MICROSCALE ORGANIC LABORATORY

WITH MATERIALS FROM
EXPERIMENTAL ORGANIC CHEMISTRY
DANIEL R. PALLEROS

DANA W. MAYO
RONALD M. PIKE
PETER K. TRUMPER

ADAPTED FOR USE IN
**CHEMISTRY 112A
ORGANIC LAB**
BY DANIEL S. BERNIER
AND THOMAS H. MORTON

Fall 2004

UNIVERSITY OF CALIFORNIA, RIVERSIDE

WILEY
CUSTOM SERVICES

Printed in the United States of America

ISBN 978-471-70282-5

10 9 8 7 6 5 4 3 2 1

MICROSCALE ORGANIC LABORATORY

with Multistep and Multiscale Syntheses

Fourth Edition

DANA W. MAYO
Charles Weston Pickard
Research Professor of Chemistry
Bowdoin College

RONALD M. PIKE
Professor of Chemistry, Emeritus
Merrimack, College

PETER K. TRUMPER
University of Maine School of Law

JOHN WILEY & SONS, INC.

New York ■ **Chichester** ■ **Weinheim** ■ **Brisbane** ■ **Toronto** ■ **Singapore**

ACQUISITIONS EDITOR	David Harris
MARKETING MANAGER	Karyn Drews
PRODUCTION EDITOR	Deborah Herbert
ILLUSTRATION EDITORS	Edward Starr/Eugene Aiello
COVER ILLUSTRATION	Lynn Rogan
COVER DESIGN	Madelyn Lesure

To order books for customer service call 1-800-CALL-WILEY (225-5945)

Library of Congress Cataloging in Publication Data:
Mayo, Dana W.
  Microscale organic laboratory: with multistep and multiscale
syntheses/Dana W. Mayo, Ronald M. Pike, Peter K. Trumper.—4th
ed.
    p. cm.
  Includes index.
  ISBN 0-471-32185-0 (cloth: alk. paper)
  1. Chemistry, Organic Laboratory manuals.   I. Pike, Ronald M.
II. Trumper, Peter K.   III. Title.
QD261.M38 1999
547'.0078—dc21   99-30131
                                                      CIP
ISBN-0-471-32185-0

Printed in the United States of America

EXPERIMENTAL ORGANIC CHEMISTRY

DANIEL R. PALLEROS

University of California, Santa Cruz

JOHN WILEY & SONS, INC.

New York ■ Chichester ■ Weinheim ■ Brisbane ■ Toronto ■ Singapore

ACQUISITIONS EDITOR	Jennifer Yee
SENIOR PRODUCTION EDITOR	Elizabeth Swain
SENIOR MARKETING MANAGER	Charity Robey
SENIOR DESIGNER	Karin Gerdes Kincheloe
ILLUSTRATION EDITORS	Sandra Rigby and Edward Starr
PHOTO EDITOR	Lisa Gee
COVER PHOTO	Paul Schraub
COVER CONCEPT	Daniel R. Palleros
ILLUSTRATIONS	Fine Line Illustrations, Inc.

This book was set in 10/12 Palatino Light by Laser Words and printed and bound by Courier/Westford. The cover was printed by Lehigh.

This book is printed on acid-free paper. ∞

To order books or for customer service, call 1(800)-CALL-WILEY (225-5945).

Library of Congress Cataloging in Publication Data:

Palleros, Daniel R.
     Experimental organic chemistry / Daniel R. Palleros.
          p.   cm.
     Includes bibliographical references and index.
     ISBN 0-471-28250-2 (cloth : alk. paper)
     1. Chemistry, Organic Laboratory manuals.   I. Title.
     QD261.P335   1999
     547'.078–dc21
     99-35417
     CIP

Printed in the United States of America

10 9 8 7 6 5 4 3 2 1

Contents

Contents

FORMAT FOR LABORATORY NOTEBOOKS

Keeping a legible, accurate notebook is essential to your success in this class. Several general guidelines regarding notebook format are given below:

a. The laboratory notebook may **not** be loose leaf or spiral bound. (See (e) below). It must be designed so that it permanently contains the original pages of your Pre-lab (Part I), and Results (Part II).

b. Number pages consecutively.

c. Use ballpoint (permanent ink) pen only.

d. Textbooks, lab manuals, loose sheets of paper, etc. will not be allowed in the lab during sessions. The complete outline of procedures must be written in your laboratory notebook prior to carrying out the experiment.

e. **Copies** of lab notebook pages will be required. Duplicate-paged notebooks with carbon paper can be purchased from the bookstore. These are designed such that **copies** of all the original pages can be removed for submission to your TA. If you purchase a bound notebook without duplicate pages: (1) Use carbon paper and looseleaf unlined pages to make copies of the original pages for submission, or (2) obtain good quality Xerox copies of your original notebook pages for submission. The original pages must remain securely attached to the lab notebook and must not be removed.

f. Your TA may periodically inspect your notebook.

YOUR LAB REPORT CONSISTS OF 3 PARTS:

Part I - **Lab Preparation Write-up** (copy of notebook pages due before beginning each experiment).

Part II - **Results** (copy of notebook pages(s) containing observations noted during the lab session).

Part III - **Discussion and Conclusion** (summary of results, etc. and answers to questions. This part can be written on separate loose-leaf paper).

I. Lab Preparation Write-up (40% of report grade)

This is Part I of your lab report. It must be written in your laboratory notebook. A copy of the original pages of this write-up will be collected prior to beginning any experiment and it will be returned after your entire lab report has been collected and graded. It will consist of:

a. Your name, lab section, etc. (on each page).

b. Experiment No.: Title of experiment.

c. Objectives. This should include hypotheses about the outcome, which you are going to test by experiment (for instance, "ballpark estimates" of quantitative determinations that you can perform in lab). As an example, the prelab exercises for the distillation experiment (the next lab after check-in) ask you to make predictions, which you should compare with your own results. <u>It is your responsibility to propose what you will measure in the course of the experiment.</u>

d. List of chemicals: Weights or volumes, look up molecular weights and calculate moles, if appropriate, show boiling points (BP's), melting points (MP's), or other physical data (color, density, refractive index, *etc.* as appropriate).

e. List of equipment: Itemize and include sketches for complex apparatus.

f. Outline of procedure: It is most worthwhile to show this in outline form; note precautions, including comments on safety in the margin.

g. Prelab questions (if any). A set of 4 prelab problems must be worked prior to the distillation experiment. They are intended to provide background for the Discussion and Conclusions that you will write in your final report, in which you compare what you predict with what you find.

The copy of Part I should be turned in as directed by your TA. It must be completed and ready to turn in before you begin the experiment.

II. Results (10% of report grade)

This section should be started on a new page of the notebook following Part I. A **copy** of Part II and Part III will be stapled together and turned in **after** the experiment as directed by your TA.

This should be completed during the laboratory session while doing the experiment and includes:

a. Name, lab section, etc. on each page

b. Experiment No.: Title

c. Results: Date, time, weights, volumes, bp's, mp's and other observations or comments actually recorded **during** the lab session.

d. Attach any spectra, chart paper, etc.

III. Discussion and Conclusions (50% of report grade)

This section need not be included in your lab notebook. It can be written on separate sheets stapled to Part II. It is to be done as homework after you have completed the experiment and includes:

a. Name, lab section, etc. on each page.

b. Summary of Results (tabular or outline form): calculate yields, describe product, and give physical data, etc.; show any graphs you may have plotted from the raw data.

c. Analysis of Results: In 5-10 sentences, comment on the quality of your results. Describe problems which may have occurred, possible solutions, etc. How (and why) did the outcome differ from what you predicted in your prelab? What was learned?

d. Critique of experiment.

e. Homework questions, if any.

Staple Parts II and III together and turn them in by the due date listed on the course syllabus or as directed by your TA. Also, if applicable, turn in products in a properly labeled vial at this time. Parts I-III will be returned to you after grading. For your benefit, you should keep a copy of Part III. The originals of Parts I and II are already in your notebook.

Chemistry Department   **University of California, Riverside**

LABORATORY SAFETY INSTRUCTIONS AND RULES

1. **EYE PROTECTION**: One of the most common (and damaging) types of laboratory accidents involves the eyes.

    EYE PROTECTION IS MANDATORY AT ALL TIMES IN ALL TEACHING AND RESEARCH LABORATORIES. NO EXCEPTIONS. PERSONS WITH INADEQUATE EYE PROTECTION WILL BE TOLD TO LEAVE THE LABORATORY.

    a. All persons in a laboratory must wear safety goggles.
    b. Persons who normally wear prescription glasses must wear safety goggles over their glasses. Regular prescription glasses do not provide adequate protection for chemical laboratories.
    c. Persons who normally wear contact lenses must not wear them in the laboratory. Contact lenses are a hazard in the laboratory. In case of an accident, they could become chemically welded to your eye. If you normally wear contact lenses, you should obtain prescription glasses to be worn under safety goggles. You will be allowed to wear contact lenses (coupled with safety goggles) only if your provide a statement from a physician that you are unable to wear prescription glasses. Since the department cannot adequately monitor this rule, your signature transfers responsibility for following this rule to you.

2. **PROPER ATTIRE**: Proper lab attire consists of full-length pants or dress or a full-length lab apron. Shorts or skirts will not be allowed in the lab except under a full-length apron, such as the plastic ones available in the Bookstore. Long lab coats are satisfactory as long as your legs are protected to within 12 inches of the floor. Sandals and other footwear that do not completely enclose the foot up to the ankle are not permitted. For your protection, you will not be allowed to attend lab without appropriate attire.

3. **MEDICAL CONDITIONS**: Notify the supervising laboratory instructor immediately if you have any medical conditions (such as pregnancy, allergies, diabetes, etc.) that may require special precautionary measures in the laboratory.

4. **EMERGENCY EQUIPMENT**: Know the locations of the lab fire extinguishers, safety showers, eyewash fountains, hallway emergency telephones, fire alarms, and lab and building exits.

5. **FIRE**: Immediately alert the TA, who will give instructions. A fire confined to a small container or flask can usually be extinguished by covering the container with something nonflammable (e.g. a large beaker). Use a fire extinguisher if necessary, but only if it appears that the fire can be easily contained; if not, pull the fire alarm and exit the building. Go directly to the designated assembly area. Do not use the elevator.

    If a person's clothing is on fire, use the safety shower to put out the flames. If the shower is not readily available, douse the individual with water or wrap the person in a coat or whatever is available to extinguish the fire and roll the person on the floor. Fire blankets must be used with caution because wrapping someone while they are in the vertical position can force flames toward the face and neck.

6. **INJURY**: Immediately report any injury to a Teaching Assistant, no matter how minor. The TA will initiate emergency procedures and arrange for transportation to a medical care facililty. Do not transport a seriously injured person. Call for help. Complete an Incident Report in consultation with your TA as soon as possible, and submit it to the Stockroom staff (see Item 10).

    NOTE: The Student Health Center is open only during the day, from 8:00 – 4:30. Laboratory injuries after these hours will be treated at the Emergency Room at Riverside Community Hospital or a nearby Urgent Care Center. Students (or their health insurance company) will be assessed Emergency Room charges for off campus treatment. The Chemistry Department (or University) cannot pay. Students under 18 years must submit in advance, a treatment release form signed by parents or guardians to be held on file in the stockroom.

7. **CHEMICAL SPILLS:** Chemical contact with eyes and skin must be <u>washed</u> immediately with lots of water for no less than 15 minutes. USE THE EYE WASH AND SAFETY SHOWER. Quickly remove all contaminated clothing. Report chemical spills on persons, tables, or floors to a TA <u>immediately</u> regardless of how minor they appear.

8. **EARTHQUAKE:** Exit the laboratory if possible, but <u>stay in the building</u> and protect yourself from <u>breaking windows</u> or <u>objects falling</u> from above. When the quake subsides, quickly check, if possible, that all gas valves are closed and all electrical heating devices are turned off to stop reactions and prevent fires. Exit the building to the designated assembly area (see item 9). Do not use elevators.

9. **BUILDING ALARM:** Leave the building immediately and quietly to the designated assembly area (grassy area between Pierce Hall and the bookstore). Do not return until specifically told to re-enter. Note: During an earthquake, do not leave the building until the shaking has subsided.

10. **REPORT OF INCIDENT:** All incidents of fire, explosion, injury, or chemical spills (including mercury from broken thermometers) should be reported immediately to a TA. A written report is required after the incident; the stockroom has forms for filing written reports.

11. **PREPARATION FOR LABORATORY:** All students are expected to have read the experiment thoroughly prior to starting the lab work. Questions about procedures or precautions should be resolved by asking the TA or professor before the experiment.

12. **ADDITIONAL LABORATORY RULES:**
    a. You may not bring nor consume any food or beverage in the laboratories. Smoking and application of cosmetics is not permitted in the labs.
    b. You may not remove chemicals, equipment or supplies from the laboratories or stockrooms without written permission of the instructor, teaching assistant, or Laboratory Coordinator.
    c. Do not deliberately smell or taste chemicals.
    d. Do not mix reagents unless you are instructed to do so or know the likely results.
    e. Do not use unlabeled chemicals. Report them to the TA.
    f. Never adulterate reagents by "pouring back" unused portions into stock bottles or using a contaminated pipet.
    g. Do not dump chemicals into trash cans or sinks. Waste chemicals are to be disposed of in specially labeled containers only.
    h. Extinguish matches with water and dispose of them in trash cans, <u>never</u> in the sinks.
    i. Absolutely no horseplay of any kind is permitted in the labs.
    j. Do not store chemicals in your lab drawer, unless specifically instructed to do so by your TA (e.g., when an experiment requires more than one lab period). All containers for storing chemicals must be clearly labeled (your name, experiment, and the full chemical name(s) of the contents).
    k. No visiting by friends is allowed during lab sessions. Pets or children are not allowed.
    l. Do not drink water from lab faucets. This water may not be safe.
    m. The instructional staff may inspect student lab drawers at any time without informing the student.

**SAFETY DEPENDS UPON AN ATTITUDE OF CAREFULNESS AT ALL TIMES
BE ALERT
THINK AHEAD AND PREVENT ACCIDENTS**

2

Safety

C₂H₄, Ethylene
a substance of natural origin,
released by ripening fruit.

Research laboratories vary widely with respect to facilities and support given to safety. Large laboratories may have several hundred chemists and an extensive network of co-workers, supervisors, safety officers, and hazardous waste managers. In small laboratories, the chemist may be left pretty much alone to work things out. Large laboratories may have an extensive set of safety procedures and detailed practices for the storage of hazardous wastes. The individual chemist in the small laboratory may have to take care of all of those things. Some laboratories may routinely deal with very hazardous materials and may conduct all chemistry in hoods. Others may deal mainly with relatively innocuous compounds and have very limited hood facilities.

Our approach is to raise some questions for the individual to think about and to suggest places to look for further information. This chapter will not present a large list of safety precautions for use in all situations. We do present a list of very basic precautionary measures. A bibliography offers a list of selected references at the end of the chapter. Many laboratories may have safety guidelines that will supersede this very cursory treatment. This chapter is no more than a starting point.

Murphy's law states in brief, "If anything can go wrong, it will." Although it is often taken to be a silly law, it is not. Murphy's law means that if sparking switches are present in areas that contain flammable vapors, sooner or later there will be a fire. If the glass container can move to the edge of the shelf as items are moved around or because the building vibrates, it will come crashing to the floor at some time. If the pipet can become contaminated, then the mouth pipetter is going to ingest a contaminant sometime.

MAKING THE LABORATORY A SAFER PLACE

We cannot revoke Murphy's law, but we can do a lot to minimize the damage. We can reduce the incidence of sparks and flames and flammable vapors. We can make sure that if the accident does occur, we have the means to contain the damage and take care of any injuries that result. All this means thinking about the laboratory environment. Think about what can go wrong and then do what can be done to minimize the chance of an accident and be prepared to respond if one does occur.

Nature of Hazards

The chemistry laboratory presents a wide assortment of risks. These risks are outlined briefly here so that you can begin to think about the steps necessary to make the laboratory safer.

1. *Physical hazards.* Injuries resulting from flames, explosions, and equipment (cuts from glass, electrical shock from faulty instrumentation, or improper use of instruments).

2. *External exposure to chemicals.* Injuries to skin and eyes resulting from contact with chemicals that have splashed or have been left on the bench top or on equipment.

3. *Internal exposure.* Longer term (usually) health effects resulting from breathing hazardous vapors or ingesting chemicals.

Reduction of Risks

Many things can be done to reduce risks. The rules below may be absolute in some laboratories. In others, the nature of the materials and apparatus used may justify the relaxation of some of these rules or the addition of others.

1. *Stick to the procedures described by your supervisor.* This attention to detail is particularly important for the chemist with limited experience. In other cases, variation of the reagents and techniques may be part of the work.

2. *Wear approved safety goggles.* We can often recover quickly from injuries affecting only a few square millimeters on our bodies, *unless* that area happens to be in our eyes. Often, larger industrial laboratories require that laboratory work clothes and safety shoes be worn. *Wear them,* if requested.

3. *Do not put anything in your mouth while in the laboratory.* This rule includes food, drinks, and pipets. There are countless ways that surfaces can become contaminated in the laboratory. Since there are substances that must *never* be pipetted by mouth, one should get into the habit of *not* mouth pipetting anything.

4. *Be cautious with flames and flammable solvents.* Remember that the flame at one end of the bench can ignite the flammable liquid at the other end in the event of a spill or improper disposal. Flames must never be used when certain liquids are present in the laboratory, and flames must always be used with care.

5. *Be sure that you have the proper chemicals for your reaction.* Check labels carefully, and return unused chemicals to the proper place for storage or disposal.

6. *Minimize the loss of chemicals to air or water and dispose of waste properly.* Some water-soluble materials may be safely disposed of in the water drains. Other wastes should go into special receptacles. Pay attention to the labels on these receptacles.

7. *Minimize skin contact with any chemicals.* Use impermeable gloves, when necessary, and wash any chemical off your body promptly. If you have to wash something off with water, use lots of it. Be sure that you know where the nearest water spray device is located.

8. *Tie back, or otherwise confine, long hair and loose items of clothing.* You do not want them falling into a reagent or getting near flames.

9. *Do not work alone.* Too many things can happen to a person working alone that might leave him/her unable to obtain assistance. In the rare event that you *are* working alone, be sure that someone checks on you at regular intervals.

10. *Exercise care in assembling glass and electrical apparatus.* Separating standard taper glassware, as well as other operations with glass, all involve the risk that the glass may break and that lacerations or punctures may result. Seek help or advice with glassware, if necessary. Electrical shock can result in many ways. When making electrical connections, make sure that your hands, the laboratory bench, and the floor are all dry and that *you* do not complete an electrical path to ground. Be sure that electrical equipment is properly grounded and insulated.

11. *Report any injury or accident to the appropriate person.* Reporting injuries and accidents is important so that medical assistance can be obtained, if necessary. It is also essential for others to be made aware of any safety problems. These problems may be correctable.

12. *Keep things clean.* Put unused apparatus away. Immediately wipe up or care for spills on the bench top or on the floor.

13. *Attend safety programs* as requested. Many laboratories offer excellent seminars and lectures on a wide variety of safety topics. *Pay careful attention* to the advice and counsel of the *safety officer.*

Locate the nearest

Precautionary Measures

- Fire extinguisher
- Eye wash
- Spray shower
- Fire blanket
- Exit

Know who to call (have the numbers posted) for

- Fire
- Medical emergency
- Spill or accidental release of chemicals

Know where to go

- In case of injury
- To evacuate the building

The smaller quantities used in the microscale laboratory carry with them a reduction in hazards caused by fires and explosions. Hazards associated with skin contact are also reduced; however, care must be exercised when working in close proximity to even the small quantities involved.

There is a great potential for reducing the exposure to chemical vapors, but these reductions will be realized only if everyone in the laboratory is careful. One characteristic of vapors emitted outside hoods is that they mix rapidly throughout the lab and will quickly reach the nose of the

THINKING ABOUT THE RISKS IN USING CHEMICALS

person on the other side of the room. For this reason some operations may have to be performed in hoods. In some laboratories, the majority of the reactions may be carried out in hoods. When reactions are carried out in the open laboratory, each experimenter becomes a "polluter" whose emissions affect the people nearby the most, but these emissions become added to the laboratory air and to the burden each of us must bear.

The concentration of vapor in the general laboratory air space depends on the vapor pressure of the liquids, the area of the solid or liquid exposed, the nature of air currents near the sources, and the ventilation characteristics of the laboratory. One factor over which each individual has control is evaporation, which can be reduced by the following practices.

- Certain liquids must remain in hoods.
- Reagent bottles must be recapped when not in use.
- Spills must be quickly cleaned up and the waste discarded.

Storage of Chemicals

Chemicals must be properly stored when not in use. Some balance must be struck between the convenience of having the compound in the laboratory where you can easily put your hands on it and the safety of having the compound in a properly ventilated and fire-safe storage room. Policies for storing chemicals will vary from place to place. There are limits to the amounts of flammable liquids that should be stored in glass containers, and fire-resistant cabinets must be used for storage of large amounts of flammable liquids. Chemicals that react with one another should not be stored in close proximity. There are plans for sorting chemicals by general reactivity classes in storerooms; for instance, Flinn Scientific Company (1989) includes a description of a storage system with their chemical catalog.

Disposal of Chemicals

Chemicals must also be segregated into categories for disposal. The categories used will depend on the disposal services available, and upon federal, state, and local regulations. For example, some organic wastes are readily incinerated, while those containing chlorine may require much more costly treatment. Other wastes may have to be buried. For safety and economic reasons, it is important to place waste material in the appropriate container.

Material Safety Data Sheets

Although risks are associated with the use of most chemicals, the magnitudes of these risks vary greatly. A short description of the risks is provided by a Material Safety Data Sheet, commonly referred to as an **MSDS**. These sheets are normally provided by the manufacturer or vendor of the chemical, and users are required to keep files of the MSDS of each material stored or used.

As an example, the MSDS for acetone is shown here. This sheet is provided by the J. T. Baker Chemical Company. Sheets from other sources will be very similar. Much of the information on these sheets is self-explanatory, but let us review the major sections of the acetone example.

Section I provides identification numbers and codes for the compound and includes a summary of the risks associated with the use of acetone. Because these sheets are available for many thousands of compounds and mixtures, there must be a means of unambiguously identifying the substance. A standard reference number for chemists is the Chemical Abstract Service Number, or CAS No.

J. T. BAKER CHEMICAL CO. 222 RED SCHOOL LANE, PHILLIPSBURG, NJ 08865
M A T E R I A L   S A F E T Y   D A T A   S H E E T
24-HOUR EMERGENCY TELEPHONE — (201) 859-2151
CHEMTREC # (800) 424-9300 — NATIONAL RESPONSE CENTER # (800) 424-8802

A0446 –01   ACETONE   PAGE: 1
EFFECTIVE: 10/11/85   ISSUED: 01/23/86

SECTION I – PRODUCT IDENTIFICATION

PRODUCT NAME: ACETONE
FORMULA: (CH3)2CO
FORMULA WT: 58.08
CAS NO.:   00067-64-1
NIOSH/RTECS NO.:   AL3150000
COMMON SYNONYMS: DIMETHYL KETONE; METHYL KETONE; 2-PROPANONE
PRODUCT CODES: 9010,9006,9002,9254,9009,9001,9004,5356,A134,9007,9005,9008

PRECAUTIONARY LABELLING

BAKER SAF-T-DATA(TM) SYSTEM

                     HEALTH   – 1
                     FLAMMABILITY   – 3 (FLAMMABLE)
                     REACTIVITY   – 2
                     CONTACT   – 1

LABORATORY PROTECTIVE EQUIPMENT

SAFETY GLASSES; LAB COAT; VENT HOOD; PROPER GLOVES; CLASS B EXTINGUISHER

PRECAUTIONARY LABEL STATEMENTS

DANGER
EXTREMELY FLAMMABLE
HARMFUL IF SWALLOWED OR INHALED
CAUSES IRRITATION
KEEP AWAY FROM HEAT, SPARKS, FLAME. AVOID CONTACT WITH EYES, SKIN, CLOTHING.
AVOID BREATHING VAPOR. KEEP IN TIGHTLY CLOSED CONTAINER. USE WITH ADEQUATE
VENTILATION. WASH THOROUGHLY AFTER HANDLING. IN CASE OF FIRE, USE WATER SPRAY,
ALCOHOL FOAM, DRY CHEMICAL, OR CARBON DIOXIDE. FLUSH SPILL AREA WITH WATER
SPRAY.

SECTION II – HAZARDOUS COMPONENTS

COMPONENT	%	CAS NO
ACETONE	90-100	67-64-1

SECTION III – PHYSICAL DATA

BOILING POINT:	56 C (133 F)	VAPOR PRESSURE(MM HG):	181
MELTING POINT:	−95 C (−139 F)	VAPOR DENSITY(AIR=1):	2
SPECIFIC GRAVITY:	0.79	EVAPORATION RATE:	5.6
(H2O=1)		(BUTYL ACETATE=1)	

SOLUBILITY(H2O):   COMPLETE (IN ALL PROPORTIONS) % VOLATILES BY VOLUME: 100

APPEARANCE & ODOR: CLEAR, COLORLESS LIQUID WITH FRAGRANT SWEET ODOR.

SECTION IV – FIRE AND EXPLOSION HAZARD DATA

FLASH POINT: −18 C (0 F)   NFPA 704M RATING: 1-3-0

FLAMMABLE LIMITS: UPPER –   13 %   LOWER –   2 %

FIRE EXTINGUISHING MEDIA
      USE ALCOHOL FOAM, DRY CHEMICAL OR CARBON DIOXIDE.
      (WATER MAY BE INEFFECTIVE.)

SPECIAL FIRE-FIGHTING PROCEDURES
      FIREFIGHTERS SHOULD WEAR PROPER PROTECTIVE EQUIPMENT AND SELF-CONTAINED
      (POSITIVE PRESSURE IF AVAILABLE) BREATHING APPARATUS WITH FULL FACEPIECE.
      MOVE EXPOSED CONTAINERS FROM FIRE AREA IF IT CAN BE DONE WITHOUT RISK.
      USE WATER TO KEEP FIRE-EXPOSED CONTAINERS COOL.

UNUSUAL FIRE & EXPLOSION HAZARDS
      VAPORS MAY FLOW ALONG SURFACES TO DISTANT IGNITION SOURCES AND FLASH BACK.
      CLOSED CONTAINERS EXPOSED TO HEAT MAY EXPLODE. CONTACT WITH STRONG
      OXIDIZERS MAY CAUSE FIRE.

SECTION V – HEALTH HAZARD DATA

THRESHOLD LIMIT VALUE (TLV/TWA):   1780 MG/M3 (750 PPM)

SHORT-TERM EXPOSURE LIMIT (STEL): 2375 MG/M3 (1000 PPM)

TOXICITY: LD50 (ORAL-RAT)(MG/KG)   – 9750
               LD50 (IPR-MOUSE)(G/KG)   – 1297

EFFECTS OF OVEREXPOSURE
    CONTACT WITH SKIN HAS A DEFATTING EFFECT, CAUSING DRYING AND IRRITATION.
    OVEREXPOSURE TO VAPORS MAY CAUSE IRRITATION OF MUCOUS MEMBRANES, DRYNESS
    OF MOUTH AND THROAT, HEADACHE, NAUSEA AND DIZZINESS.

EMERGENCY AND FIRST AID PROCEDURES
    CALL A PHYSICIAN.
    IF SWALLOWED, IF CONSCIOUS, IMMEDIATELY INDUCE VOMITING.
    IF INHALED, REMOVE TO FRESH AIR.   IF NOT BREATHING, GIVE ARTIFICIAL
    RESPIRATION.   IF BREATHING IS DIFFICULT, GIVE OXYGEN.
    IN CASE OF CONTACT, IMMEDIATELY FLUSH EYES WITH PLENTY OF WATER FOR AT
    LEAST 15 MINUTES.   FLUSH SKIN WITH WATER.

SECTION VI – REACTIVITY DATA

STABILITY: STABLE   HAZARDOUS POLYMERIZATION: WILL NOT OCCUR

CONDITIONS TO AVOID: HEAT, FLAME, SOURCES OF IGNITION

INCOMPATIBLES: SULFURIC ACID, NITRIC ACID, STRONG OXIDIZING AGENTS

SECTION VII – SPILL AND DISPOSAL PROCEDURES

STEPS TO BE TAKEN IN THE EVENT OF A SPILL OR DISCHARGE
    WEAR SUITABLE PROTECTIVE CLOTHING.   SHUT OFF IGNITION SOURCES; NO FLARES,
    SMOKING, OR FLAMES IN AREA.   STOP LEAK IF YOU CAN DO SO WITHOUT RISK.   USE
    WATER SPRAY TO REDUCE VAPORS.   TAKE UP WITH SAND OR OTHER NON-COMBUSTIBLE
    ABSORBENT MATERIAL AND PLACE INTO CONTAINER FOR LATER DISPOSAL.   FLUSH
    AREA WITH WATER.

    J. T. BAKER SOLUSORB(R) SOLVENT ADSORBENT IS RECOMMENDED
    FOR SPILLS OF THIS PRODUCT

DISPOSAL PROCEDURE
    DISPOSE IN ACCORDANCE WITH ALL APPLICABLE FEDERAL, STATE, AND LOCAL
    ENVIRONMENTAL REGULATIONS.

EPA HAZARDOUS WASTE NUMBER: U002 (TOXIC WASTE)

SECTION VIII – PROTECTIVE EQUIPMENT

VENTILATION: USE GENERAL OR LOCAL EXHAUST VENTILATION TO MEET
                          TLV REQUIREMENTS.

RESPIRATORY PROTECTION: RESPIRATORY PROTECTION REQUIRED IF AIRBORNE
                          CONCENTRATION EXCEEDS TLV   AT CONCENTRATIONS UP
                          TO 5000 PPM, A GAS MASK WITH ORGANIC VAPOR
                          CANNISTER IS RECOMMENDED.   ABOVE THIS LEVEL, A
                          SELF-CONTAINED BREATHING APPARATUS WITH FULL FACE
                          SHIELD IS ADVISED.

EYE/SKIN PROTECTION: SAFETY GLASSES WITH SIDESHIELDS, POLYVINYL ACETATE
                          GLOVES ARE RECOMMENDED.

SECTION IX – STORAGE AND HANDLING PRECAUTIONS

SAF-T-DATA(TM) STORAGE COLOR CODE: RED

SPECIAL PRECAUTIONS
    BOND AND GROUND CONTAINERS WHEN TRANSFERRING LIQUID.   KEEP CONTAINER
    TIGHTLY CLOSED.   STORE IN A COOL, DRY, WELL-VENTILATED, FLAMMABLE LIQUID
    STORAGE AREA.

SECTION X – TRANSPORTATION DATA AND ADDITIONAL INFORMATION

DOMESTIC (D.O.T.)

PROPER SHIPPING NAME	ACETONE
HAZARD CLASS	FLAMMABLE LIQUID
UN/NA	UN1090
LABELS	FLAMMABLE LIQUID

INTERNATIONAL (I.M.O.)

PROPER SHIPPING NAME	ACETONE
HAZARD CLASS	3.1
UN/NA	UN1090
LABELS	FLAMMABLE LIQUID

(TM) AND (R) DESIGNATE TRADEMARKS.
N/A = NOT APPLICABLE OR NOT AVAILABLE
—

THE INFORMATION PUBLISHED IN THIS MATERIAL SAFETY DATA SHEET HAS BEEN COMPILED
FROM OUR EXPERIENCE AND DATA PRESENTED IN VARIOUS TECHNICAL PUBLICATIONS. IT IS
THE USER'S RESPONSIBILITY TO DETERMINE THE SUITABILITY OF THIS INFORMATION FOR
THE ADOPTION OF NECESSARY SAFETY PRECAUTIONS. WE RESERVE THE RIGHT TO REVISE
MATERIAL SAFETY DATA SHEETS PERIODICALLY AS NEW INFORMATION BECOMES AVAILABLE.

A quick review of the degree of risks is given by the numerical scale under Precautionary Labeling. This particular scale is a proprietary scale that ranges from 0 (very little or nonexistent risk) to 4 (extremely high risk). The National Fire Protection Association (NFPA) uses a similar scale, but the risks considered are different. Other systems may use different scales, and there are some that represent low risks by the highest number! Be sure that you understand the scale being used. Perhaps some day, one scale will become standard.

Section II covers risks from mixtures. Because a mixture is not considered here, the section is empty. Selected physical data are described in Section III. Section IV contains fire and explosion data, including a description of the toxic gases produced when the compound is exposed to a fire. The MSDSs are routinely made available to fire departments that may be faced with fighting a fire in a building where large amounts of chemicals are stored.

Health hazards are described in Section V. The entries of most significance for evaluating risks from vapors are the Threshold Limit Value (or TLV) and the Short-Term Exposure Limit (STEL). The TLV is a term used by the American Conference of Governmental Industrial Hygienists (ACGIH). This organization examines the toxicity literature for a compound and establishes the TLV. This standard is designed to protect the health of workers exposed to the vapor 8 hours/day, 5 days a week. The Occupational Safety and Health Administration (OSHA) adopts a value to protect the safety of workplaces in the United States. Their value is termed the Time Weighted Average (TWA) and in many cases is numerically equal to the TLV. The STEL is a value not to be exceeded for even a 15-min averaging time. The TLV/TWA and STEL values for many chemicals are also summarized in a small handbook available from the ACGIH; they are also collected in the *CRC Handbook of Chemistry and Physics*.

The toxicity of acetone is also described in terms of the toxic oral dose. In this case, the LD_{50} is the dose that will cause the death of 50% of the mice or rats given that dose. The dose is expressed as milligrams of acetone per kilogram of body weight of the subject animal. The figures for small animals are often used to estimate the effects on humans. If, for example, we used the mouse figure of 1297 mg/kg and applied it to a 60-kg chemist, a dose of 77,820 mg ($\sim$ 98.5 mL) would kill 50% of the subjects receiving that dose. As a further example, chloroform has an LD_{50} of 80 mg/kg. For our 60-kg chemist, a dose of 4800 mg ($\sim$ 3 mL) would be fatal in 50% of these cases. The effects of exposure of skin to the liquid and vapor are also described.

Section VI describes the reactivity of acetone and the classes of compounds with which it should not come in contact. For example, sodium metal reacts violently with a number of substances (including water) and should not come in contact with them. Strong oxidizing agents (such as nitric acid) should not be mixed with organic compounds (among other things). The final sections (Sections VII–X) are self-explanatory.

Estimating the Risks from Vapors

Other things (availability and suitability) being equal, one would, of course, choose the least toxic chemical for a given reaction. Some very toxic chemicals play very important roles in synthetic organic chemistry, and the toxicity of the chemicals in common use varies greatly. Bromine and benzene have TLVs of 0.7 and 30 mg/m^3, respectively, and are at the more toxic end of the spectrum of routinely used chemicals. Acetone has a TLV of 1780 mg/m^3. These representative figures do not mean that acetone is "harmless" or that bromine cannot be used. In general, one should exercise care at all times (make a habit of good laboratory practice) and should take special precautions when working with highly toxic materials.

The TLV provides a simple means to evaluate the relative risk of exposure to the vapor of any substance used in the laboratory. If the quantity of the material evaporated is represented by m (in milligrams per hour) and the TLV is expressed by L (in milligrams per cubic meter), a measure of relative risk to the vapor is given by m/L. This quantity actually represents the volume of clean air required to dilute the emissions to the TLV. As an example, the emission of 1 g of bromine and 10 g of acetone in 1 hour lead to the values of m/L of 1400 m³/hour for the bromine and 5.6 m³/hour for acetone. These numbers provide a direct handle on the *relative* risks from these two vapors. It is difficult to assess the absolute risk to these vapors without a lot of information about the ventilation characteristics of the laboratory. If these releases occur within a properly operated hood, the threat to the worker in the laboratory is probably very small. (However, consideration must be given to the hood exhaust.)

Exposure in the general laboratory environment can be assessed if we assume that the emissions are reasonably well mixed before they are inhaled, and if we know something about the room ventilation rate. The ventilation rate of the room can be measured in a number of ways (Butcher et al.). Given the ventilation rate, it might be safe to assume that only 30% of that air is available for diluting the emissions. (This accounts for imperfect mixing in the room.) The effective amount of air available for dilution can then be compared with the amount of air required to dilute the chemical to the TLV.

Let us continue our example. Suppose that the laboratory has a volume of 75 m³ and an air exchange rate of two air changes per hour. This value means that (75 m³)(2/hour)(0.3) = 45 m³/hour are available to dilute the pollutants. There may be enough margin for error to reduce the acetone concentration to a low level (5.6 m³/hour are required to reach the TLV); use of bromine should be restricted to the hood. An assessment of the accumulative risk of several chemicals is obtained by adding the individual m/L $\left(\frac{\text{mg/hour}}{\text{mg/m}^3}\right)$ values.

The m/L figures may also be used to assess the relative risk of performing the experiment outside a hood. As m/L represents the volume of air required for *each* student, this may be compared with the volume of air actually available for each student. If the ventilation rate for the entire laboratory is Q, (in cubic meters per min) for a section of n students meeting for t min, the volume for each student is kQt/n cubic meters. Here k is a mixing factor that allows for the fact that the ventilation air will not be perfectly mixed in the laboratory before it is exhausted. In a reasonable worst-case mixing situation a k value of 0.3 seems reasonable. Laboratories with modest ventilation rates supplied by 15–20 linear feet of hoods can be expected to provide 30–100 m³ per student over a 3-hour laboratory period if the hoods are working properly. Let us take the figure of 50 m³ per student as an illustration. If the value of m/L for a compound (or a group of compounds in a reaction) is substantially less than 50 m³, it may be safe to do that series of operations in the open laboratory. If m/L is comparable to or greater than 50 m³, a number of options are available. (1) Steps using that compound may be restricted to a hood. (2) The instructional staff may satisfy themselves that much less than the assumed value is actually evaporated under conditions present in their laboratory. (3) The number of individual repetitions of this experiment may be reduced. The size of the laboratory section can be reduced or the experiment may be done in pairs or trios.

Conducting reactions in a hood does not automatically convey a stamp of safety. Hoods are designed to keep evaporating chemicals from entering the general laboratory space. For hoods to do their job, there must be an adequate flow of air into the hood, and this air flow must not be disturbed by turbulence at the hood face. A frequently used figure of merit for hood operation is the face velocity of 100 ft/min. This rate is an average velocity of air entering the hood opening. (There are instruments available for measuring this flow rate in the catalogs of major equipment suppliers. Prices range from less than $50 to several hundred dollars.) Even with a face velocity of 100 ft/min, vapors can be drawn out of an improperly designed hood simply by people walking by the opening, or by drafts from open windows.

Hood performance should be checked at regular intervals. The face velocity will increase as the front hood opening is decreased. If an adequate face velocity cannot be maintained with a front opening height of 15 cm, use of the hood for carrying out reactions will be limited. A low face velocity may indicate that the fans and ductwork need cleaning, that the exhaust system leaks (if it operates under lower than ambient pressure), or that the supply of make-up air is not adequate. When the hood system is properly maintained, the height of the hood opening required to provide an adequate face velocity is often indicated with a sticker.

Hoods are often used for storage of volatile compounds. A danger in this practice is that the hood space can become quickly cluttered, making work in the hood difficult, and the air flow may be disturbed. Of course, hoods used for storage should not be turned off.

This brief chapter only touches a few of the important points concerning laboratory safety. The risk from vapor exposure is discussed in some detail, but other risks are treated only briefly. Applications in some laboratories may involve reactions with a risk from radiation or infection or may involve compounds that are unstable with respect to explosion. The chemist must be aware of the potential risks and must be prepared to go to an appropriate and detailed source of information, as needed.

2-1. Think about what you would do in the following cases. (Note that you may need more information for some of these problems.)
   a. A hot solution "bumps," splashing your face.
   b. A beaker of solvent catches fire.
   c. A reagent bottle falls, spilling concentrated sulfuric acid (H_2SO_4).
   d. You hear a sizzle as you pick up a hot test tube.

2-2. A laboratory has four hoods each of which is 39 in. wide. When the hood door is open to a height of 8 in. and the hoods are operating, the average air velocity through the hood face is 170 ft/min.
   a. Evaluate the total ventilation rate for this room assuming that there are no other exhausts.
   b. The laboratory is designed for use by 30 students. Evaluate the air available per student if the mixing factor is 0.3, and experiments last for 3 hours.
   c. An experiment is considered in which each student would be required to evaporate 7 mL of methylene chloride (CH_2Cl_2). Estimate the average concentration of methylene chloride. Look up the TLV

or the TWA for methylene chloride and consider how the evaporation might be performed.

2-3. A laboratory has a ventilation system that provides 20 m³ for each student during the laboratory period. (This figure includes the mixing factor.) An experiment is considered for this program that uses the following quantities of materials A, B, and C. The TLV is also listed for each compound.

Substance	Quantity (mg)	TLV (mg/m³)
A	400	1200
B	500	200
C	200	5

Assess the relative risks of these three compounds. Is there a likely need for operations to be conducted in a hood if the compounds are assumed to be entirely evaporated?

2-4. An experiment is considered in which 1 mL of diethylamine would be used by each student. The ventilation rate for the laboratory is 5 m³/min. Look up the TLV (or TWA) for diethylamine [$(C_2H_5)_2NH$]. What restrictions might be placed on the laboratory to keep the average concentration, over a 3-hour period, less than one third of the TWA? Assume a mixing factor of 0.3.

GENERAL SAFETY REFERENCES

Committee on Chemical Safety: *Safety in Academic Chemical Laboratories*, 3rd ed.; American Chemical Society: Washington, DC, 1979.

Furr, A. K. Jr., Ed. *Handbook of Laboratory Safety*, 3rd ed.; CRC Press: Boca Raton, FL, 1990.

Green, M. E.; Turk, A. *Safety in Working with Chemicals*; Macmillan: New York, 1978.

National Research Council: *Prudent Practices for Handling Chemicals in Laboratories*; National Academy Press: Washington, DC, 1981.

National Research Council: *Prudent Practices for Disposal of Chemicals from Laboratories*; National Academy Press; Washington, DC, 1983.

BIBLIOGRAPHY

ACGIH *Threshold Limit Values for Chemical Substances and Physical Agents in the Work Environment*; Cincinnati, OH; 1984. Available from ACGIH; 6500 Glenway Avenue, Building D-5, Cincinnati, OH 45211.

Butcher, S. S.; Mayo, D. W.; Hebert, S. M.; Pike, R. M. *Laboratory Air Quality, Part I, J. Chem. Educ.* **1985**, *62*, A238 and *Laboratory Air Quality, Part II, J. Chem. Educ.* **1985**, *62*, A261.

Flinn Scientific Company, *Chemical Catalog/Reference Manual (1989)*. Available from Flinn Scientific Co., P. O. Box 219, Batavia, IL 60510.

Lide, D.R., Ed. *CRC Handbook of Chemistry and Physics*, 72nd ed., CRC Press: Boca Raton, FL, 1991–1992.

3

Introduction to Microscale Organic Laboratory Equipment and Techniques

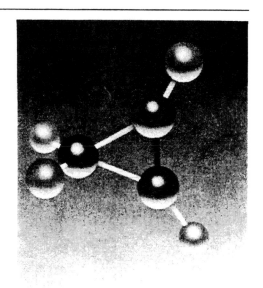

C₃H₄, Cyclopropene
Demyanov and Doyarenko (1922).

We begin this chapter with a description of the standard pieces of glassware that are employed in our microscale laboratory, many of which will be used to perform the experiments carried out in your laboratory assignments. This equipment, in one form or another, is now available from at least seven different scientific glassware manufacturers. Two principal suppliers are ACE Glass of Vineland, New Jersey and Corning Glass of Corning, New York. The following descriptions are helpful when considering what supplementary equipment may be required to carry out the experiments selected by your instructor, and what type of application is of specific interest. We next consider a series of standard experimental apparatus setups that utilize this equipment. At the end of each of these short discussions, you will find a listing of arrangements of the particular setup presented.

It should be pointed out that most of the equipment listed below is glassware that was originally developed and tested by students at Bowdoin and Merrimack Colleges for use in the undergraduate microscale organic laboratory programs at these institutions. It is believed that this particular collection of glassware offers significant advantages over earlier versions commercially available to both student and research laboratories. This conclusion is our opinion, but it is only an opinion. As you more deeply explore the experimental side of the microscale laboratory, you will find in the techniques you choose to employ a component that is very much *artistic* in nature. Two chemists may do exactly the same experiment and describe the experimental procedures in very nearly the same terms, but in fact, in the laboratory they may go about the work in different ways. This aspect of the experimental process is the *art* of doing chemical research. The esthetics of laboratory experimentation touch chemists in very personal ways. Thus, the equipment you find described in this text may be identical, similar, or only vaguely reminiscent of the components found in other texts on the subject. Historically, the equipment employed in the undergraduate instructional laboratory became an extension of that used in the chemical research laboratory. The development of the microscale instructional programs has reversed this trend by actually developing various types of instructional laboratory equipment that will be particularly useful to the modern organic research chemist. As in any laboratory work, the microscale laboratory is in large part an extension of our own personal research laboratories. We hope you find that you agree with us, and that in using this design, you will be comfortable learning the art of experimental microscale organic chemistry (see Figs. 3.1–3.7).

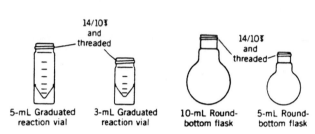

FIGURE 3.1   Reaction flasks.

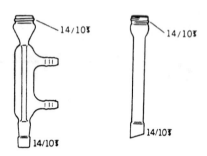

FIGURE 3.2   Condensers.

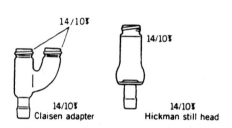

FIGURE 3.3   Distillation heads.

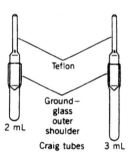

FIGURE 3.4   Recrystallization tubes.

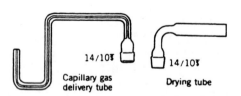

FIGURE 3.5   Miscellaneous items.

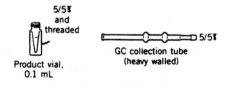

FIGURE 3.6   Gas chromatographic collection items.

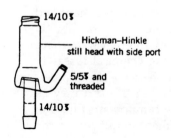

FIGURE 3.7   Hickman–Hinkle distillation column.

Listed below are the items and quantities of glassware that we have installed in our laboratories over the last few years. We list these mainly as a guide to those who are considering conversion to this type of program. This collection obviously is not meant to imply that it is the only type and quantity of apparatus that must be present on the laboratory bench. It represents, in our current view, the minimum essential content when balancing cost against experimental breadth.

MICROGLASSWARE EQUIPMENT

Thirteen Glassware Items

2   Conical vials, 5 mL, 14/10𝕋 and threaded (one thin-walled)
2   Conical vials, 3 mL, 14/10𝕋 and threaded
1   Round-bottom flask, 5 or 10 mL, 14/10𝕋
1   Water-jacketed reflux condenser, male 14/10𝕋, female 14/10𝕋
1   Air condenser, male 14/10𝕋, female 14/10𝕋
1   Claisen head, male 14/10𝕋 threaded, female 14/10𝕋
1   Craig tube, 3 mL, with Teflon® head (optional)
1   Craig tube, 2 mL, accepts above head
1   Drying tube, male 14/10𝕋
1   Capillary gas delivery tube, male 14/10𝕋
1   Hickman still head, male 14/10𝕋, female 14/10𝕋, or Hickman–Hinkle Spinning Band Head, male 14–10/10𝕋, female 14/10𝕋 with side-arm collection port

Four Gas Chromatographic Collection Items

2   Gas chromatographic collection tubes, male 5/5𝕋
2   Conical vials, 0.1 mL, 5/5𝕋 and threaded

Standard taper (𝕋) ground-glass joints are the common mechanism for assembling all conventional research equipment in the organic laboratory. The symbol 𝕋 is commonly used to indicate the presence of this type of connector. Normally, 𝕋 is either followed or preceded by #/#. The first # refers to the maximum inside diameter of a female (outer) joint or the maximum outside diameter of a male (inner) joint, measured in millimeters. The second number corresponds to the total length of the ground surface of the joint (Fig. 3.8). The advantage of this type of connection is that if the joint surfaces are lightly greased, a vacuum seal is achieved. One of the drawbacks in employing these joints, however, is that contamination of the reacting system readily occurs through extraction of the grease by the solvents present in the reaction vessel. In carrying out microscale reactions, this is particularly troublesome.

An alternative to using greased joints as connectors is to employ either outside or inside screw-threaded glass systems. This type of joint utilizes plastic Teflon-lined screw cap connectors. These threaded glass joints are commercially available; they originally suffered from the same problem as the ungreased standard taper joint, that is, they were not gas tight (at least not in the hands of most undergraduates). The more recent adaptations of these seals have minimized this problem to a reasonable extent. The glassware joints developed in the microscale experimental organic laboratory programs at Bowdoin and Merrimack, however, have the ease of assembly and physical integrity of research-grade standard taper ground-glass joints along with a number of extremely important added features. The dimensions usually are 𝕋 14/10, male or female (𝕋 7/10 systems are optional for some setups). The conical vials in which the large majority of reactions are carried out also employ this alternative type of sealing system. Note that in addition to being ground to a standard taper

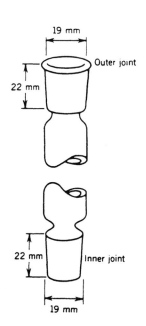

FIGURE 3.8 Standard taper joints [𝕋]. *From Zubric, James W. The Organic Chem Lab Survival Manual, 3rd ed.; Wiley: New York, 1992. (Reprinted by permission of John Wiley & Sons, Inc., New York.)*

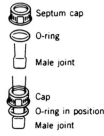

FIGURE 3.9 Threaded female joint.

Septum cap

O-ring

Male joint

Cap

O-ring in position

Male joint

FIGURE 3.10 Male joint with septum cap and O-ring.

on the inside surface, these vials also possess a screw thread on the outside surface (Fig. 3.9). This arrangement allows a standard taper male joint to be sealed to the reaction flask by a septum-type (open) plastic screw cap. The screw cap applies compression to a silicone rubber retaining O-ring positioned on the shoulder of the male joint (Fig. 3.10). The compression of the O-ring thereby achieves a *greaseless* gas-tight seal on the joint seam, while at the same time clamping the two pieces of equipment together. The ground joint provides both protection from intimate solvent contact with the O-ring, and mechanical stability to the connection. This type of joint (now available on all joints of the ACE Glass microscale line of glassware) provides a quick, easy, and reliable mechanism for assembling the glassware required for carrying out the microscale reactions. The use of this type of connector leads to a further bonus during construction of an experimental setup. Because the individual sections are small, light, and firmly sealed together, the entire arrangement often can be mounted on the support rack by a single clamp. In conventional systems, it is necessary in the majority of cases, to employ at least two clamps. This latter arrangement can easily lead to points of high strain in the glass components unless considerable care is taken in the assembly process. Clamp strain is one of the major sources of experimental glassware breakage. The ability to single-clamp essentially all microscale setups effectively eliminates this problem.

It should be emphasized that the ground-glass joint surfaces are grease free; therefore, it is important to disconnect joints soon after use or they may become locked or "frozen" together.

Joints of the size employed in these microscale experiments, however, seldom are a problem to separate, if given proper care (keep them clean!).

A complete set of glassware would involve 14 different components and a total of 17 items grouped according to function as follows (see Figs. 3.1–3.7):

Five Reaction Flasks

2   Conical vials, 5 mL, 14/10T and threaded (one thin-walled)
2   Conical vials, 3 mL, 14/10T and threaded
1   Round-bottom flask, 10 mL, 14/10T
1   Round-bottom flask, 5 mL, 14/10T (optional)

Both the conical vials and the round-bottom flasks are designed to be connected via an O-ring compression cap installed on the male joint of the adjacent part of the system (see Fig. 3.1).

Two Condensers

1   Water-jacketed reflux condenser, male 14/10T, female 14/10T
1   Air condenser, male 14/10T, female 14/10T (optional: The water-jacketed condenser can function as an air condenser)

These items form two sets of condensers for use with 14/10T jointed reaction flasks. The female joints allow connection of the condenser to the 14/10T drying tube and the 14/10 capillary gas delivery tube (see Fig. 3.2).

Two Distillation Heads

1   Hickman still head, male 14/10T, female 14/10T or
1   Hickman–Hinkle Spinning Band Head, male 14–10/10T, female 14/10T with **side-arm collection port** (optional)

The simple Hickman still is used with an O-ring compression cap to carry out semimicro simple or crude fractional distillations. The newly developed Hickman–Hinkle Spinning Band Head is a powerful modification of the simple system. The 3-cm fractionating column of this still routinely develops between five and six theoretical plates. The Hickman–Hinkle is currently available with 14/10Ŧ joints and can be conveniently operated with the 14/10Ŧ, 3- and 5-mL conical vials (see Figs. 3.3 and 3.7). The still head is also available with an optional side-arm collection port.

Two Recrystallization Tubes

1   Craig tube, 2 mL
1   Craig tube, 3 mL

Craig tubes are a particularly effective method for recrystallizing small quantities of reaction products. These tubes possess a nonuniform ground joint in the outer section. The Teflon head modification (earlier models used glass inner sections) has made these systems more durable, and much less susceptible to breakage during centrifugation (see Fig. 3.4).

Three Miscellaneous Items

1   Claisen head, male 14/10Ŧ, female 14/10Ŧ
1   Drying tube, male 14/10Ŧ
1   Capillary gas delivery tube, 14/10Ŧ

The Claisen head (see Fig. 3.3) is often employed to facilitate the syringe addition of reagents to closed moisture-sensitive systems (such as Grignard reactions) via a septum seal in the vertical upper joint. This joint can also function to position the thermometer in the well of a Hickman–Hinkle still. The Claisen adapter is also used to mount the drying tube in a protected position remote from the reaction chamber. The drying tube, in turn, is used to protect moisture-sensitive reaction components from atmospheric water vapor, while allowing a reacting system to remain unsealed. The capillary gas delivery tube is employed in transferring gases, formed during reactions, to storage containers (see Figs. 3.5 and 3.28).

Four Gas Chromatographic Collection Items

2   Gas chromatographic collection tubes, male 5/5Ŧ
2   Conical vials, 0.1 mL, 5/5Ŧ and threaded

The collection tube is connected directly to the exit port of the GC detector through a stainless steel adapter for fraction collection. The collected sample is then transferred to a 0.1-mL conical vial for storage. The system is conveniently employed in the resolution and isolation of two-component mixtures (see Fig. 3.6).

It is important to be able to carry out microscale experiments at accurately determined temperatures. Very often, transformations are successful, in part, because of the ability to maintain precise temperature control. In addition, many reactions require that reactants be intimately mixed to obtain a substantial yield of product. Therefore, the majority of the reactions you perform in this laboratory will be conducted with rapid stirring of the reaction mixture.

STANDARD EXPERIMENTAL APPARATUS

Heating and Stirring Arrangements

Heating Reactions

Many chemical reactions need to be heated in order to proceed. The stirrer/hotplate is the most convenient way to do this, but a method to conduct heat from the hotplate to the flask is necessary. One way to accomplish this is to use an aluminum block, with appropriately shaped holes and recesses to accommodate the glassware. A schematic of this block is shown below in Figure 3.11.

The temperature of the block is read by means of a digital thermometer, which is secured to it by means of a nut. Sometimes the nut comes loose, so it is wise practice to check to make sure the nut is tight and that the electrical leads are connected. Otherwise the block might get very hot without any reading appearing on the digital meter! Some blocks have a hole the size of an ordinary thermometer bulb -- *Do not insert a thermometer into those holes.* We have found that very often the thermometer gets stuck in the hole and cannot be removed without shattering it (and spilling mercury all about).

Since the block is made of aluminum, a magnetic stirrer works well for vials or flasks fitted into the block. If you do not get adequate stirring, tell your teaching assistant.

Some distillations require uniform heating of the flask, which means that you should cover the part of the flask that is not in the block with a small piece of aluminum foil. This insulates the flask and permits higher temperatures to be reached, as well as distributing the heat more evenly.

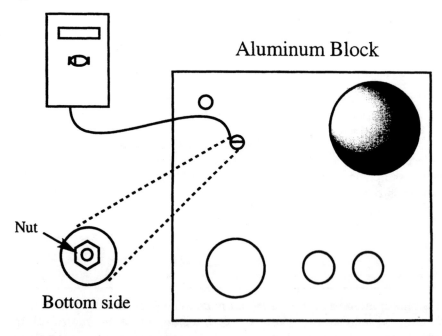

FIGURE 3.11. Aluminum block to be set on top of the hot plate for heating reaction vials, flasks, and distillations.

Removal of Solvent

The solvents used in Chem112A must be removed in the hood. They may be simply boiled off or, more efficiently, removed using a steady, slow stream of nitrogen gas.

Always be sure to weigh the vessel into which you put the solution *before* you evaporate solvent. After you have tared the vessel you can then weigh it after removal of solvent in order to figure out the mass of residue that is left.

Ether is very volatile, and it can be easily evaporated by holding the vessel containing an ether solution in your hand in the hood and blowing nitrogen over it, as drawn in Figure 3.12. You must take care that the gas flow does not push the solvent out of the vessel. Also make sure that the evaporation takes place in the hood -- you do not want to breathe ether fumes!

Some solvents need to be boiled off at higher temperatures, such as methylene chloride. In that case you should add *one* boiling stone. *It doesn't do any good to add more than one,* since its purpose is simply to prevent the solvent from overheating. After taring the vessel (with the boiling stone in it), add your solution and set on a hot plate in the fume hood. You can speed up the evaporation of solvent by blowing nitrogen gas over it, as well.

Occasionally traces of solvent will remain in a sample, even after you think you have gotten rid of it all. If you try to take a microboiling point (pp 44-47) of a sample containing volatile solvent, the sample will shoot out of the tube and be lost. Therefore you must take care that all solvent is gone before trying to take a melting or boiling point.

In some cases you should leave the sample overnight (or over a week) in a beaker or watch glass in your lab drawer, so that evaporation is complete. This is particularly true for solids that have been filtered from water, and which may require more than an hour to dry.

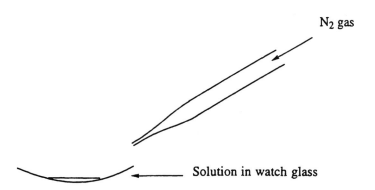

N₂ gas

Solution in watch glass

Figure 3.12 Removing solvent in a watch glass with a slow stream of nitrogen gas coming out through a glass Pasteur pipette.

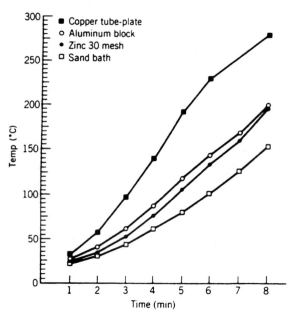

FIGURE 3.13   Temperature rise characteristics for several thermal devices.

An evaluation of copper devices also has been undertaken, as copper has nearly double the thermal conductivity of aluminum. The configuration found most attractive in this series is the **copper tube–plate device**. It requires relatively little copper, as it utilizes a 3-mm plate and 15-mm lengths of standard tubing (see Fig. 3.14). The fabrication cost should be close to that of the aluminum block systems currently on the market. As shown in Figure 3.13, compared to all other systems, the copper plate is far superior in temperature rise from room temperature. Thus, it is found at nearly 200 °C at the 5-min mark, whereas the aluminum block is barely above 100 °C at this time. It is also easier to achieve equilibrium conditions (see Fig. 3.15) compared to the aluminum block. An equilibrium temperature of 150 °C could be reached in 9 min with copper, whereas it took 19 min with aluminum under the same conditions. The copper device also cools at nearly double the rate of the aluminum block. For example, to drop from 200 to 150 °C takes the aluminum block 8.1 min, whereas the copper system reaches the lower temperature in only 4.2 min. This characteristic is important in controlling temperature overruns.

Of particular significance is the observation that when distilling or refluxing organic materials, the block temperatures when employing the copper device are measurably lower. For example, 1 mL of *p*-xylene (bp 138 °C) contained in a 5-mL reaction vial refluxes at 175 °C in the copper bath. The aluminum block requires 188 °C under the same conditions and the sand bath ranks a distant third at 208 °C.

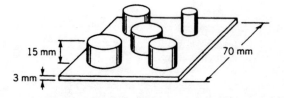

FIGURE 3.14   Copper tube heat-transfer plate.

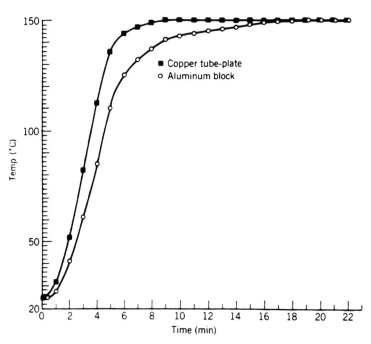

FIGURE 3.15 Time to equilibrium (control set at high until the temperature reaches 85 °C, then heat control adjusted to a lower setting to give 150 °C at equilibrium).

Stirring

Stirring the reaction mixture in a conical vial is carried out with Teflon-coated magnetic spin vanes, and in round-bottom flasks with Teflon-coated magnetic stirring bars (see Figs. 3.11 and 3.12).

It is important that the settings on the controls that adjust the current to the heating element, and to the motor that spins the magnet, are roughly calibrated to block temperatures and spin rates, respectively. You can make a rough graph of heat control setting versus temperature (Fig. 3.16) for your particular hot plate system (see sections on the Sand Bath Technique (p. 20) and Metal Heat-Transfer Devices (p. 21)). These data will save considerable time when you bring a reaction system to operating temperature. When you first enter the laboratory, it is advisable to adjust the temperature setting on the hot plate stirrer with the heating device, or bath, in place. The setting is determined from your control setting–temperature calibration curve. This procedure will allow the heated bath to reach a relatively constant temperature by the time it is required. You will then be able to make small final adjustments more quickly, if necessary.

NOTE. *If a sand bath is used, it should again be emphasized that heavy layers of sand act as an insulator on the hot plate surface. This insulation can result in damage to the heating element at high-temperature settings. Therefore, when temperatures over 150 °C are required, it is especially important to remember to use the minimum amount of sand.*

It is important to position the reaction flask as close to the bottom surface of the crystallizing dish as possible in those experiments that depend on magnetic stirring. This arrangement is good practice, in general, as it leads to use of the minimum amount of sand when this type of bath is employed.

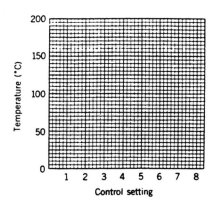

FIGURE 3.16 Plot your temperature (°C) versus hot plate control setting.

If the reaction does not require elevated temperatures, but needs only to be stirred, the system is assembled without the heating device. Some stirred reactions, on the other hand, require cooling with a crystallizing dish filled with ice water, or with ice water and salt if lower temperatures are required.

Reflux Apparatus

We often find that to bring about a successful reaction between two substances, it is necessary to intimately mix the materials together and to maintain a specific temperature. The mixing operation is conveniently achieved by dissolution of the materials in a solvent in which they are mutually soluble. If the reaction is carried out in solution under reflux conditions, the choice of solvent can be used to control the temperature of the reaction. Many organic reactions involve the use of a reflux apparatus in one arrangement or another.

What do we mean by *reflux?* The term means to "return," or "run back." This return is exactly how the reflux apparatus functions. When the temperature of the reaction system is raised to the solvent's boiling point (constant temperature), *all* vapors are condensed and returned to the reaction flask or vial; this operation is not a distillation and the liquid phase remains at a stable maximum temperature. In microscale reactions, two basic types of reflux condensers are utilized: the air-cooled condenser, or *air condenser*, and the *water-jacketed condenser*. The air condenser operates, as its name implies, by condensing solvent vapors on the cool vertical wall of an extended glass tube that dissipates the heat by contact with laboratory room air. This arrangement functions quite effectively with liquids boiling above 150 °C. Indeed, a simple test tube can act as a reaction chamber and air condenser all in one unit, and many simple reactions can be most easily carried out in test tubes. Air condensers can occasionally be used with lower boiling systems; however, the water-jacketed condenser, which employs flowing cold water to remove heat from the vertical column and thus facilitate vapor condensation, is more often employed in these situations. The latter apparatus is highly efficient at condensing vapor from low-boiling liquids. Both styles of condensers accommodate various sizes of reaction flasks and are available in standard taper joint size 14/10𝕋. The tops of both condenser columns possess the female 14/10𝕋 joint.

In refluxing systems that do not require significant mixing or agitation, the stirrer (magnetic spin vane or bar) usually is replaced by a "boiling stone." These sharp-edged stones possess highly fractured surfaces that are very efficient at initiating bubble formation as the reacting medium approaches the boiling point. The boiling stone acts to protect the system from disastrous boil-overs and also reduces "bumping." (Boiling stones should be used only once and **must never** be added to a hot solution. In the first case, the vapor cavities become filled with liquid upon cooling, and thus a boiling stone becomes less effective after its first use. In the second case, **adding the boiling stone to the hot solution may initiate uncontrollable vapor eruption leading to catastrophic boil-over.**)

Various Arrangements of Reflux Apparatus (see Figs. 3.17–3.19)

Air condenser with a 3- or 5-mL conical vial, arranged for heating and magnetic stirring.

Water-jacketed condenser with a 3- or 5-mL conical vial, arranged for heating and magnetic stirring.

Water-jacketed condenser with a 10-mL round-bottom flask, arranged for heating and stirring.

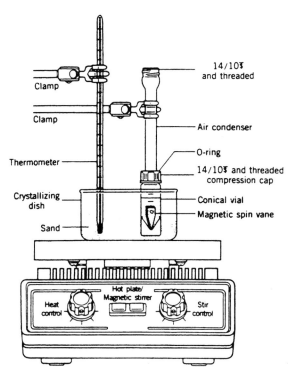

FIGURE 3.17 Air condenser with conical vial, arranged for heating and magnetic stirring.

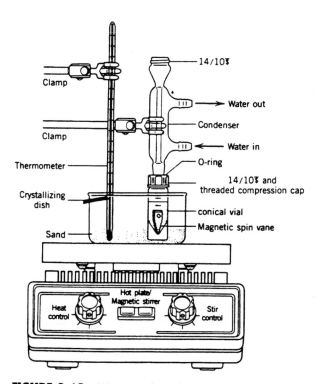

FIGURE 3.18 Water-jacketed condenser with conical vial, arranged for heating and magnetic stirring.

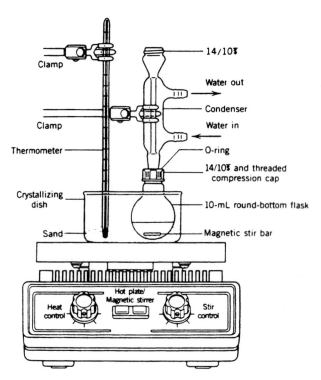

FIGURE 3.19 Water-jacketed condenser with 10-mL round-bottom flask, arranged for heating and magnetic stirring.

Distillation Apparatus

Distillation is a laboratory operation used to separate substances that have different boiling points. The mixture is heated, vaporized, and then condensed, with the more volatile component being enriched in the early fractions of condensate. Unlike the reflux operation, in distillations none, or only a portion, of the condensate is returned to the flask where vaporization is taking place. Many distillation apparatus have been designed to carry out this basic operation. These apparatus differ mainly in small features that are used to solve particular types of separation problems. In microscale experiments, a number of simple *semimicroscale* distillations are often required. For these distillations, the Hickman still head (Fig. 3.20) is ideally suited. This system has a 14/10ℑ male joint for connection to either the 3- or 5-mL conical vials or the 5- or 10-mL round-bottom (RB) flasks. The still head functions as both an air condenser and a condensate trap. For a detailed discussion of this piece of equipment see Distillation Experiments [3A] and [3B]. In 1987, a new modification of the basic Hickman still was developed, the Hickman–Hinkle spinning band still (Fig. 3.21), and named for the Bowdoin College undergraduate student who first proposed this arrangement. The modified still (plain or side-arm types) functions in much the same way as the simple Hickman still, except that a Teflon spinning band element is mounted in the slightly extended section between the male joint and the collection collar. In addition, this system has a built-in thermometer well that allows fairly accurate measurement of vapor temperature. When the band is spun at 1500 rpm by a magnetic stirring hot

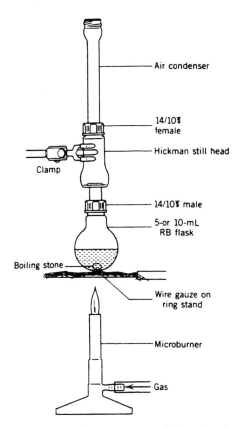

FIGURE 3.20 Hickman still head and air condenser with 5-mL round-bottom flask, arranged for microburner heating.

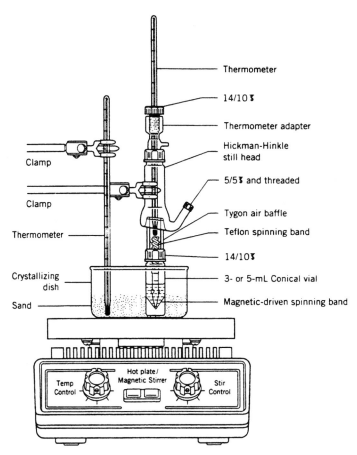

FIGURE 3.21 Hickman–Hinkle still head with side port 3- or 5-mL conical vial, Teflon® spinning band, and thermometer adapter and arranged for heating and magnetic stirring.

plate, this still is transformed into a very effective short-path fractional distillation column (see Distillation, Experiment [3D]).

The most powerful system currently available for both the instructional and research laboratories, however, is the 2.5-in. vacuum-jacketed microscale spinning band distillation column (see Fig. 3.22a and Experiment [3C] for description and details). This still utilizes the same type of band drive as the Hickman–Hinkle columns, but in addition the system is designed for conventional downward distillate collection, nonstopcock reflux control, and reasonably accurate temperature sensing. The column, which can develop nearly 12 theoretical plates, possesses the highest resolution of any standard distillation apparatus presently in use in the introductory organic laboratory.

The high-performance low-cost atmospheric pressure 2.5-in. micro-spinning band distillation column has been modified to accommodate reduced pressure fractional distillation (Fig. 3.22b) by: (a) replacing the air condenser and suspended thermometer with a 14/10$\intercal$, vacuum-tight, threaded thermometer adapter; (b) replacing the heavy-walled 3-mL conical collection vial with a thin-walled, 3-mL conical vial, which has, mounted near the bottom, a side arm with a threaded 5/5 $\intercal$ joint (a septum cap and silicone septum form a vacuum-tight seal on the side arm); and (c)

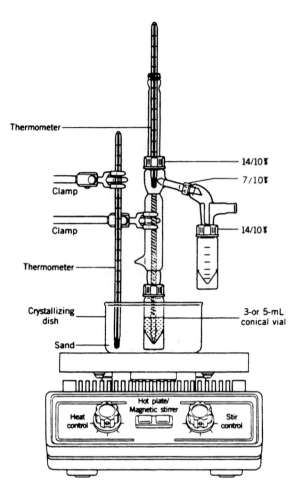

FIGURE 3.22a Micro spinning band distillation column (2.5 in.).

a vacuum tubing nipple replacing the Teflon stopper (7/10⅜) used to establish a vapor lock on the collection side of the system in the atmospheric still.

The system is evacuated via the vacuum tubing nipple. Fractions are efficiently collected with a gas-tight syringe and needle inserted through a septum mounted in the side arm of the 3-mL collection vial. The collection vial may be cooled externally during collection. This arrangement allows convenient collection of distillate fractions down to pressures of approximately 100 torr (successful collections have been made at pressures as low as 10 torr).

The system continues to function very effectively under reduced pressure, even though the vapor lock has been removed. Data indicate that height equivalent/theoretical plate values will remain near 0.25 in. per plate in these columns.

Various Distillation Apparatus (see Figs. 3.20 and 3.21)

Hickman still head and air condenser with 5- and 10-mL round-bottom flasks, or 3- and 5-mL conical vials arranged for microburner or hot plate heating (see Experiments [3A] and [3B]).

Hickman–Hinkle still head with 5-mL conical vial (thin-walled), arranged for heating and magnetic spinning (see Experiment [3D].)

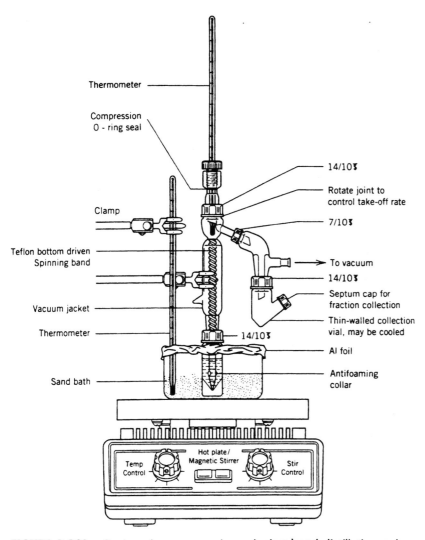

Thermometer

Compression
0 - ring seal

Clamp

Teflon bottom driven
Spinning band

Vacuum jacket

Thermometer

Sand bath

14/10ℑ

Rotate joint to
control take-off rate

7/10ℑ

To vacuum

14/10ℑ

Septum cap for
fraction collection

Thin-walled collection
vial, may be cooled

14/10ℑ

Al foil

Antifoaming
collar

Hot plate/
Magnetic Stirrer

Temp
Control

Stir
Control

FIGURE 3.22b   Reduced pressure microspinning band distillation column.

Many organic reagents react rapidly and preferentially with water. *The success or failure of many experiments depends to a large degree on how well atmospheric moisture is excluded from the reaction system.* The "drying tube," which is packed with a desiccant, such as anhydrous calcium chloride, is a handy way to carry out a reaction in apparatus that is not totally closed to the atmosphere, but which is reasonably well protected from water vapor. The microscale apparatus described here are designed to be used with the 14/10ℑ drying tube. The reflux condensers discussed earlier are constructed with female 14/10ℑ joints at the top of the column, which allows convenient connection of the drying tube, if the refluxing system is moisture sensitive.

Because many reactions are highly sensitive to moisture, successful operation at the microscale level can be rather challenging. If anhydrous reagents are to be added after an apparatus has been dried and assembled, it is important to be able to introduce these reagents without exposing the system to the atmosphere, particularly when operating under humid atmospheric conditions. In reactions not requiring reflux conditions and conducted at room temperature, this addition procedure is best accomplished

**Moisture-Protected
Reaction Apparatus**

by use of the microscale Claisen head adapter. The adapter has a vertical screw-threaded standard taper joint that will accept a septum cap. The septum seal allows syringe addition of reagents and avoids the necessity of opening the apparatus to the laboratory atmosphere.

In a few instances reactions that are unusually moisture sensitive will be encountered. In this situation, reactions are best carried out in completely sealed systems that are scrupulously dry. The use of the Claisen head adapter with a balloon substituted for the drying tube provides a satisfactory solution to the problem. Occasionally, it becomes important to maintain dry conditions during a distillation. The Hickman stills are constructed with a 14/10\$ joint at the top of the head that readily accepts the drying tube (or Claisen head plus drying tube)

Various Moisture-Protected Reaction Apparatus (see Figs. 3.23–3.26)

Moisture-protected water-jacketed condenser with a 3- or 5-mL conical vial, arranged for heating and stirring.

Moisture-protected Claisen head with a 3- or 5-mL conical vial, arranged for syringe addition and magnetic stirring.

Sealed Claisen head with a 3- or 5-mL conical vial, arranged for nitrogen (N$_2$) flushing, heating, and magnetic stirring.

Moisture-protected Hickman still head with a 10-mL round-bottom flask, arranged for heating and stirring.

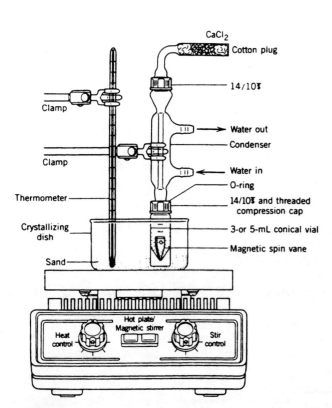

FIGURE 3.23   Moisture-protected water-jacketed condenser with 3- or 5-mL conical vial, arranged for heating and magnetic stirring.

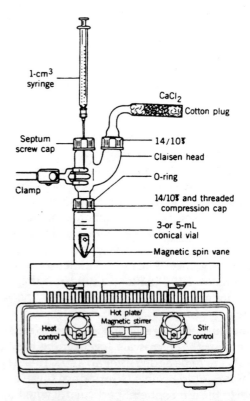

FIGURE 3.24   Moisture-protected Claisen head with 3- or 5-mL conical vial, arranged for syringe addition and magnetic stirring.

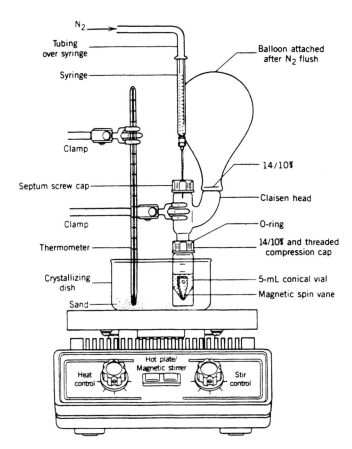

FIGURE 3.25 Sealed Claisen head with 3- or 5-mL conical vial, arranged for N₂ flushing, heating, and magnetic stirring.

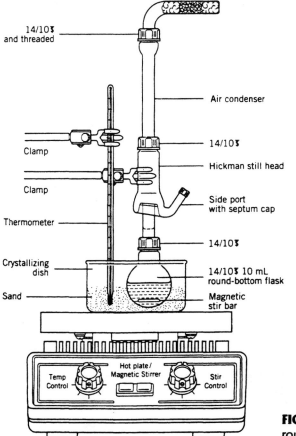

FIGURE 3.26 Moisture-protected Hickman still head with 10-mL round-bottom flask, arranged for heating and stirring.

Specialized Pieces of Equipment

Collection of Gaseous Products

Some experiments lead to gaseous products. The collection, or trapping, of gases is conveniently carried out by using the capillary gas delivery tube. This item is designed to be attached directly to a 1- or 3-mL conical vial, or to the female 14/10$ joint of a condenser connected to a reaction flask or vial. The tube leads to the collection system, which may be a simple, inverted, graduated cylinder; a blank-threaded septum joint; or an air condenser filled with water (where the gaseous product, or products, are not soluble in the aqueous phase). The 0.1-mm capillary bore considerably reduces dead volume, and increases the efficiency of product transfer (see Figs. 3.27 and 3.28).

Collection of Gas Chromatographic Effluents

The trapping and collection of gas chromatographic liquid fractions becomes a particularly important exercise at the microscale level of experi-

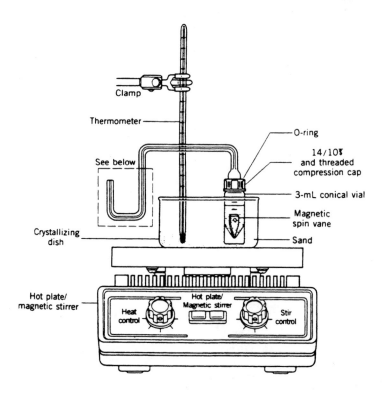

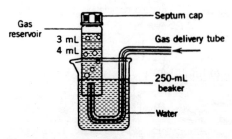

FIGURE 3.27   Conical vial (3-mL) and capillary gas delivery tube arranged for heating and magnetic stirring.

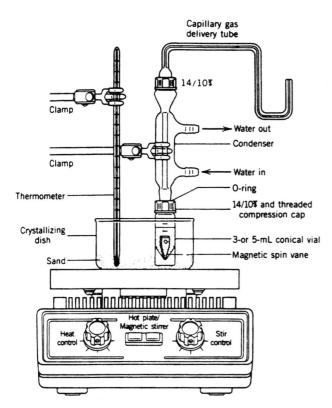

FIGURE 3.28 Water-jacketed condenser with 3- or 5-mL conical vial and capillary gas delivery tube, arranged for heating and stirring.

mentation. When liquid product yields drop below 100 μL, conventional distillation, even utilizing microtechniques, becomes impractical. In this case, preparative gas chromatography replaces conventional distillation as the route of choice to product purification. A number of the reaction products in the experimental section of the text depend on this approach for successful purification and isolation. The ease and efficiency of carrying out this operation is greatly facilitated by employing the 5/5Ŧ collection tube and the 0.1-mL 5/5Ŧ conical collection vial (see Fig. 3.29).

Various Sample Collection Apparatus (see Figs. 3.27–3.29)

Conical vial (1-mL) and capillary gas delivery tube, arranged for heating and stirring.

Water-jacketed condenser with 3- or 5-mL conical vial and capillary gas delivery tube, arranged for heating and stirring.

Gas chromatographic collection tube and 0.1-mL conical vial.

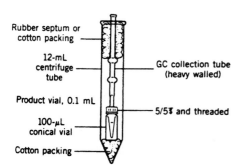

FIGURE 3.29 Gas chromatographic collection tube and 0.1 mL conical vial.

MICROSCALE LAWS

Rules of the Trade for Handling Organic Materials at the Microscale Level

Now that we have briefly looked at the equipment we will be using to carry out microscale organic reactions, let us examine the specific techniques that are used to deal with the small quantities of material involved. Microscale synthetic organic reactions, as defined by Cheronis,[2] start with 15–150 mg of the limiting reagent. These quantities sound small, and they are. Although 150 mg of a light, powdery material will fill one-half of a 1-mL conical vial, you will have a hard time observing 15 mg of a clear liquid in the same container, even with magnification. On the other hand, this volume of liquid is reasonably easy to observe when placed in a 0.1-mL conical vial. A vital part of the game of working with small amounts of materials is to become familiar with microscale techniques and to practice them as much as possible in the laboratory.

Rules for Working with Liquids at the Microscale Level

1. *Liquids are never poured at the microscale level.* Liquid substances are transferred by pipet or syringe. As we are working with small, easy-to-hold glassware at the microscale level, the best technique for transfer is to hold both containers with the fingers of one hand, with the mouths as close together as possible. The free hand is then used to operate the pipet (syringe) to withdraw the liquid and make the transfer. This approach reduces to a minimum the time that the open tip is not in, or over, the reservoir or the reaction flask. We employ three different pipets and two standard syringes for most experiments in which liquids are involved. *This equipment can be a prime source of contamination.* Be very careful to thoroughly clean the pipets and syringes after each use.

   a. *Pasteur pipet*, often called a capillary pipet, is a simple glass tube with the end drawn to a fine capillary. These pipets can hold several milliliters of liquid (Fig. 3.30*a*), and are filled using a small rubber bulb or one of the very handy, commercially available pipet pumps. Since many transfers are made using the Pasteur pipet, it is suggested that several of them be calibrated for approximate delivery of 0.5, 1.0, 1.5, and 2.0 mL of liquid. This calibration is easily done by drawing the measured amount of a liquid from a 10-mL graduated cylinder and marking the level of the liquid in the pipet. This mark can be made with transparent tape, or by scratching with a file. Indicate the level with a marking pen before trying to tape or file the pipet.

   b. *Pasteur filter pipet.* A very handy adaptation of the Pasteur pipet is a filter pipet. This pipet is constructed by taking a small cotton ball and placing it in the large open end of the standard Pasteur pipet. Hold the pipet vertically and tap it gently to position the cotton ball in the drawn section of the tube (Fig. 3.30*b*). Now form a plug in the capillary section by pushing the cotton ball down the pipet with a piece of copper wire (Fig. 3.30*c*). Finish by seating the plug flush with the end of the capillary (Fig. 3.30*d*). The optimum-size plug will allow easy movement along the capillary while it is being positioned by the copper wire. Compression of the cotton will build enough pressure against the walls of the capillary (once the plug is in position) to prevent plug slippage while the pipet is filled with liquid. If the ball is too big, it will wedge in the capillary

---

[2] Cheronis, N. D., *Semimicro Experimental Organic Chemistry*, Hadrion Press, Inc., New York, 1958.

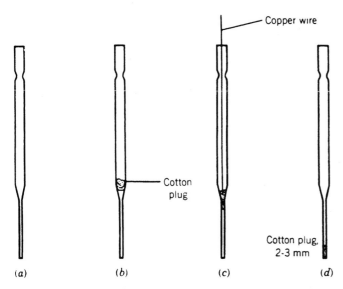

Copper wire

Cotton
plug

Cotton plug,
2-3 mm

(a)   (b)   (c)   (d)

FIGURE 3.30   Preparation of Pasteur filter pipet.

before the end is reached, and wall pressure will be so great that liquid flow will be shut off. Even some plugs that are loose enough to be positioned at the end of the capillary will still have developed sufficient lateral pressure to make the filling rate unacceptably slow. If the cotton filter, however, is positioned too loosely, it may be easily dislodged from the pipet by the solvent flow. These plugs can be quickly and easily inserted with a little practice. Once in place, the plug is rinsed with 1 mL of methanol, 1 mL of hexane, and dried before use.

The purpose of placing the cotton plug in the pipet is two-fold. First, a particular problem with the transfer of volatile liquids via the standard Pasteur pipet is the rapid build up of back pressure from solvent vapors in the rubber bulb. This pressure quickly tends to force the liquid back out of the pipet and can cause valuable product to drip on the bench top. The cotton plug tends to resist this back pressure and allows much easier control of the solution once it is in the pipet. The time-delay factor becomes particularly important when the Pasteur filter pipet is employed as a microseparatory funnel (see the discussion on extraction techniques in Technique 4, p. 73).

Second, each time a transfer of material is made, the material is automatically filtered. This process effectively removes dust and lint, which are a constant problem when working at the microscale level with unfiltered room air. A second stage of filtration may be obtained by employing a disposable filter tip on the original Pasteur filter pipet as described by Rothchild.[3]

c. *Automatic pipet (considered the Mercedes-Benz of pipets).* Automatic pipets quickly, safely, and reproducibly measure and dispense specific volumes of liquids. These pipets are particularly valuable at the microscale level, as they generate the precise and accurate liquid measurements that are absolutely necessary when handling microliter volumes of reagent. The automatic pipet adds consider-

[3] Rothchild, R. *J. Chem. Educ.* **1990,** *67,* 425.

able insurance for the success of an experiment, as any liquid can be efficiently measured, transferred, and delivered to the reaction flask. Automatic pipets have become almost an essential instrument in the active microscale laboratory.

The automatic pipet system consists of a calibrated piston pipet with a specially designed disposable plastic tip. It is possible to encounter any one of three pipet styles: single volume, multirange, or continuously adjustable (see Fig. 3.31). The first type is calibrated to deliver only a single volume. The second type is adjustable to two or three predetermined delivery volumes. The third type is the most versatile and can be user set to deliver any volume within the range of the pipet. Obviously, the price of these valuable laboratory tools goes up with increasing features. These pipets are expensive, and often must be shared in the laboratory. Treat them with respect!

The automatic pipet is designed so that the liquid comes in contact only with the disposable tip. Never load the pipet without the tip in place. Never immerse the tip completely in the liquid that is being pipetted. Always keep the pipet vertical when the tip is attached. If these three rules are followed, most automatic pipets will give many years of reliable service. A few general rules for improving reproducibility with an automatic pipet should also be followed.

- Try to effect the same uptake and delivery motion for all samples. Smooth depression and release of the piston will give the most consistent results. Never allow the piston to snap back.
- *Always* depress the piston to the first stop before inserting the tip into the liquid. If the piston is depressed after submersion, formation of an air bubble in the tip becomes likely, and bubble formation will result in a filling error.
- *Never* insert the tip more than 5 mm into the liquid. It is good practice not to allow the body of the pipet to contact any surface, or bottle neck, that might be wet with a chemical.
- If an air bubble forms in the tip during uptake, return the fluid, discard the tip, and repeat the sampling process.

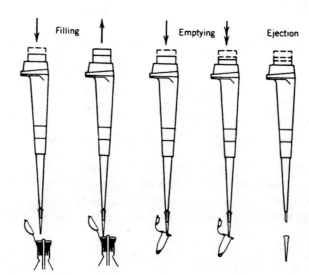

FILLING   EMPTYING   EJECTION

FIGURE 3.31 Operation of automatic delivery pipet. *(Courtesy of Brinkmann Instruments Co., Westbury, NY)*

d. *Syringes.* Syringes are particularly helpful pieces of equipment when transferring liquid reagents or solutions to sealed reaction systems from sealed reagent or solvent reservoirs. Syringe needles can be inserted through a septum, which avoids opening the apparatus to the atmosphere. Syringes are also routinely employed in the determination of ultramicro boiling points (10-μL GC syringe). It is critically important to clean the syringe needle after each use. Effective cleaning of a syringe requires as many as a dozen flushes. For many transfers, the microscale laboratory utilizes a low-cost glass 1-mL insulin syringe in which the rubber plunger seal is replaced with a Teflon seal (ACE Glass). For preparative GC injections, the standard 50- or 100-μL syringes are preferred (see Technique 1).

2. *Liquid volumes may be converted easily to mass measures by the following relationship:*

$$\text{Volume (mL)} = \frac{\text{mass (g)}}{\text{density (g/mL)}}$$

3. *Work with liquids in conical vials,* and work in a vial whose capacity is approximately twice the volume of the material. The trick here is to reduce the surface area of the flask in contact with the sample to an absolute minimum. Conical systems are far superior to the spherical surface of the conventional round-bottom flask.

Liquids may also be weighed directly. A tared container (vial) should be used. After addition of the liquid, the vial should be kept capped throughout the weighing operation. This procedure prevents loss of the liquid material by evaporation. If the density of the liquid is known, the approximate volume of the liquid should be transferred to the container using an automatic delivery pipet or a calibrated Pasteur pipet. Use the above expression relating density, mass, and volume to calculate the volume required by the measured mass. Adjustment of the mass to give the desired value can then be made by adding or removing small amounts of liquid from the container by Pasteur pipet.

NOTE. *Before you leave the balance area, be sure to replace all caps on reagent bottles and clean up any spills. A modern balance is a precision instrument that can easily be damaged by contamination.*

Rules for Working with Solids at the Microscale Level

1. *General considerations.* Working with a crystalline solid is much easier than working with the equivalent quantity of a liquid. Unless the solid is in solution, a spill on a clean glass working surface usually can be recovered quickly and efficiently. *Be careful, however, when working in solution. ALWAYS use the same precautions that you would use if you were handling a pure liquid.*

2. *The transfer of solids.* Solids are normally transferred with a microspatula, a technique that is not difficult to develop.

3. *Weighing solids at the milligram level.* The current generation of single-pan electronic balances has removed much of the drudgery from weighing solids. These systems can automatically tare an empty vial. Once the vial is tared, the reagent is added in small portions. The weight of each addition is instantly registered; material is added until the desired quantity has been transferred.

Most solids are weighed in glass containers (vials or beakers), in plastic or aluminum weighing boats, or on glazed weighing paper. Filter paper or other absorbing materials are not the best choice for this measurement, as small quantities of the weighed material will often adhere to the fibers of the paper.

THE LABORATORY NOTEBOOK	Written communication is the most important method by which chemists transmit their work to the scientific community. It begins with the record kept in a laboratory notebook. The reduction to practice of an experiment originally recorded in the laboratory notebook is the source of information used to prepare scientific papers published in journals or presented at meetings. For the industrial chemist, it is especially critical in obtaining patent coverage.

It is important that potential scientists, whatever the field, learn to keep a detailed account of their work. A laboratory notebook has several key components. Note how each component is incorporated into the example that follows.

Key Components of a Laboratory Experiment Writeup

 1. Date experiment was conducted.
 2. Title of experiment.
 3. Purpose for running the reaction.
 4. Reaction scheme.
 5. Table of reagents and products.
 6. Details of procedure used.
 7. Characteristics of the product(s).
 8. References to product or procedure (if any).
 9. Analytical and spectral data.
10. Signature of person performing the experiment and that of a witness, if required.

In reference to point 6, it is the obligation of the person doing the work to list the equipment, the amounts of reagents, the experimental conditions, and the method used to isolate the product. Any color or temperature changes should be carefully noted and recorded.

Several additional points can be made about the proper maintenance of a laboratory record.

11. A hardbound, permanent notebook is essential.
12. Each page of the notebook should be numbered in consecutive order. For convenience, an index at the beginning or end of the book is recommended and blank pages should be retained for this purpose.
13. If a page is not completely filled, an ''X'' should be used to show that no further entry was made.
14. Always record your data in ink. If a mistake is made, draw a neat line through the word or words so that they remain legible. Data are always recorded directly into the notebook, *never* on scrap paper!
15. Make the record clear and unambiguous. Pay attention to grammar and spelling.
16. In industrial research laboratories, your signature, as well as that of a witness, is required, because the notebook may be used as a legal document.
17. Always write and organize your work so that someone else could come into the laboratory and repeat your directions without confusion or uncertainty. *Completeness* and *legibility* are key factors.

For those of you undertaking study in the organic laboratory for the first time, it is likely that the reactions you will be performing have been worked out and checked in detail. Because of this, your instructor may not require you to keep your notebook in such a meticulous fashion. For example, when you describe the procedure (item 6), it may be acceptable to make a clear reference to the material in the laboratory manual and to note any modifications or deviations from the prescribed procedure. In some cases, it may be more practical to use an outline method. In any event, the following example should be studied carefully. It may be used as a reference when detailed records are important in your work.

NOTE. *Because of its length, the example is presented typed. Normally, the entry in the notebook is handwritten. However, now that computers are gaining wide acceptance in laboratory work, many chemists are using this means to record their data.*

The circled numbers refer to list on page 38

EXAMPLE OF A LABORATORY NOTEBOOK ENTRY

16 Aug. 1985 ①

PREPARATION OF DIPHENYL SUCCINATE ②

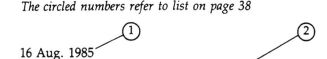

$$\begin{matrix} CH_2CO_2H \\ | \\ CH_2CO_2H \end{matrix} + 2\ C_6H_5OH + POCl_3 \rightarrow \begin{matrix} CH_2CO_2C_6H_5 \\ | \\ CH_2CO_2C_6H_5 \end{matrix} + HPO_3 + 3\ HCl \quad \Big\}$$ ④

Diphenyl succinate is being prepared as one of a series of dicarboxylic acid esters that are to be investigated as growth stimulants for selected fungi species. ③

This procedure was adapted from that reported by Daub, G. H.; Johnson, W. S. *Organic Syntheses*; Wiley: New York, 1963; Collect Vol. IV, p. 390. ⑧

Physical Properties of Reactants and Products

Compound	MW[a]	Amounts	mmol	mp(°C)	bp(°C)
Succinic acid	118.09	118 mg	1.0	182	
Phenol	94.4	188 mg	2.0	40–42	182
Phosphorus oxychloride	153.33	84 μL	0.9		105.8
Diphenyl succinate	270.29			121	

⑤

[a] MW = molecular weight.

In a 3.0-mL conical vial containing a magnetic spin vane and equipped with a reflux condenser protected by a calcium chloride drying tube were placed succinic acid (118 mg, 1.0 mmol), phenol (188 mg, 2.0 mmol), and phosphorous oxychloride (84 μL, 0.9 mmol). The reaction mixture was heated with stirring at 115 °C in a sand bath in the **hood** for 1.25 hours. It was necessary to conduct the reaction in the **hood**, as hydrogen chloride (HCl) gas evolved during the course of the reaction. The drying tube was removed, toluene (0.5 mL) was added through the top of ⑥ the condenser using a Pasteur pipet, and the drying tube replaced. The mixture was then heated for an additional 1 hour at 115 °C.

The hot toluene solution was separated from the red syrupy residue of phosphoric acid using a Pasteur pipet. The toluene extract was filtered by gravity using a fast-grade filter paper and the filtrate collected in a 10-mL Erlenmeyer flask. The phosphoric acid residue was then extracted with two additional 1.0-mL portions of hot toluene. These extracts were also separated using the Pasteur pipet and filtered, and the filtrate was collected in the same Erlenmeyer flask. The combined toluene solutions were concentrated to a volume of approximately 0.6 mL by warming them in a sand bath under a gentle stream of nitrogen (N_2) gas in the **hood**. The pale yellow liquid residue was then allowed to cool to room temperature; the diphenyl succinate precipitated as colorless crystals. The solid was collected by vacuum filtration using a Hirsch funnel and the filter cake washed with three 0.5-mL portions of cold diethyl ether. The product was dried in a vacuum oven at 30 °C (3 mm) for 30 min.

⑦
⑧   There was obtained 181 mg (67%) of diphenyl succinate having a mp = 120–121 °C (lit. value 121 °C: CRC *Handbook of Chemistry and Physics*, 72nd ed.; CRC Press: Boca Raton, FL, 1991–1992; no. 13559, p. 3–471).

⑨   The IR spectrum exhibits the expected peaks for the compound. [*At this point, the data may be listed, or the spectrum pasted on a separate page of the notebook.*]

Marilyn C. Waris

⑩

witnessed by
D. Jeanne d'Arc Mailhiot   16/Aug./1985

Almost without exception, in each of the experiments presented in this text, you are requested to calculate the percentage yield. For any reaction, it is always important for the chemist to know how much of a product is *actually* produced (experimental) in relation to the *theoretical* amount (maximum) that could have been formed. The percentage yield is calculated on the basis of the relationship

CALCULATION OF YIELDS

$$\% \text{ yield} = \frac{\text{actual yield (experimental)}}{\text{theoretical yield (calculated maximum)}} \times 100$$

The percentage yield is generally calculated on a weight (gram or milligram) or on a mole basis. In the present text, the calculations are made using milligrams.

Several steps are involved in calculation of the percentage yield.

1. Write a *balanced* equation for the reaction. For example, consider Experiment [22A], the Wiliamson synthesis of propyl *p*-tolyl ether.

CH$_3$—⬡—OH + CH$_3$CH$_2$CH$_2$—I $\xrightarrow[\text{(C}_4\text{H}_9)_4\text{N}^+, \text{Br}^-]{\text{NaOH}}$ CH$_3$—⬡—O—(CH$_2$)$_2$CH$_3$ + Na$^+$, I$^-$

     p-Cresol   Propyl iodide   Propyl *p*-tolyl ether

2. Identify the *limiting* reactant. The ratio of reactants is calculated on a millimole (or mole) basis. In the example, 0.78 mmol of *p*-cresol is used compared with 0.77 mmol of propyl iodide. Note that the sodium hydroxide is used as a reagent but *does not* appear in the product, propyl *p*-tolyl ether. Therefore, it is not considered in the calculations. Nor is the quaternary salt considered; it is used as a phase transfer catalyst. The reaction is run essentially on a 1 : 1 molar ratio and, thus, calculation of the theoretical yield can be based on the *p*-cresol or the propyl iodide.

3. Calculate the *theoretical* (maximum) amount of the product that could be obtained for the conversion, based on the limiting reactant. In the present case, referring to the balanced equation, one mole of propyl iodide affords one mole of the ether product. Therefore, if we start with 0.77 mmol of the propyl iodide, the maximum amount of propyl *p*-tolyl ether that can be produced is 0.77 mmol, or 115.7 mg.

4. Determine the *actual* (experimental) yield (milligrams) of product isolated in the reaction. This amount is invariably less than the theoretical quantity, unless the material is impure (one common contaminant is water). For example, student yields for the preparation of propyl *p*-tolyl ether average 70 mg.

5. Calculate the *percentage yield* using the weights determined in steps 3 and 4. The percentage yield is then

$$\% \text{ yield} = \frac{70 \text{ mg (actual)}}{115.7 \text{ mg (theoretical)}} \times 100 = 60.5\%$$

As you carry out each reaction in the laboratory, strive to obtain as high a percentage yield of product as possible. The reaction conditions have been carefully developed and, therefore, it is essential that you master the microscale techniques concerned with transfer of reagents and the isolation of products as soon as possible.

4

Determination of Physical Properties

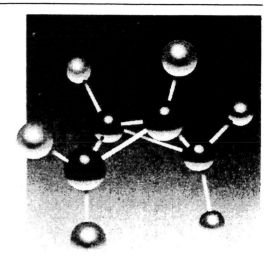

C_4H_6, Bicyclo[1.1.0]butane
Lemal, Menger and Clark (1963).

Determination of physical properties is important for substance identification, and as an indication of material purity. Historically, the physical constants of prime interest include: the boiling point, density, and refractive index in liquids and the melting point in solids. In special cases, optical rotation and molecular weight determinations may be required. Today, with the widespread availability of spectroscopic instrumentation, powerful new techniques may be applied to the direct identification and characterization of materials, including the analysis of individual components of very small quantities of complex mixtures. The sequential measurement of the infrared (IR) and mass spectrometric (MS) characteristics of a substance resolved "on the fly" by capillary gas chromatography (GC) can be quickly determined and interpreted. This particular combination (GC-IR-MS), which stands out among a number of "hyphenated" techniques just becoming available, is perhaps the most powerful system yet developed for molecular identification. The rapid development of high-field multinuclear nuclear magnetic resonance (NMR) spectrometers also has added another powerful dimension to identification techniques. The NMR sensitivities, however, are still considerably lower than either IR or MS. The IR spectrum alone, obtained with one data point per wavenumber, can add more than 4000 measurements to the few classically determined properties. *Indeed, even compared to high-resolution MS, and pulsed ^1H and ^{13}C NMR, the IR spectrum of a material still remains a powerful set of physical properties (transmission elements) available to the organic chemist for the identification of an unknown compound.*[1]

[1] Griffiths, P. R.; de Haseth, J. A.; Azaraga, L. V. *Anal. Chem.* **1983,** *55,* 1361A.

At the present time, simple physical constants are determined mainly to assist in establishing the purity of *known* materials. As the boiling point or the melting point of a material can be very sensitive to small quantities of impurities, these data can be particularly helpful in determining whether or not a starting material needs further purification, or whether a product has been isolated in acceptable purity. Gas (GC), high-performance liquid (HPLC), and thin-layer (TLC) chromatography, however, now provide considerably more powerful purity information when such data are required. When a new composition of matter has been formed, an elemental (combustion) analysis is normally reported, if sufficient material is available for this destructive analysis. For new substances, we are, of course, interested in establishing not only the identity, but also the molecular structure of the materials. In this situation, other modern techniques, such as ^{1}H and ^{13}C NMR spectroscopy, high-resolution MS, and single-crystal X-ray diffraction, can provide sensitive structural information.

When comparisons are made between experimental data and values obtained from the literature, it is essential that the latter information be obtained from the most reliable sources available. Certainly, judgment, which improves with experience, must be exercised in accepting any value as a standard. The known classical properties of a large number of compounds are found in the *CRC Handbook of Chemistry and Physics*. This reference work is a valuable source that lists inorganic, organic, and organometallic compounds. The handbook is kept current, and a new edition is published each year.

LIQUIDS

ULTRAMICRO-BOILING POINT

Upon heating, the vapor pressure of a liquid increases, though in a nonlinear fashion. When the pressure reaches the point where it matches the local pressure, the liquid boils. That is, it spontaneously begins to form vapor bubbles, which rapidly rise to the surface. If heating is continued, both the vapor pressure and the temperature of the liquid will remain constant until the substance has been completely vaporized (Fig. 4.1).

Since microscale preparations generally yield quantities of liquid products in the range 30–70 μL, the allocation of 5 μL or less of material to boiling point measurements becomes highly desirable. The modification of the Wiegand ultramicro boiling point procedure described here has established that reproducible and reasonably accurate (± 1 °C) boiling points can be observed on 3–4 μL of most liquids[2] thermally stable at the required temperatures.

Procedure

Ultramicro boiling points can be conveniently determined in standard (90-mm length) Pyrex capillary melting point tubes. The melting point tube replaces the conventional 3–4 mm (o.d.) tubing used in the Siwoloboff procedure.[3] The sample (3–4 μL) is loaded into the melting point capillary via a 10-μL syringe and centrifuged to the bottom if necessary.

A small glass bell, which replaces the conventional melting point tube as the bubble generator in microboiling point determinations, is formed by

---

[2] Wiegand, C. *Angew. Chem.* **1955**, *67*, 77. Mayo, D. W.; Pike, R. M.; Butcher, S. S.; Meredith, M. L. *J. Chem. Educ.* **1985**, *62*, 1114.

[3] Siwoloboff, A. *Chem. Ber.* **1886**, *19*, 795.

heating 3-mm (o.d.) Pyrex tubing with a microburner and drawing it out to a diameter small enough to be readily accepted by the melting point capillary. A section of the drawn capillary is fused and then cut to yield two small glass bells approximately 5 mm long (Fig. 4.2a). It is important that the fused section be reasonably large. This section is more than just a seal. The fused glass must add sufficient weight to the bell so that it will firmly seat itself in the bottom of the melting point tube.

An alternate technique to prepare the glass bells is as follows: heat the midsection of an open-ended melting point capillary tube and then draw the glass to form a smaller capillary section. This section is then broken approximately in the middle and each end of the open end sealed. The appropriate length for the bell is then broken off. Thus two bells are obtained, one from each section. The sealing process (be sure that a significant section of glass is fused during the tube closure in order to give sufficient weight to the bell) can be repeated on each remaining glass section and thus a series of bells can be prepared in a relatively short period.

One of the glass bells is inserted into the loaded melting point capillary, open end first (down), and allowed to fall (centrifuged if necessary) to the bottom. The assembled system (Fig. 4.2b) is then inserted onto the stage of a Thomas-Hoover Uni-Melt® Capillary Melting Point apparatus (Fig. 4.3)[4] or similar system (such as Mel-Temp®).

The temperature is rapidly raised to 15–20 °C below the expected boiling point (the temperature should be monitored carefully in the case of unknown substances), and then is adjusted to a maximum 2 °C/min rise rate until a fine stream of bubbles is emitted from the glass bell. The heat control is then adjusted to drop the temperature. The boiling point is recorded at the point where the last escaping bubble collapses (i.e., when the vapor pressure of the substance equals the atmospheric pressure). The heater is then rapidly adjusted to again raise the temperature at 2 °C/min and induce a second stream of bubbles. This procedure may then be repeated several times. *It should be emphasized that a precise and sensitive temperature control system is essential to the successful application of this cycling technique. Although this control is a desirable feature it is not, however, essential for obtaining satisfactory boiling point data.*

Utilization of the conventional melting point capillary as the "boiler" tube has the particular advantage that the system is ideally suited for observation in a conventional melting point apparatus. The illumination and magnification available make the observation of rate changes in the bubble stream readily apparent. Economical GC injection syringes (10 µL) appear to be the most successful instrument for dealing with the small quantities of liquids involved in these transfers. The 3-in. needles normally supplied with the 10-µL barrels will not reach the bottom of the capillary; however, liquid samples deposited on the walls of the tube are easily and efficiently moved to the bottom by centrifugation. After the sample is packed in the bottom of the capillary tube, the glass bell is introduced. Use of the glass bell is necessary because, if a conventional Siwoloboff fused capillary insert is employed (it would extend beyond the top of the melting point tube), capillary action between the "boiler" tube wall and the capillary insert will draw the majority of the sample from the bottom of the tube up onto the walls. This effect often precludes the formation of the requisite bubble stream.

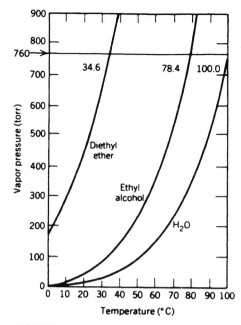

FIGURE 4.1 Vapor-pressure curves. *From Brady, J. E.; Humiston, G. E. General Chemistry, 3rd ed.; Wiley: New York, 1982. (Reprinted by permission of John Wiley & Sons, New York)*

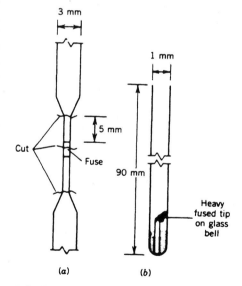

FIGURE 4.2 (a) Preparation of small glass bell for ultramicro boiling point determination. (b) Ultramicro boiling point assembly. *From Mayo, D. W.; Pike, R. M.; Butcher, S. S.; Meredith, M. L. J. Chem. Educ. 1985, 62, 1114.*

[4] Thomas Scientific, 99 High Hill Road, P.O. Box 99, Swedesboro, NJ 08085.

FIGURE 4.3 Thomas-Hoover melting point determination device. *(Courtesy of Thomas Scientific, Swedesboro, NJ.)*

Little loss of low-boiling liquids occurs (see Table 4.1). Furthermore, if the boiling point is overrun and the sample is suddenly evaporated from the bottom section of the "boiler" capillary, it rapidly will condense on the upper (cooler) sections of the tube, which extend above the heat-transfer fluid. The sample can easily be recentrifuged to the bottom of the tube, and a new determination of the boiling point begun. It should be pointed out that if the bell cavity fills completely during the cooling point of a cycle, it is often difficult to reinitiate the bubble stream without first emptying the entire cavity by overrunning the boiling point.

Observed boiling points for a series of compounds, which boil over a wide range of temperatures, are summarized in Table 4.1.

TABLE 4.1 Observed Boiling Points (°C)[a]

Compound	Observed	Literature Value	Reference
Methyl iodide	42.5	42.4	b
Isopropyl alcohol	82.3	82.4	c
2,2-Dimethoxypropane	80.0	83.0	d
2-Heptanone	149–150	151.4	e
Cumene	151–153	152.4	f
Mesitylene	163	164.7	g
p-Cymene	175–178	177.1	h
Benzyl alcohol	203	205.3	i
Diphenylmethane	263–265	264.3	j

REFERENCE(S)

[a] Observed values are uncorrected for changes in atmospheric pressure (corrections all estimated to be less than ±0.5 °C).

[b] *CRC Handbook of Chemistry and Physics*, 72nd ed.; CRC Press: Boca Raton, FL, 1991–1992; no. 9082, p. 3–320.

[c] *CRC Handbook of Chemistry and Physics*, 72nd ed.; CRC Press: Boca Raton, FL, 1991–1992; no. 11972, p. 3–417.

[d] *Dictionary of Organic Compounds*, 4th ed.; Oxford University Press: London, 1965; Vol. I, p. 11.

[e] *CRC Handbook of Chemistry and Physics*, 72nd ed.; CRC Press: Boca Raton, FL, 1991–1992; no. 7627, p. 3–268.

[f] *CRC Handbook of Chemistry and Physics*, 72nd ed.; CRC Press: Boca Raton, FL, 1991–1992; no. 5394, p. 3–191.

[g] *CRC Handbook of Chemistry and Physics*, 72nd ed.; CRC Press: Boca Raton, FL, 1991–1992; no. 8987, p. 3–317.

[h] *CRC Handbook of Chemistry and Physics*, 72nd ed.; CRC Press: Boca Raton, FL, 1991–1992; no. 2192, p. 3–85.

[i] *CRC Handbook of Chemistry and Physics*, 72nd ed.; CRC Press: Boca Raton, FL, 1991–1992; no. 3160, p. 3–116.

[j] *CRC Handbook of Chemistry and Physics*, 72nd ed.; CRC Press: Boca Raton, FL, 1991–1992; no. 9074, p. 3–320.

Materials that are thermally stable at their boiling point will give identical values on repeat determinations. Substances that begin to decompose will give values that slowly drift after the first few measurements. The observation of color and/or viscosity changes, together with a variable boiling point, all signal the need for caution in making repetitive measurements.

Comparison of the boiling points obtained experimentally at various atmospheric pressures with reference boiling points at 760 torr is greatly

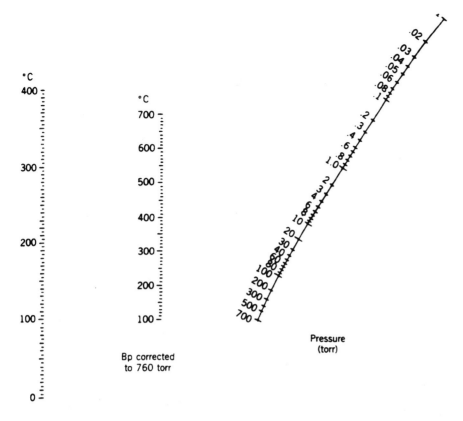

°C

°C

Pressure
(torr)

Bp corrected
to 760 torr

Observed bp

FIGURE 4.4   Pressure-temperature nomograph.

facilitated by the use of pressure–temperature nomographs, such as that shown in Figure 4.4. A straight line from the observed boiling point to the observed pressure will pass through the corrected boiling point value. These values can be of practical importance when carrying out reduced-pressure distillations.

DENSITY

Density, defined as mass per unit volume, is generally expressed as grams per milliliter (g/mL) or grams per cubic centimeter (g/cm^3) for liquids. Accurate procedures have been developed for the measurement of this physical constant at the microscale level. A micropycnometer (density meter), developed by Clemo and McQuillen,[5] requires approximately 2 μL of liquid (Fig. 4.5). This very accurate device determines the density to three significant figures. The system is self-filling, and the fine capillary ends do not need to be capped while coming to temperature equilibrium, or while weighing (the measured values tend to degrade for substances boiling under 100 °C and when room temperatures are much above 20 °C). In addition, the apparatus must first be tared, filled, and then reweighed on an *analytical* balance. A technique that results in less precise densities (good to about two significant figures), but one that is far easier to use is simply to substitute a 50- or 100-μL syringe for the pycnometer. The method simply

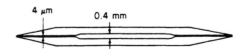

4 μm   0.4 mm

FIGURE 4.5   Pycnometer of Clemo and McQuillen. *From Schneider, F. L Monographien aus dem Gebiete der qualitativen Mikroanalyse, Qualitative Organic Microanalysis, Vol. II; Benedetti-Pichler, A. A., Ed.; Springer-Verlag: Vienna, Austria, 1964.*

[5] Clemo, G. R.; McQuillen, A. *J. Chem. Soc.* **1935**, 1220.

requires weighing the syringe before and after filling it to a measured volume as in the conventional technique. With the volume and the weight of the liquid known, the density can be calculated. A further advantage of the syringe technique is that the pycnometer is not limited to a fixed volume. Although much larger samples are required, it is not inconvenient to utilize the entire sample obtained in the reaction for this measurement, as the material can be efficiently recovered from the syringe for additional characterization studies. Since density changes with temperature, these measurements should be obtained at a constant temperature.

An alternative to the syringe method is to use *Drummond Disposable Microcaps* as pycnometers. These precision-bore capillary tubes, calibrated to contain the stated volume from end to end (accuracy ±1%), are available from a number of supply houses.[6] These tubes are filled by capillary action or by suction using a vented rubber bulb (provided). The pipets can be obtained in various sizes, but as with the syringe, volumes of 50, 75, or 100 μL are recommended. When using this method, be sure to handle the micropipet with forceps and not with your fingers (heat). The empty tube is first *tared*, and then filled and weighed again. The difference in these values is the weight of liquid in the pipet. For convenience, the pipet may be placed in a small container (10-mL beaker or Erlenmeyer flask) when the weighing procedure is carried out.

REFRACTIVE INDEX

It is commonly observed that a beam of light "bends" as it passes from one medium to another. For example, an oar looks bent as one views (from the air) the portion under the water. This effect is a consequence of the refraction of light. It results from the change in velocity of the light at the interface of the media, and the angle of refraction, (ϕ'). It is related to the velocity change as follows (see Fig. 4.6):

$$\frac{\sin \phi}{\sin \phi'} = \frac{\text{velocity in vacuum}}{\text{velocity in sample}} = n \text{ (refractive index)}$$

where ϕ is the angle of incidence between the beam of light and the interface.

Since the velocity of light in a medium must be less than that in a vacuum, the index of refraction (n) will always be greater than 1. In practice, n is taken as the ratio of the velocity of light in air relative to the medium being measured. The refractive index is wavelength dependent.

The wavelength dependence gives rise to the effect of dispersion or the spreading of white light into its component colors. When we measure n, therefore, we must specify the wavelength at which the measurement is made. The standard wavelength for refractive index determinations has become the (yellow) sodium 589-nm emission, the sodium D line. Sodium, unfortunately, is a poor choice of wavelength for these measurements with organic substances, but as the sodium lamp represented one of the easiest-to-obtain monochromatic sources of light in the past, it has become widely used. Because the density of the medium is sensitive to temperature, the velocity of radiation also changes with temperature, and therefore, refractive index measurements must be made at constant temperatures. Many values in the literature are reported at 20 °C. The refractive index can be

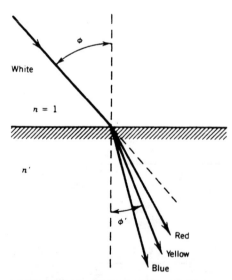

FIGURE 4.6 Upon refraction, white light is spread out into a spectrum. This is called dispersion.

---

[6] Drummond Disposable Microcaps are available from Thomas Scientific, 99 High Hill Road, P.O. Box 99, Swedesboro, NJ 08085; VWR Scientific, P. O. Box 626, Bridgeport, NJ 08014.

measured optically quite accurately to four decimal places. Since this measurement is particularly sensitive to the presence of impurities, the refractive index can be a valuable physical constant for tracking the purification of liquid samples.

For example, the measurement is reported as

$$n_D^{20} = 1.4628$$

In the Abbe-3L refractometer (Fig. 4.7), white light is used as the source, but compensating prisms give indexes for the D line. This refractometer is commonly used in many organic laboratories.

Samples (~10 μL) are applied between the horizontal surfaces of a pair of hinged prisms (Fig. 4.8). A sampling procedure recently developed by Ronald[7] significantly reduces the amount of sample required and allows accurate measurements on highly volatile materials. The technique involves placing a small precut 6-mm disk of good-quality lens paper at the center of the bottom prism. The sample is loaded onto the disk with a micro Pasteur pipet or a microliter syringe (see Table 4.2).

CAUTION: **Do not touch the prisms with the Pasteur pipet or syringe tip as they may be easily and permanently marred or scratched, and the refractometer will, from then on, give erroneous results.**

The refractometer is adjusted so that the field of view has a well-defined light and dark split image (see your instrument manual for the correct routine for making adjustments on your particular refractometer).

FIGURE 4.7 Abbe-3L refractometer. *(Courtesy of Milton Roy Co., Rochester, NY.)*

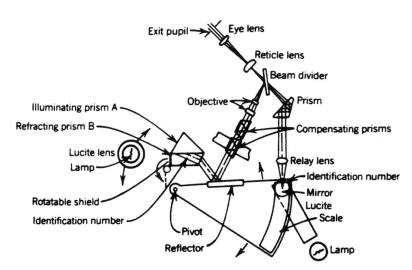

FIGURE 4.8 Diagram of a typical refractometer. *(Courtesy of Milton Roy Co., Rochester, NY.)*

[7] Ronald, B. P. Department of Chemistry, Idaho State University, Pocatello, ID (personal communication).

TABLE 4.2 Refractive Index Measurements Utilizing Lens Paper Disk Technique

Substance	T(°C)	n^t (normal) 100 μL	n^t (microdisk) 2–4 μL
Water	24.5	1.3224	1.3226
Diethyl ether	24	1.3508	1.3505
Chlorobenzene	24.5	1.5225	1.5219
Iodobenzene	24.5	1.6151	1.6151

When using the refractometer, always clean the prisms with alcohol and lens paper before and after use. Record the temperature at which the reading is taken. A reasonably good extrapolation of temperature effects can be obtained by assuming that the index of refraction changes 0.0004 unit per degree Celsius, and that it varies inversely with temperature.

SOLIDS

MELTING POINTS

In general, the crystalline lattice forces holding organic solids together are distributed over a relatively narrow energy range. The melting points of organic compounds, therefore, are usually relatively sharp, that is, less than 2 °C. The range and maximum temperature of the melting point, however, are very sensitive to impurities. Small amounts of sample contamination by soluble impurities will nearly always result in melting point depressions.

The drop in melting point is usually accompanied by an expansion of the melting point range. Thus, in addition to the melting point acting as a useful guide in identification, it also can be a particularly effective indication of sample purity.

Procedure

In the microscale laboratory, two different types of melting point determinations are carried out: (1) simple capillary melting points and (2) evacuated melting points.

Simple Capillary Melting Point

Because the microscale laboratory utilizes the Thomas-Hoover Uni-Melt apparatus or a similar system for determining boiling points, melting points are conveniently obtained on the same apparatus. The Uni-Melt system utilizes an electrically heated and stirred silicone oil bath. The temperature readings require no correction in this case as the depth of immersion is held constant. (This assumes, of course, that the thermometer is calibrated to the operational immersion depth.) Melting points are determined in the same capillaries as boiling points. The capillary is loaded by introducing about 1 mg of material into the open end. The sample is then tightly packed (~2 mm) into the closed end by dropping the capillary down a length of glass tubing held vertically to the bench top. The melting point tube is then ready for mounting in the metal stage, which is immersed in the silicone oil bath of the apparatus. If the melting point of the substance is expected to occur in a certain range, the temperature can be rapidly raised to about 20 °C below the expected value. At that point, the

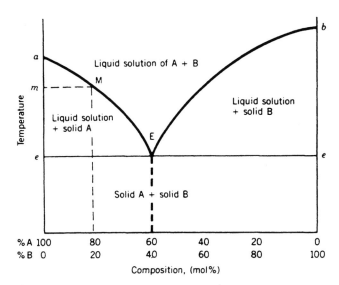

FIGURE 4.9 Melting point composition diagram for the binary mixture, A + B. In this diagram, *a* is the melting point of the solid A, *b* of solid B, *e* of eutectic mixture *E*, and *m* of the 80% A:20% B mixture, M.

temperature rise should be adjusted to a maximum of 2 °C/min, which is the standard rate of change at which the reference determinations are obtained. The melting point range is recorded from the temperature at which the first drop of liquid forms (point *e* on Fig. 4.9) to that at which the last crystal melts (point *m* on Fig. 4.9).

Evacuated Melting Points

Many organic compounds begin to decompose at their melting points. This decomposition often begins as the melting point is approached and may adversely affect the values measured. The decomposition can be invariably traced to reaction with oxygen at elevated temperatures. If the melting point is obtained in an evacuated tube, therefore, much more accurate melting points can be obtained. These more reliable values arise not only from increased sample stability, but because several repeat determinations can often be made on the same sample. The multiple measurements may then be averaged to provide more accurate data.

Evacuated melting points are quickly and easily obtained with a little practice. The procedure is as follows: Shorten the capillary portion of a Pasteur pipet to approximately the same length as a normal melting point tube (see Fig. 4.10*a*). Seal the capillary end by rotating in a microburner flame. Touch the pipet only to the very edge of the flame, and keep the large end at an angle below the end being sealed (see Fig. 4.10*b*). This technique will prevent water from the flame being carried into the tube where it will condense in the cooler sections. Then load 1–2 mg of sample into the drawn section of the pipet with a microspatula (see Fig. 4.10*c*). Tap the pipet gently to seat the solid powder as far down the capillary as it can be worked (see Fig. 4.10*d*). Then push the majority of the sample partially down the capillary with the same diameter copper wire that you used to seat the cotton plug in constructing the Pasteur filter pipet (see Fig. 4.10*e*). Next, connect the pipet to a mechanical high-vacuum system with a piece of vacuum tubing. Turn on the vacuum and evacuate the pipet for 30 seconds (see Fig. 4.10*f*). With a microburner, gently warm the surface of

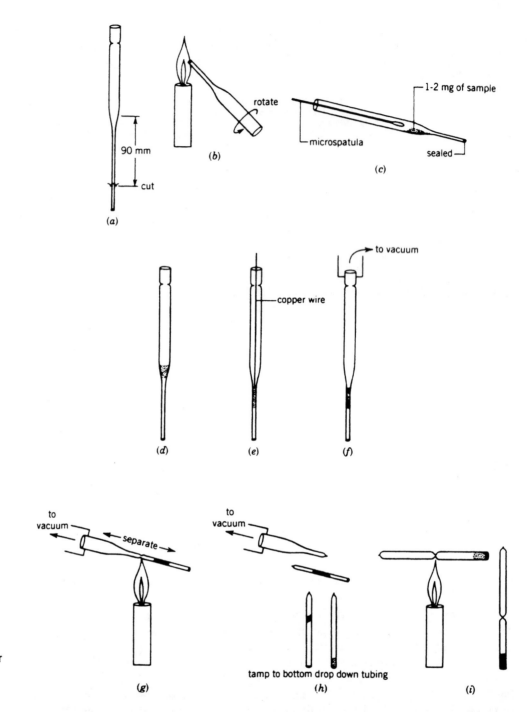

FIGURE 4.10 Procedure for obtaining evacuated melting point capillaries.

the capillary tubing just below the drawn section. On warming, the remaining fragments of the sample (the majority of which has been forced further down in the tube) will sublime in either direction away from the hot section. Once the traces of sample have been "chased" away, the heating is increased, and the capillary tube collapsed, fused, and separated from the shank, which remains connected to the vacuum system (see Fig. 4.10g). The vacuum system is then vented and the shank is discarded. The sample is tightly packed into the initially sealed end of the evacuated capillary by dropping down a section of glass tubing, as in the case of packing open melting point samples. After the sample is packed (~2 mm in length, see Fig. 4.10h), a section of the evacuated capillary about 10–15 mm above the sample is once more gently heated and collapsed by the microburner flame (see Fig. 4.10*i*).

This procedure is required to trap the sample below the surface of the heated silicone oil in the melting point bath, and thus avoid sublimation up the tube to cooler sections during measurement of the melting point. The operation is a little tricky and should be practiced a few times. It is very important that complete fusion of the tubing take place. Now the sample is ready to be placed in the melting point apparatus. The procedure beyond this point is the same as in the open capillary case, except that after the sample melts, it can be cooled, allowed to crystallize, remelted several times, and the average value of the range reported. If these latter values begin to drift downward, the sample can be considered to be decomposing even under evacuated, deoxygenated conditions. In this case, the first value observed should be recorded as the melting point, and the decomposition noted (mp = xx dec, where dec = decompose).

MIXTURE MELTING POINTS

Additional information can often be extracted from the sensitivity of the melting point to the presence of impurities. Where two different substances possess identical melting points (not an uncommon occurrence), it would be impossible to identify an unknown sample as either material based on the melting point alone. If reference standards of the two compounds are available, however, then mixtures of the unknown and the two standards can be prepared. It is important to prepare several mixtures of varying concentrations for melting point comparisons, as the point of maximum depression need not occur on the phase diagram at the 50:50 ratio (see Fig. 4.9). The melting points of the unknown and the mixed samples are conveniently obtained simultaneously (the Uni-Melt stage will accept up to seven capillaries at one time). The unknown sample and the mixture of the unknown with the correct reference will have identical values, but the mixture of the reference with a different substance will give a depressed melting point. This procedure is a classical step in the positive identification of crystalline solids. Only very rarely do mixtures of two different compounds fail to exhibit mixture melting point depression.

5

Development of Microscale Techniques

C$_5$H$_6$, Propellane
Wiberg and Walker (1982).

This chapter introduces the microscale organic laboratory techniques employed throughout the experimental sections of the text. These operations must be mastered in order to be successful when working at this scale. Detailed discussions are given for each individual experimental technique. At the end of each of these discussions, you will find a note listing the experiments described in Chapters 6–8 in which that particular technique plays a significant role. These lists should prove useful to instructors assembling experiments to be covered in the laboratory part of a course. The lists also will be handy for students who wish to examine the application of a particular technique to other experiments not covered in their laboratory sequence.

One of the principal hurdles in dealing with experimental chemistry is the isolation of materials in their pure state. Characterization of a substance requires a pure sample of the material. In organic chemistry, this is a particularly difficult demand since most organic reactions generate several products. We are generally satisfied if the desired product is the major component of the mixture obtained. Thus, in this chapter a heavy emphasis is placed on separation techniques.

TECHNIQUE 1

Microscale Separation of Liquid Mixtures by Preparative Gas Chromatography

INTRODUCTION

Technique 1 begins the discussion of the resolution (separation) of microliter quantities of liquid mixtures via preparative gas chromatography. Techniques 2 and 3 deal with semimicro adaptations of classical distillation routines that focus on the separation of liquid mixtures involving one to several milliliters of material.

The methods of chromatography have revolutionized experimental organic chemistry over the past 30-odd years. These methods are by far the most powerful of the techniques for separating mixtures and isolating pure substances, either solids or liquids. Chromatography can be defined as the resolution of a multicomponent mixture (several hundred in some cases) by distribution between two phases, one stationary and one mobile. The various methods of chromatography are categorized by the phases involved: column, thin-layer, and paper (solid–liquid); partition (liquid–liquid); and vapor phase (gas–liquid). The principal mechanism on which these separations depend is differential solubility, or adsorbtivity, of the mixture components with respect to the two phases involved. That is, the components must exhibit different partition coefficients.

Gas chromatography (GC, or sometimes termed vapor-phase chromatography, VPC) is an extraordinarily powerful technique for the separation of mixtures. In this case, the stationary phase is a high-boiling liquid and the mobile phase is a gas (the carrier gas). The GC systems develop resolutions vastly superior to those obtained via distillation techniques.

Prep-GC separations, which involve processing greater than submicroliter quantities of materials, require relatively sophisticated instrumentation and, even then, considerable time may be expended to develop the appropriate operating conditions.

On the other hand, **analytical-GC** separations, which require small quantities of material (often <0.1 μL), are extremely powerful. The necessity of working with small quantities of materials in GC separations, however, becomes advantageous at the microscale level. Note that this analytical mode is utilized in assaying distillation fractions in Experiments [3C] and [3D].

The instrumentation required to carry out GC can range from straightforward, and relatively simple systems, to those containing highly automated and relatively expensive components. A diagram of a common and simple instructional laboratory GC is given in Figure 5.1.

Injection port: The analysis begins in a heated injection port. The sample mixture is introduced by syringe through a septum into the high-temperature chamber (injection port) through which the inert carrier gas (the mobile phase) is flowing. Helium and nitrogen are commonly used as carrier gases. The solubility of the sample in the carrier gas depends to a large extent on the vapor pressure of the substances in the mixture. Thus, heating the injection port helps to insure vaporization of less volatile samples. These requirements place two major constraints on GC: (1) the sample must be stable at the temperature required to cause vaporization, and (2) the sample must possess sufficient vapor pressure to be completely soluble in the carrier gas at the column operating temperatures.

NOTE.   *When injecting a sample, remember to always have your thumb positioned over the syringe plunger. This technique prevents a blow-back of the sample by the carrier gas pressure in the injection port.*

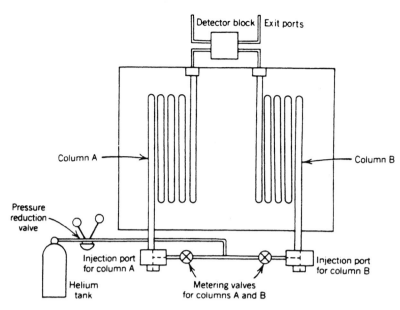

FIGURE 5.1   Block diagram of a dual-column gas chromatograph showing essential parts. *(Courtesy of GOW-MAC Instrument Co., Bound Brook, NJ.)*

Column: The vaporized mixture is swept by the carrier gas from the injection port onto the column. Bringing the sample mixture into intimate contact with the column constitutes the key stage in the separation process. The stationary liquid phase, in which the sample will dissolve and partition with the mobile gas phase, is physically and/or chemically bonded to inert packing (often referred to as the "support") material contained in the column. Gas chromatographic columns are available from manufacturers in a variety of sizes and shapes. In the diagram of the GOW-MAC instrument (Fig. 5.1), two parallel coiled columns are mounted in a well-insulated oven. Considerable oven space can be saved, and better temperature regulation achieved, if the columns are coiled. Temperature regulation is particularly important, as column resolution degrades rapidly if the entire column is not at the same temperature, and most liquid mixtures will require oven temperatures above ambient to maintain reasonable vapor pressures during the course of the separation.

Resolution of the mixture occurs as the carrier gas sweeps the sample through the column. Most columns are constructed of stainless steel, glass, or fused silica. The diameter and length of the column are critical factors in determining how the internal part of the column is designed to achieve maximum separation of the sample mixture.

Packed Columns: In these columns the surface area of the liquid phase, in contact with the sample contained in the moving gas phase, is maximized by coating a finely divided inert support with a nonvolatile liquid material (stationary phase). The coated support is carefully loaded into the column to avoid void channels. Columns prepared in this fashion are termed "packed columns." Packed columns are usually 1/4 or 1/8 in. in diameter and range from 4 to 12 ft long. These columns are particularly attractive for use in the microscale laboratory as they can function in both the analytical and preparative modes. Numerous examples are known where simple mixtures ranging from 20 to 80 μL can be resolved into their pure components and collected at the exit port of the detector. On the other hand, samples in the 0.2–2-μL range will exhibit quite good analytical resolution.

Capillary Columns: Research grade columns are also available that have no packing; the liquid phase is simply applied directly to the walls of the column. These columns are referred to as wall-coated or open-tubular columns. The reduction in surface area is compensated for by making the diameter very small (0.1 mm) and the length very long (100 m would not be uncommon). Termed capillary columns, they are the most efficient columns employed for analytical separations. Mixtures of several hundred compounds can be completely resolved in a single pass through one of these systems. Capillary columns, generally, require a more sophisticated and expensive operating system, and, in addition, they are restricted to very small sample loading (0.1 μL or less). Thus, capillary columns cannot be used for preparative separations.

Liquid phase: Once the sample is introduced on the column (in the carrier gas), it will undergo partition with the liquid phase. The choice of the liquid phase is particularly important since it directly affects the relative distribution coefficients.

In general, the stationary liquid phase controls the partitioning of the sample by two criteria: (1) If little or no interaction occurs between the sample components and the stationary phase, the boiling point of the materials will determine the order of elution. Under these conditions, the highest boiling species will be the last to elute. (2) The functionality of the components may interact directly with the stationary phase to establish different partition coefficients. Elution in this latter case will depend on the particular binding properties of the sample components.

Some typical materials employed as stationary phases are shown below.

Name	Stationary Phase[a]	Maximum Temperature (°C)	Mechanism of Interaction
Silicone oil DC 710, etc.	$R_3Si[OSiR_2]_nOSiR_3$	250	According to boiling point
Polyethylene glycol (Carbowax®)	$HO[CH_2CH_2O]_nCH_2CH_2OH$	150	Relatively selective toward polar compounds
Diisodecyl phthalate	$o\text{-}C_6H_4[CO_2\text{-isodecyl}]_2$	175	According to boiling point

[a] R = alkyl substituent

Oven temperature: The temperature of the column will also affect the separation. In general, the elution period of the sample components will decrease as the temperature is increased. That is, the retention times on the column are shorter at higher temperatures. Higher boiling components tend to undergo diffusion broadening at low column temperatures because of the increase in retention times. Programmed oven temperature increases, which speed up elution of the higher boiling components, tend to suppress peak broadening, and therefore, increase resolution. If the oven temperature is too high, however, equilibration with the stationary phase will not be established and the component mixture may elute together or, at best, undergo incomplete resolution. Obviously, temperature-programming capabilities require more costly ovens and controllers.

Flow rate: The flow rate of the carrier gas constitutes another important parameter. The rate must be slow enough to allow equilibration between the phases, but sufficiently rapid to ensure that diffusion will not overcome resolution of the components.

Column Length: As noted, the length of the column also is an important factor in separation performance. As we will see in the distillation discussions, distillation column efficiency is proportional to column height, as it determines the number of evaporation–condensation cycles. In a similar manner, increasing the length of the GC column allows more partition cycles to occur. Difficult-to-separate mixtures, such as the xylenes (very similar boiling points, o-xylene, 144.4 °C, m-xylene, 139.1 °C, and p-xylene, 138.3 °C), will have a better chance of being resolved on longer columns. In fact, both GC and distillation resolution data are described using the same term, **theoretical plates** (see Technique 3 and Experiments [3C] and [3D]).

Detector and Exit Port: A successfully resolved mixture will elute as individual components, sequentially with time, at the exit port (also temperature controlled) of the instrument. To monitor the exiting vapors, a detector is placed in the gas stream just prior to the above outlet (Fig. 5.1). After passing through the detector, the carrier gas and the separated sample components are then vented.

A widely used detector is the nondestructive, thermal conductivity sensor, often referred to as a hot-wire detector. A heated element in the gas stream changes electrical resistance when a substance dilutes the carrier gas and changes its thermal conductivity. Helium possesses a higher thermal conductivity than most organic substances. When samples other than helium are present, the conductivity of the gas stream decreases and the resistance of the heated wire changes. The change in resistance is measured by differences (Wheatstone bridge), with a reference detector mounted on a second (parallel) gas stream. This signal is plotted by a recorder. On the plot, the horizontal axis is time and the vertical axis is the magnitude of the resistance difference. The plot of resistance difference versus time is referred to as the **chromatogram**. Retention time (t_R) is defined as the time from sample injection to the time of maximum peak intensity. The baseline width (W_b) of a peak is defined as the distance between two points where tangents to the points of inflection cross the baseline (Fig. 5.2).

Theoretical Plates: It is possible to estimate the number of theoretical plates (directly related to the number of distribution cycles) present in a column for a particular substance. The parameters are given in the relationship[1]

$$n = 16[t_R/W_b]^2$$

where the units of retention time (t_R) and baseline width (W_b) are the same (minutes, seconds, or centimeters). As in distillation columns, the larger the number of theoretical plates, n, the higher the resolution of the column.

The efficiency of a system may also be expressed as the *height equivalent theoretical plate* (HETP) in centimeters (or inches)/plate. This parameter is related to the number of theoretical plates n by

$$HETP = \frac{L}{n}$$

[1] Berg, E. W. *Physical and Chemical Methods of Separation*; McGraw-Hill: New York, 1963, p. 111.

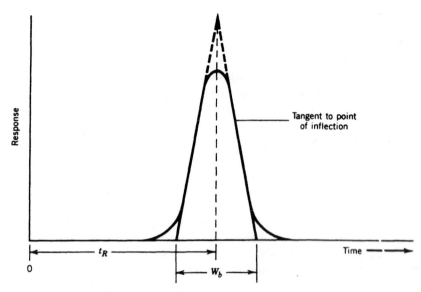

FIGURE 5.2 Schematic chromatogram.

where L is the length of the column, usually reported in centimeters. The smaller the HETP, the more efficient the column.

The number of theoretical plates available in fractional distillation columns is limited by column holdup (see Techniques 2A and 2B). Thus, distillations of less than 500 μL are not practical. Gas chromatographic columns, on the other hand, operate **most efficiently at the microscale or submicroscale levels**, where 500 μL would be an order (even 3–5 orders in the case of capillary columns) of magnitude too large.

Fraction Collection: Sequential collection of the separated materials can be made by attaching suitable sample condensing tubes to the exit port (see Fig. 3.6).

Procedure for Preparative Collection

The collection tube (oven dried until 5 min before use) is attached to the heated exit port by the metal 5/5 joint. Sample collection is initiated 30 s prior to detection of the expected peak on the recorder (time based on previously determined retention values)[2] and continued until 30 s following the return to baseline. After the collection tube is detached, the sample is transferred to the 0.1-mL conical GC collection vial. The transfer is facilitated by the 5/5 joint on the conical vial. After the collection tube is joined to the vial (preweighed with cap), the system is centrifuged (see Fig. 5.3). The collection tube is then removed, and the vial capped and reweighed.

The efficiency of collection can exceed 90% with most materials, even relatively low-boiling substances. In the latter case, the collection tube, after attachment to the instrument, is wrapped with a paper tissue. As the tube is being wrapped, it is also being flushed by the carrier gas. The wrapping is then saturated with liquid nitrogen.

The role of preparative GC in the microscale laboratory is that of a powerful replacement for the technique of fractional distillation in product purification. As all liquid product mixtures in the microscale laboratory are less than 500 μL, distillation techniques are impractical in most cases.

---

[2] Refer to your local laboratory instructions.

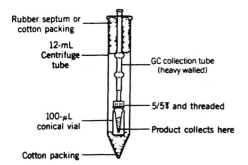

Rubber septum or
cotton packing

12-mL
Centrifuge
tube

100-μL
conical vial

Cotton packing

GC collection tube
(heavy walled)

5/5℥ and threaded

Product collects here

FIGURE 5.3 Gas chromatographic collection tube and
0.1-mL conical vial.

Refer to Experiment [2] for specific experimental details on preparative GC as applied to the separation of a number of binary mixtures. These
are designed as practice examples to give you experience at sample collection.

NOTE. *Gas chromatographic purification of reaction products is suggested in the
following list of experiments: Experiments [2], [3C], [3D], [5A], [5B], [8C], [9],
[10], [13], [17], and [32].*

Semimicroscale Distillation

TECHNIQUE 2

INTRODUCTION

Distillation is the process of heating a liquid to the boiling point, condensing the heated vapor by cooling, and returning either a portion of, or none
of, the condensed vapors to the distillation vessel. Distillation varies from
the process of reflux (see p. 24) only in that at least some of the condensate
is removed from the boiling system. Distillations in which a fraction of the
condensed vapors are returned to the boiler are often referred to as being
under "partial reflux." Three types of distillations will be described under
the headings Techniques 2A, 2B and 3.

Distillation Theory

Distillation techniques often can be used for separating two or more components on the basis of differences in their vapor pressures. Separation can
be accomplished by taking advantage of the fact that the vapor phase is
generally richer in the more volatile (lower boiling) component of the liquid
mixture. Molecules in a liquid are in constant motion and possess a range
of kinetic energies. Those with higher energies (a larger fraction for the
lower boiling component) moving near the surface have a greater tendency
to escape into the vapor (gas) phase. If a pure liquid (e.g., hexane) is in a
closed container, eventually hexane molecules in the vapor phase will
reach equilibrium with hexane molecules in the liquid phase. The pressure
exerted by the hexane vapor molecules at a given temperature is called the
vapor pressure and is represented by the symbol P_H° where the superscript °
indicates a pure component. For any pure component A, the vapor pressure would be P_A°. Suppose a second component (e.g., toluene) is added to
the hexane. The total vapor pressure (P_{total}) is then the sum of the individual component *partial vapor pressures* (P_H, P_T), where P_H is the partial

pressure of hexane, and P_T is the partial pressure of toluene as given by *Dalton's law*.

$$P_{total} = P_H + P_T$$

or in general

$$P_{total} = P_A + P_B + P_C + \ldots + P_n$$

Assuming that the vapors are ideal, the mole fraction of hexane in the **vapor phase** is given by

$$Y_H = P_H/P_{total} \tag{5.1}$$

It is important to realize that the vapor pressure (P_A°) and the partial vapor pressure (P_A) are not equivalent, since the presence of a second component in the liquid system has an effect on the vapor pressure of the first component. If the solution is ideal, the partial vapor pressure of hexane is given by Raoult's law

$$P_H = P_H^\circ X_H \tag{5.2}$$

where X_H is the mole fraction of hexane in the **liquid system**.

For ideal solutions, Eqs. 5.1 and 5.2 may be combined to obtain the phase diagram shown in Figure 5.4. In this figure and elsewhere we will drop the subscripts from X_H and Y_H. Here X and Y will represent the mole fractions of the <u>m</u>ost <u>v</u>olatile <u>c</u>omponent (MVC) (hexane in this case) in the liquid and vapor phases, respectively.

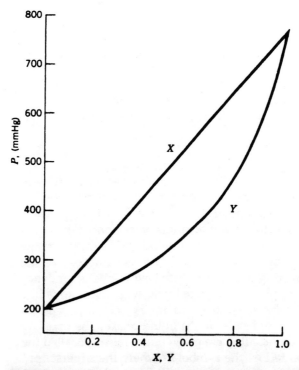

FIGURE 5.4   Pressure as a function of liquid composition (X) and vapor composition (Y), for hexane and toluene (temperature held constant at 69 °C).

Figure 5.4 describes hexane and toluene mixtures at a fixed temperature. For the region above the X curve, there will be only liquid present. For the region below the Y curve, there will be only vapor. In the area between (the sloping, lens-shaped region), liquid and vapor will be present in equilibrium. This area is the only region of interest to us in examining the distillation process.

To understand what the phase diagram tells us about the composition of the liquid and vapor phases, let us imagine that the total pressure of the system is 500 torr, shown by the horizontal line in Figure 5.5. At this pressure a liquid of composition X_1 will be in equilibrium with a vapor of composition Y_1. These two points are defined by the intersection of the constant pressure line with the X and Y curves. It is important to note here that Y will be greater than X for the equilibrium system. That is, the vapor in equilibrium with a given liquid will be richer in the more volatile component than in the liquid.

Diagrams such as Figure 5.5 are not very useful in describing the distillation process. We need a phase diagram for the mixture at constant pressure instead of constant temperature. Figure 5.4 may be transformed to the desired diagram if we know how P_H° and P_T° depend on T. This information may be supplied by the Clausius–Clapeyron equation or by appropriate experimental data.

We will obtain a qualitative diagram for temperature as a function of composition by the following reasoning: (1) The substance having the *higher* vapor pressure at a given temperature will have the *lower* boiling point at a given pressure. (2) At *low* temperatures, only the liquid phase will be present, and at *high* temperatures only the vapor phase will be

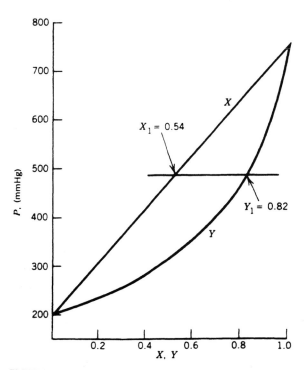

FIGURE 5.5 Pressure as a function of liquid composition (X) and vapor composition (Y), for hexane and toluene (temperature held constant at 69 °C).

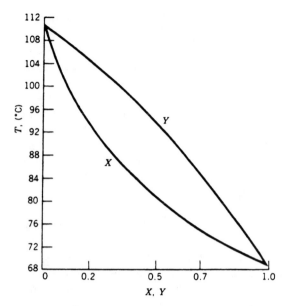

FIGURE 5.6 Temperature as a function of liquid composition (X) and vapor composition (Y).

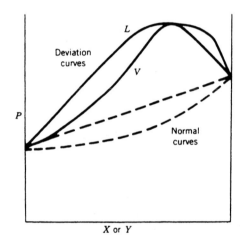

FIGURE 5.7 Positive deviation from Raoult's law; L = liquid, V = vapor.

present. Thus, the temperature-composition diagram is shown by Figure 5.6. Note that this figure may also be obtained (qualitatively) by turning Figure 5.4 upside down.

Many pairs of liquids do not obey Raoult's law. Often, pairs of liquids encountered in organic chemistry exhibit a positive deviation from Raoult's law. The *positive deviation* means that the pressure above the solution is *greater than* would be predicted by Raoult's law. If this deviation is large, the pressure composition curve may exhibit a maximum, as shown in Figure 5.7. Here the curves for normal Raoult's law behavior are shown as dashed lines for reference. Mixtures in which one of the components is polar and the other component is at least partly nonpolar often exhibit positive deviations from Raoult's law.

The temperature–composition diagram for systems showing a positive deviation from Raoult's law is again obtained by the simple inversion process. Such a diagram is shown in Figure 5.8. In this diagram at a temperature of T_1 a liquid of composition X_1 will be in equilibrium with a vapor

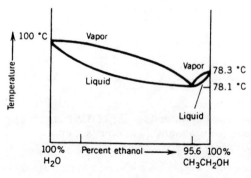

FIGURE 5.8 Ethanol–water minimum boiling point phase diagram.

of Y_1. At a temperature of T_{az}, however, the composition of the liquid and vapor will be the same. This mixture is an *azeotropic* or constant-boiling mixture. Water (H_2O) and ethanol (CH_3CH_2OH) form one of the more familiar azeotropic systems. This mixture exhibits a positive deviation from Raoult's law and has a minimum boiling azeotrope at 78.1 °C, which consists of 95.6% ethanol by volume.

Technique 2A Simple Distillation at the Semimicroscale Level

Process

Simple distillation involves the use of the distillation process to separate a liquid from minor components that are nonvolatile, or that have boiling points at least 30–40 °C above that of the major component. A typical setup for a macroscale distillation of this type is shown in Figure 5.9. At the microscale level, when one is working with volumes smaller than 500 μL, GC techniques (see Technique 1) have replaced conventional microdistillation processes.[3] Semimicroscale simple distillation in the volume range 0.5–2 mL still remains an effective separation technique. Apparatus have been developed that achieve effective separation of mixture samples in this

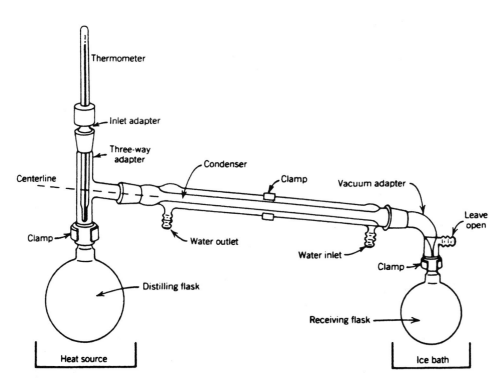

FIGURE 5.9 A complete simple distillation setup. *From Zubric, James W.* The Organic Chem Lab Survival Manual, *3rd ed.; Wiley: New York, 1992. (Reprinted by permission of John Wiley & Sons, Inc., New York.)*

[3] Schneider, F. L. *Monographien aus dem Gebiete der qualitativen Mikroanalyse*, Vol. II: *Qualitative Organic Microanalysis*; A. A. Benedetti-Pichler, Ed.; Springer-Verlag: Vienna, Austria, 1964; p. 31.

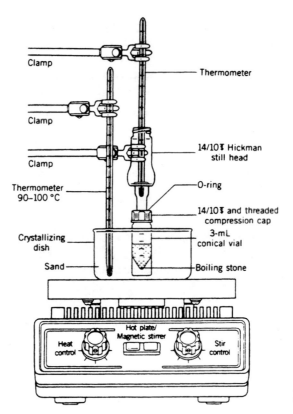

Clamp

Thermometer

Clamp

Clamp

14/10$ Hickman still head

Thermometer 90–100 °C

O-ring

14/10$ and threaded compression cap

3-mL conical vial

Crystallizing dish

Sand

Boiling stone

Hot plate/ Magnetic stirrer

Heat control

Stir control

FIGURE 5.10 Hickman still [14/10$ with conical vial (3 mL)].

range. One of the most significant of these designs is the classic Hickman still, shown in Figure 5.10.

This still is employed in several modes in microscale experiments described in Chapters 6–8; such as the purification of solvents, carrying out reactions, and concentration of solutions for recrystallization. An introduction to the use of the Hickman still is given in Experiment [3].

In a distillation where a liquid is separated from a nonvolatile solute, the vapor pressure of the liquid is lowered by the presence of the solute, but the vapor phase consists only of one component. Thus, except for the incidental transfer of nonvolatile material by splashing, the material condensed should consist only of the volatile component.

We can understand what is going on in a simple distillation of two volatile components by referring to the phase diagrams shown in Figures 5.11 and 5.12. Figure 5.11 is the phase diagram for hexane and toluene. The boiling points of these liquids are separated by 42 °C. Figure 5.12 is the phase diagram for methylcyclohexane and toluene. Here the boiling points are separated by only 9.7 °C.

Imagine a simple distillation of the hexane–toluene pair in which the liquid in the pot is 50% hexane. In Figure 5.11, when the liquid reaches 80.8 °C it will be in equilibrium with a vapor having a composition of 77% hexane. This result is indicated by the line *A–B*. If this vapor is condensed to a liquid of the same composition, as shown by line *B–C*, we will have achieved a significant enrichment of the condensate with respect to hexane. This change in composition is referred to as a simple distillation. The process of evaporation and condensation is achieved by the theoretical construct known as a *theoretical plate*. When this distillation is actually done with a Hickman still, some of the mixture will go through one evaporation and condensation cycle, some will go through two of these cycles, and some may be splashed more directly into the collar. A resolution of between one and two theoretical plates is generally obtained.

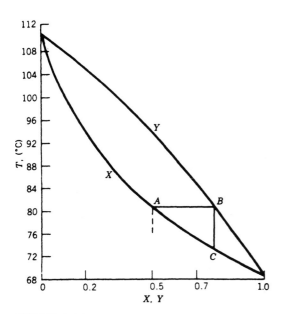

FIGURE 5.11 Temperature as a function of liquid composition (*X*) and vapor composition (*Y*): hexane and toluene.

Referring to Figure 5.12, if we consider the same process for a 50% mixture of methylcyclohexane and toluene, the methylcyclohexane composition will increase to 58% for one theoretical plate. Thus, simple distillation may provide adequate enrichment of the MVC if the boiling points of the two liquids are reasonably well separated, as they are for hexane and toluene. If the boiling points are close together, as they are for methylcyclohexane and toluene, the simple distillation will not provide much improvement.

As we continue the distillation process and remove some of the MVC by condensing it, the residue in the heated flask becomes less rich in the MVC. This means that the next few drops of condensate will be less rich in the MVC. As the distillation is continued the condensate becomes less and less rich in the MVC.

We can improve upon simple distillation by repeating the process. For example, we could collect the condensate until about one third is obtained. Then we could collect a second one-third aliquot in a separate container. Our original mixture would then be separated into three fractions. The first one third would be richest in the MVC and the final one

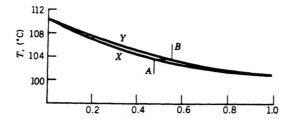

FIGURE 5.12 Temperature as a function of liquid composition (*X*) and vapor composition (*Y*): methylcyclohexane and toluene.

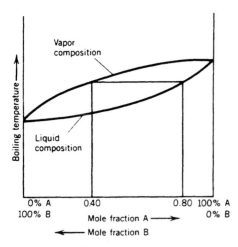

FIGURE 5.13 Liquid–vapor composition curve.

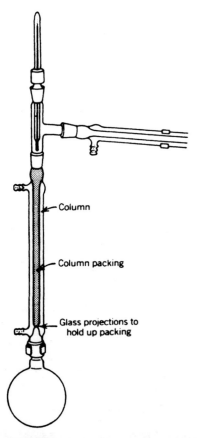

FIGURE 5.14 The fractional distillation setup. *From Zubric, James W. The Organic Chem Lab Survival Manual, 3rd ed.; Wiley: New York, 1992. (Reprinted by permission of John Wiley & Sons, Inc., New York.)*

third in the pot would be richest in the least volatile component. If the MVC were the compound of interest we could redistill the first fraction collected (in a clean flask!) and collect the first one third of the material condensing in that process. This simplest of all fractional distillation strategies is employed in Experiment [3B].

Technique 2B   Fractional Distillation at the Semimicroscale Level

Process

Fractional distillation is the application of a distillation system containing more than one theoretical plate. This process must be used if fairly complete separation is desired when the boiling points of the components differ by less than 30–40 °C. In this situation a fractionating column is required to increase the efficiency of the separation. As discussed previously, it may be seen from a liquid–vapor composition curve (Fig. 5.13) that the lower boiling component of a binary mixture makes a larger contribution to the vapor composition than does the higher boiling component. On condensation, the liquid formed will be richer in the lower boiling component. This condensate will not be pure, however, and, in the case of closely boiling components, it may show only slight enrichment. If the condensate is volatilized a second time, the vapor in equilibrium with this liquid will show a further enrichment in the lower boiling component. Thus, the trick to separating liquids that possess similar boiling points is to repeat the vaporization–condensation cycle many times. Each cycle is one *theoretical plate*. A number of different column designs are available for use at the macro level, which achieve varying numbers of theoretical plates (see Fig. 5.14).

In most distillation columns, the design is such that increased fractionation efficiency is dependent on a very large increase in the surface area in contact with the vapor phase. This increased surface area is normally accomplished by packing the fractionating column with wire gauze or glass beads. Unfortunately, a large volume of liquid must be distributed over the column surface in equilibrium with the vapor. Furthermore, the longer the column the more efficient it becomes, but longer columns also require additional liquid phase. The column requirement of the liquid phase is termed *column holdup*. Column holdup is defined as the amount of liquid distributed over the column packing required to maintain the system in equilibrium. This material is essentially lost from the liquid phase held in the distillation pot. The amount of column holdup can be large compared with the total volume of material available for the distillation. With mixtures of less than 2 mL, column holdup precludes the use of the most common fractionation columns. Microfractionating columns constructed of rapidly spinning bands of metal gauze or Teflon have very low column holdup and have a large number of plates relative to their height (Fig. 5.15). These columns are, however, rather expensive and normally are available only for research purposes.

In the development of the microscale laboratory, several new distillation systems have been designed. The microscale spinning band distillation apparatus (Fig. 5.16) can achieve nearly 12 theoretical plates and operates simply enough to be used in the instructional laboratory. This system contains a Teflon band that fits rather closely inside an insulated glass tube. The Teflon band has spiral grooves which, when the band is spun, rapidly return condensed vapor to the distillation pot. The Teflon band is rotated at 1000–1500 rpm when the column is fully operational. A powerful extension of this type of instructional apparatus uses a short spinning band inside a modified Hickman still head (see Fig. 3.21). These stills are referred to as Hickman–Hinkle stills, and 4-cm Hickman–Hinkle columns have been rated in excess of 10 theoretical plates! The commercially available 2.5-cm model is rated at 6 plates. Distillation Experiments [3C] and [3D] involve fractional distillation with spinning band columns.

An alternative to the microscale spinning band distillation column is the concentric-tube column. In these columns the fractionating section is constructed of two concentric tubes in which the vapor–liquid equilibrium is established within the annular space between the two columns. The resolution of the concentric tube system is inversely proportional to the thickness of the annular ring. Columns of this type can achieve very good separations with the number of theoretical plates approaching three per centimeter. In addition, column holdup can be close to 10 μL per theoretical plate. The major constraint in the use of these columns is the very low throughput, which can be as little as 100 μL/hour. Concentric tube columns also have the nasty habit of flooding even in experienced hands. These factors cause long residence times at elevated temperatures for the liquid components. When time and thermal stability are not a problem, the concentric-tube column can be a powerful system for mixture separations.

Experiment [3B] utilizes the Hickman still in a simple demonstration of fractional distillation. The system is arranged so that the thermometer is positioned directly down the center of the still column with the bulb ex-

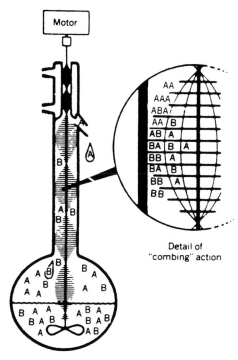

FIGURE 5.15 Schematic of a metal mesh spinning band still.

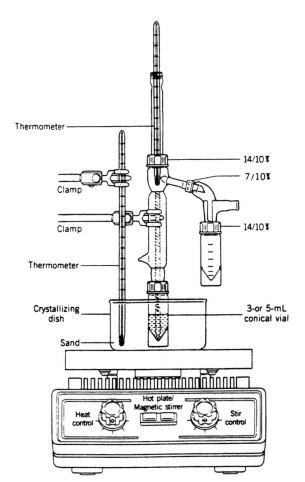

FIGURE 5.16 Micro-spinning band distillation column (3 in.).

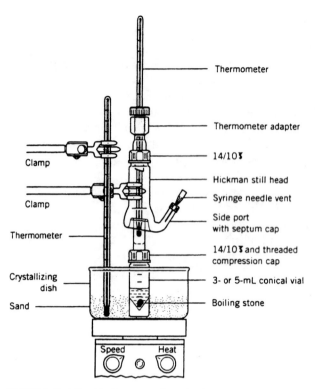

FIGURE 5.17 Hickman still with thermometer adapter.

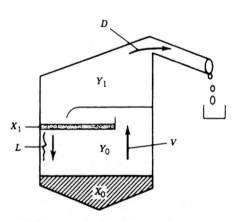

FIGURE 5.18 Model for fractional distillation with partial reflux.

tending just to the bottom of the well. As assembled, the system functions as a very rough concentric tube fractionating column. Thus, it is very important to position both the still and the thermometer as close to the vertical as possible, and in no circumstances should the two elements come into direct contact (see Fig. 5.17). A successful, two-theoretical-plate distillation is obtained with a two-component mixture by carrying out two *sequential* fractional distillations with this system.

To understand how the spinning band improves the performance of the column, and to see some of the important characteristics of these fractionating systems, we will analyze them a bit further. Figure 5.18 shows a very simple distillation column possessing just one plate. Overall, however, this system has two theoretical plates.

The compositions of the liquid in the pot and of the infinitesimal amount of liquid at the first plate are X_0 and X_1, respectively. Both Y_0 and Y_1 are compositions of the vapor in equilibrium with each of the liquids, X_0 and X_1, respectively. Since we are talking about the MVC, $Y_0 > X_0$, $Y_1 > X_1$, and we may assume that $Y_1 > Y_0$ (i.e., we have already established that the vapor will be enriched in the MVC). The parameter V is the *rate* at which vapor is transported upward, L is the rate of downward transport of liquid back to the pot, and D is the rate at which material is distilled. The parameters L, D, and V are related by $V = L + D$. (What goes up, must come down.)

We will first look at the process qualitatively. If D and V are comparable (L is small), as vapor at composition Y_1 is removed, X_1 becomes smaller—the liquid in the first plate becomes less rich in the MVC as the MVC rich vapor is removed. If, on the other hand, L and V are both large compared with D, the composition at plate 1 will be maintained at Y_0 by the large supply of incoming vapor with composition Y_0. This relationship may also be seen in the following quantitative discussion.

The first relationship we have already seen:

$$V = L + D \tag{5.3}$$

In addition, if an insignificant amount of material is held up at plate 1, the moles of MVC going into plate 1 must equal the moles of MVC leaving plate 1;

$$V \cdot Y_0 = L \cdot X_1 + D \cdot Y_1 \tag{5.4}$$

We may eliminate $V = (L + D)$ from Eq. 5.4 and rearrange to get

$$X_1 = Y_0 - (D/L) \cdot (Y_1 - Y_0) \tag{5.5}$$

Now, in Eq. 5.5, $Y_1 - Y_0$ will always be greater than 0 under ideal conditions (since they both represent the MVC). Both D and L are positive. Therefore, the *upper limit* for X_1 is Y_0. This situation would be the case when $D/L = 0$ (and nothing is being distilled). In the real world something is being distilled ($D > 0$) and X_1 will be less than Y_0 (and down the line the condensate will be less rich in the MVC; there will be less separation). You should be able to generalize this result for one plate for the situations in which we have n plates. When D/L is small the composition of the first plate is at a maximum; therefore, Y_1 is also a maximum and, furthermore, X_2 will be a maximum, and so on.

The purpose of the spinning band is to make D/L as small as possible so that X_1 approaches its upper limit of Y_0. The spinning band ensures that the optimum separation of a pair of liquids will be achieved. We will have a lot of vapor going up, a lot of liquid being returned by the spinning action of the spiral band, and a relatively small amount of material actually being distilled. This result also implies that if we want to achieve a high degree of separation, the distillation rate should be low. There is, of course, a compromise between the low rate of distillation required to obtain maximum separation and a rate that will allow someone else to use the apparatus and you to get on to other things.

NOTE. *The following list of experiments utilize Technique 2A: Experiments [3A], [3B], [11C], [29], [32], and [3A_adv]. The following Experiments utilize Technique 2B: Experiments [3C] and [3D].*

Steam Distillation   **TECHNIQUE 3**

THEORY

If two substances are immiscible (as the term "steam distillation" implies, one of the substances will be water), the **total vapor pressure** (P_t) above the two-phase liquid mixture is equal to the **sum of the vapor pressures** of the pure individual components (P_i) according to Dalton's law.

$$P_t = P_1 + P_2 + \ldots + P_i$$

In other words, with an *immiscible* pair of liquids, neither component lowers the vapor pressure of the other. The two liquids would exert the same vapor pressure (at a given temperature) even if they were in separate containers. If a mixture of these two liquids is heated, **boiling** will occur when the **combined vapor pressures** of the liquids equals atmospheric pressure. At this point, distillation will commence. **Condensation** of the vapors gives a **two-phase mixture (condensate** or **distillate)** of the organic species and water. The composition of this distillate is determined by the vapor pressure and molecular weight of the compounds.

To illustrate this concept let us take an insoluble mixture of bromobenzene (bp = 156 °C) and water. At 30 °C the vapor pressure of bromobenzene is 6 torr; water is 32 torr. Therefore, the vapor pressure of the mixture is **the sum** of 6 + 32 or 38 torr, at this temperature. At 95 °C, the vapor pressure of bromobenzene is 120 torr; water is 640 torr. It follows that the **sum** is now equal to 760 torr or 1 atm. That is, $P_A^o + P_B^o = 1$ atm.

As a result, the mixture boils and the bromobenzene and water distill together. A further example is the isolation of cyclohexanone from nonvolatile reaction byproducts by steam distillation. The normal boiling point of pure cyclohexanone is 156 °C and that for water is 100 °C. At about 94.5 °C, the vapor pressure of cyclohexanone is 112 torr and the vapor pressure of water is 648 torr. The vapor pressures of cyclohexanone and water add up to 760 torr. Thus the two compounds steam distill at 94.5 °C.

Several important aspects of steam distillation are summarized below:

1. The mixture **boils below** the boiling point of either pure component. In this regard the technique is similar to reduced pressure distillation in that the liquid distills and condenses at a temperature below its normal boiling point. This result occurs because compounds that are immiscible in water have very large, positive deviations from Raoult's law.

2. The **boiling point** of the mixture will **hold constant** as long as both substances are present to saturate the vapor volume.

3. The molar ratio of the two species in the **distillate** remains constant as long as aspect 2 holds.

From Dalton's law, the condensate in a steam distillation will consist of water and the compound in the same *molar* ratio as the ratio of their vapor pressures (P^o) at the steam distillation temperature. The relationship is

$$\frac{\text{Moles water}}{\text{Moles of organic species}} = \frac{P^o \text{ water}}{P^o \text{ organic species}}$$

This relationship may be altered to show the weight relationship of the organic substance to that of water.

Substituting grams per molecular weight (g/MW) for moles we obtain

$$\frac{\text{g/MW water}}{\text{g/MW organic species}} = \frac{P^o \text{ water}}{P^o \text{ organic species}}$$

Transposition and rearrangement of this expression leads to

$$\frac{\text{g water}}{\text{g organic species}} = \frac{P^o \text{ water} \times \text{MW water}}{P^o \text{ organic species} \times \text{MW organic species}}$$

Based on this relationship, the weight of water required per weight of organic species can be calculated. Note that if the vapor pressure of water is known at the boiling temperature of the mixture that is being steam distilled, the vapor pressure of the organic substance is 760 torr $- P^o_{\text{water}}$.

NOTE.   *These two experiments utilize Technique 3: Experiments [11C] and [32].*

Solvent Extraction

Solvent extraction is a technique frequently used in the organic laboratory to separate or isolate a desired species from a mixture of compounds or from impurities. Solvent extraction methods are readily adapted to micro-scale work, since small quantities are easily manipulated in solution. This method is based on the solubility characteristics of the organic substances involved in relation to the solvents used in a particular separation procedure.

Substances vary greatly in their solubility in various solvents, but based on observations, many of which were made in the very early days, a useful principle has evolved that allows the chemist to predict rather accurately the solubility of a particular substance.[4] It is generally true that *a substance tends to dissolve in a solvent that is chemically similar to itself. In other words, like dissolves like.*

Thus, for a particular substance to exhibit solubility in water requires that species to possess some of the characteristics of water. For example, an important class of compounds, the organic alcohols, have the hydroxyl group (—OH) bonded to a hydrocarbon chain or framework (R—OH). The hydroxyl group can be viewed as being effectively one half a water (H_2O) molecule, and it has a similar polarity to that of water. This results from a charge separation arising from the difference in electronegativity between the hydrogen and oxygen atoms. The O—H bond, therefore, is considered to have *partial ionic character.*

$$\overset{\delta^-}{-\ddot{O}}\overset{\delta^+}{-H}$$

Partial ionic character of the hydroxyl group

This *polar*, or partial ionic, character leads to relatively strong hydrogen bond formation between molecules having this entity. Strong hydrogen bonding is evident in molecules that contain a hydrogen atom attached to an oxygen, nitrogen, or fluorine atom, as shown here for the (ethanol-water) system. This polar nature of a functional group is present when there are sufficient differences in electronegativity between the atoms making up the group.

$$CH_3-CH_2-\overset{\delta^-}{\ddot{O}}\overset{\delta^-}{\cdots}\underset{H}{}$$

Ethanol

Hydrogen bond formation

In ethanol (CH_3CH_2OH), it is apparent that the hydroxyl end of the molecule is very similar to water (HOH). When ethanol is added to water, therefore, they are miscible in all proportions. That is, ethanol is completely soluble in water and water is completely soluble in ethanol. This solubility results because the attractive forces set up between the two molecules are nearly as strong as between two water molecules; however, the

[4] This section is repeated in Experiment [4], and is presented here for the sake of continuity.

attraction in the first case is somewhat weakened by the presence of the nonpolar alkyl ethyl group, CH_3CH_2—. Hydrocarbon groups attract each other only weakly, as evidenced by their low melting and boiling points. Three examples of the contrast in boiling points between compounds of different structure, but similar molecular weight, are summarized in Table 5.1. Clearly, those molecules that attract each other weakly have lower boiling points.

TABLE 5.1 Comparison of Boiling Point Data

Name	Formula	MW	bp(°C)
Ethanol	CH_3CH_2OH	46	78.3
Propane	$CH_3CH_2CH_3$	44	−42.2
Methyl acetate	$CH_3CO_2CH_3$	74	54
Diethyl ether	$(CH_3CH_2)_2O$	74	34.6
Ethylene	$CH_2{=}CH_2$	28	−102
Methylamine	CH_3NH_2	31	−6

When we compare the water solubility of ethanol (a two-carbon (C_2) alcohol that, as we have seen, is completely miscible with water) with that of octanol (a straight-chain eight-carbon (C_8) alcohol), we find that the solubility of octanol is less than 2% in water. Why the difference in solubilities between these two alcohols? The answer lies in the fact that the dominant structural feature of octanol has become the nonpolar nature of its alkyl group.

$$CH_3{-}CH_2{-}CH_2{-}CH_2{-}CH_2{-}CH_2{-}CH_2{-}CH_2{-}\overset{\delta-}{\ddot{O}}{:}\underset{H}{\overset{\delta+}{\diagdown}} \qquad\qquad CH_3{-}CH_2{-}\ddot{O}{-}CH_2{-}CH_3$$

Octanol   Diethyl ether

As the bulk of the hydrocarbon section of the alcohol molecule increases, the intramolecular attraction between the polar hydroxyl groups of the alcohol and the water molecules is no longer sufficiently strong to overcome the *hydrophobic character* (lack of attraction to H_2O) of the nonpolar hydrocarbon section of the alcohol. On the other hand, octanol has a large nonpolar hydrocarbon group as its dominant structural feature. We might, therefore, expect octanol to exhibit enhanced solubility in less polar solvents. In fact, octanol is found to be completely miscible with diethyl ether. Ethers are solvents of weak polarity (here the polarity depends on the magnitude of C—O bond dipoles, which are considerably less than those present in O—H bonds). Since the nonpolar characteristics are significant in both molecules, mutual solubility is observed. In general, it has been empirically demonstrated that if a compound has both polar and nonpolar groups present in its structure, those compounds having five or more carbon atoms in the hydrocarbon portion of the molecule will be more soluble in nonpolar solvents, such as pentane, diethyl ether, or methylene chloride. Figure 5.19 summarizes the solubilities of a number of straight-chain alcohols, carboxylic acids, and hydrocarbons in water. As expected, those compounds with more than 5 carbon atoms are shown to possess solubilities similar to those of the hydrocarbons.

Several additional relationships between solubility and structure have been observed and are pertinent to the discussion.

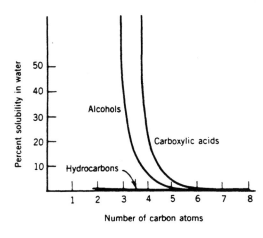

FIGURE 5.19 Solubility curve of acids, alcohols, and hydrocarbons. *From Kamm, O.* Qualitative Organic Analysis, *2nd ed.; Wiley: New York, 1932. (Reprinted with permission of John Wiley & Sons, New York.)*

1. Branched-chain compounds have greater water solubility than their straight-chain counterparts, as illustrated in Table 5.2 with a series of alcohols.

TABLE 5.2 Water Solubility of Alcohols[a]

Name	Formula	Solubility (g/100 g H_2O)
Pentanol	$CH_3(CH_2)_3CH_2OH$	4.0
2-Pentanol	$CH_3(CH_2)_2CH(OH)CH_3$	4.9
2-Methyl-2-butanol	$(CH_3)_2C(OH)CH_2CH_3$	12.5

[a] Data at 20°C.

2. The presence of more than one polar group in a compound will increase that compound's solubility in water and decrease its solubility in nonpolar solvents. For example, high molecular weight sugars, such as cellobiose, that contain multiple hydroxyl and/or acetal groups, are water soluble, and ether insoluble—whereas cholesterol (C_{27}), which possesses only a single hydroxyl group, is water insoluble and ether soluble.

Cholesterol

Cellobiose

3. The presence of a chlorine atom, even though it lends some partial ionic character to the mostly covalent C—Cl bond, does not normally impart water solubility to a compound. In fact, such compounds as methylene chloride (CH_2Cl_2), chloroform ($CHCl_3$), and carbon tetrachloride (CCl_4) have long been used as solvents for the extraction of aqueous solutions. It should be noted that use of the latter two solvents is no longer recommended, unless strict safety precautions are exercised, because of their potential carcinogenic nature.

4. Most functional groups that are capable of forming a hydrogen bond with water, if it constitutes the dominant structural feature of a molecule, will impart increased water solubility characteristics to a substance (the five-carbon rule obviously applies here in determining just what is a dominant feature). For example, certain alkyl amines (organic relatives of ammonia) might be expected to have significant water solubility. This finding is indeed the case, and the water-solubility data for a series of amines is summarized in Table 5.3.

TABLE 5.3 Water Solubility of Amines[a]

Name	Formula	Solubility (g/100 g H_2O)
Ethylamine	$CH_3CH_2NH_2$	∞
Diethylamine	$(CH_3CH_2)_2NH$	∞
Trimethylamine	$(CH_3)_3N$	91
Triethylamine	$(CH_3CH_2)_3N$	14
Aniline	$C_6H_5NH_2$	3.7
p-Phenylenediamine	$H_2NC_6H_4NH_2$	3.8

[a] Data at 25 °C.

It is important to realize that the solubility characteristics of any given compound will uniquely govern that substance's distribution (*partition*) between the phases of two immiscible solvents (in which the material has been dissolved) when these phases are intimately mixed. In this experiment we determine the partition coefficient (distribution coefficient) of benzoic acid between two immiscible solvents, methylene chloride, and water.

PARTITION COEFFICIENT

A given substance, if placed in a mixture of two immiscible solvents, will distribute (partition) itself in a manner that is a function of its relative solubility in the two solvents. For example, a solute X will be distributed between two immiscible solvents according to the following equilibrium distribution.

$$X_{solvent\,1} \rightleftharpoons X_{solvent\,2}$$

Then,

$$K_{eq} = \frac{[X_{solvent\,2}]}{[X_{solvent\,1}]}$$

The equilibrium constant (K_{eq}) is the *ratio* of the concentrations of the species in each solvent for a given system at a given temperature. This particular equilibrium constant is designated the *partition coefficient* (also referred to as the *distribution coefficient*). This coefficient is similar to the partitioning of a species that occurs in chromatographic separations.

The basic equation used to express the coefficient K is

$$K = \frac{(g/100 \text{ mL})_{\text{organic layer}}}{(g/100 \text{ mL})_{\text{water layer}}}$$

This expression uses grams per 100 mL or grams per deciliter (g/dL), but grams per liter (g/L), parts per million (ppm), and molarity (M) are also valid. The partition coefficient is dimensionless so that any concentration units may be used, provided the units are the same for both phases. If equal volumes of both solvents are used, the equation reduces to the ratio of the weights of the given species in the two solvents.

$$K = \frac{\delta_{\text{organic layer}}}{\delta_{\text{water layer}}}$$

Determination of the partition coefficient for a particular compound in various immiscible-solvent combinations often can give information valuable to the isolation and purification of the species using extraction techniques.

Let us now look at a typical calculation for the extraction of an organic compound P from an aqueous solution using diethyl ether. We will assume that the $K_{\text{ether/water}}$ value (*partition coefficient* of P between ether and water) is 3.5 at 20 °C.

If an aqueous solution containing 100 mg of P in 300 μL of water is extracted at 20 °C with 300 μL of ether, the following expression holds:

$$K_{\text{ether/water}} = \frac{C_e}{C_w} = \frac{W_e/300 \ \mu L}{W_w/300 \ \mu L}$$

where

W_e = weight of P in the ether layer
W_w = weight of P in the water layer
C_e = concentration of P in the ether layer
C_w = concentration of P in the water layer

Since $W_w = 100 - W_e$, the preceding relationship can be written as

$$K_{\text{ether/water}} = \frac{W_e/300 \ \mu L}{(100 - W_e)/300 \ \mu L} = 3.5$$

If we solve for the value of W_e, we obtain 77.8 mg; the value for W_w = 22.2 mg. Thus, we see that after one extraction with 300 μL of ether, 77.8 mg of P (77.8% of the total) is removed by the ether and 22.2 mg (22.2% of the total) remains in the water layer. The question often comes up whether it is preferable to make a single extraction with the total quantity of solvent available, or to make multiple extractions with portions of the solvent. The second method is usually preferable in terms of efficiency of extraction. To illustrate, let us consider the following.

In relation to the foregoing example, let us now extract the 100 mg of P in 300 μL of water with **two 150-μL** portions of ether **instead of one** 300-μL portion as previously done.

For the first 150-μL extraction,

$$\frac{W_e/150 \ \mu L}{W_w/300 \ \mu L} = \frac{W_e/150 \ \mu L}{(100 - W_e)/300 \ \mu L}$$

Solving for the value of W_e, we obtain 63.6 mg. The amount of P remaining in the water layer (W_w) is then 36.4 mg. The aqueous solution is now extracted with the second portion of ether (150 μL). We then have

$$\frac{W_e/150 \ \mu L}{(36.4 - W_e)/300 \ \mu L} = 3.5$$

As before, by solving for W_e, we obtain 23.2 mg for the amount of P in the ether layer; $W_w = 13.2$ mg.

The two extractions, each with 150 μL of ether, removed a total of 63.6 mg + 23.2 mg = 86.8 mg of P (86.8% of the total). The P left in the water layer is then 100 − 86.8 or 13.2 mg (13.2% of the total).

Based on the preceding calculations, it can be seen that the multiple extraction technique is the more efficient. Whereas the single extraction removed 77.8% of P, the double extraction increased this to 86.8%. To extend this relationship, multiple extractions with one third of the total quantity of the ether solvent in three portions would be even more efficient. You might wish to calculate this extension to prove the point. Of course, there is a practical limit to the number of extractions that can be performed based on time and the degree of efficiency realized.

EXTRACTION

.

The two major types of extractions utilized in the organic laboratory are the solid–liquid and liquid–liquid methods.

Solid–Liquid Extraction

The simplest form of solid–liquid extraction is the treatment of a solid with a given solvent in a beaker or Erlenmeyer flask followed by the decantation or filtration of the solvent extract from the solid sample. An example of this technique (see Experiment [11A]) is the extraction of usnic acid from its native lichen using acetone as the extraction solvent. This approach is most useful when only one main component of the solid phase has appreciable solubility in the solvent. The extraction of caffeine from tea (see Experiment [11B]) is a further example of this method and is accomplished by heating the tea in an aqueous solution of sodium carbonate. This approach works well because the solubility characteristics of the compounds involved are improved, and also because the water swells the tea leaves and allows the caffeine to be removed more readily.

The usual method of choice, however, is to carry out solid–liquid extractions on a continuous basis employing a *countercurrent* process. Various types of apparatus have been developed over the years, but perhaps the best known is the "Soxhlet" extractor, first described in 1879. It is pictured in Figure 5.20. The solid sample is placed in a porous thimble. The extraction-solvent vapor, generated by refluxing the extraction solvent contained in the distilling pot, passes up through the vertical side tube into the condenser.

The liquid condensate then drips onto the solid, which is extracted. The extraction solution passes through the pores of the thimble, eventually filling the center section of the Soxhlet. The siphon tube also fills with this extraction solution and when the liquid level reaches the top of the tube, the siphoning action commences and the extract is returned to the distillation pot. The cycle is automatically repeated numerous times. In this manner the desired species is concentrated in the distillation pot. Equilibrium is not generally established in the system, since the extraction is usually a slow process. However, the rate of extraction can be influenced by choices

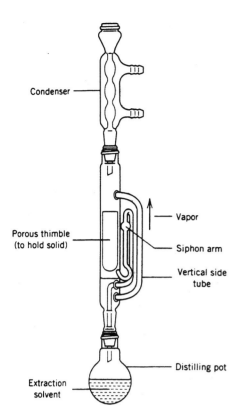

Condenser

Vapor

Porous thimble
(to hold solid)

Siphon arm

Vertical side
tube

Distilling pot

Extraction
solvent

FIGURE 5.20   Soxhlet
extractor.

of solvent, temperature, and so on. The method is classified as a discontinuous-infusion process, since the thimble containing the solid must fill with solvent before the extraction solution returns to the distillation pot. The extraction solution collected in the pot is then concentrated to isolate the desired compound.

Soxhlet extractors are available from many supply houses and can be purchased in various sizes. Of particular interest to us is the micro variety, which is effective for small amounts of material. Numerous designs for microextractors have been reported in the literature. Two examples are shown in Figure 5.21a and 5.21b. The apparatus developed by Garner (Fig. 5.21a) consists of a small cold-finger condenser inserted into a test tube. The test tube has indentations near the bottom to support a small funnel. The sample is carefully wrapped in filter paper and placed in the funnel. The Blount extractor (Fig. 5.21b) is designed for the simultaneous extraction and recrystallization of small amounts of material. In this arrangement, the sample is placed in a small fritted-glass filter crucible that is hung from the bottom of the condenser. Soxhlet microextractors also have been described, and are now commercially available.[5]

Recently, a new apparatus has become commercially available. It is reported to be much more efficient than the traditional Soxhlet method. Named the "Soxtec," it has been demonstrated to be applicable for extraction of petroleum, food, textiles, plastics, chemicals, and so on.[6] Enhanced safety, the claim of shorter extraction times, a built-in solvent recovery system, and indirect heating by circulating oil from an electronically controlled service unit are some of the advantages of this system. The three

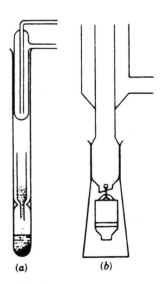

(a)   (b)

FIGURE 5.21   Apparatus for continuous extraction of a solid. (a) Garner microextractor.(b) Blount microextractor. *From Schneider, F. L.* Monographien aus dem Gebiete der qualitativen Mikroanalyse, Qualitative Organic Microanalysis, Vol. II; Benedetti-Pichler, A. A., Ed.; Springer-Verlag: Vienna, Austria, 1964.

[5] Microscale Soxhlet equipment is available from Wheaton, 1501 North Tenth St., Millville, NJ 08332.

[6] The "Soxtec" extractor is available from Tecator, Inc., P.O. Box 405, Herndon, VA 22070.

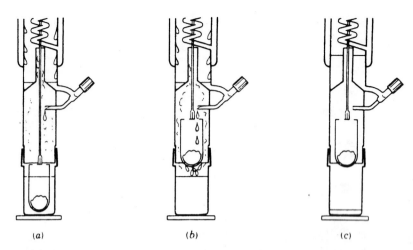

(a)   (b)   (c)

FIGURE 5.22 The Soxtec principle. (a) Boiling. Rapid pre-extraction in hot solvent. (b) Rinsing. Condensed solvent washes the last traces of soluble matter from the sample. (c) Recovery. Solvent is evaporated, condensed, and collected. *(Courtesy of Tecator, a Perstorp Analytical Co., 2875C Towerview Road, Herndon, VA 22071.)*

stages of the process: boiling, rinsing, and solvent recovery, are shown in Figure 5.22.

Liquid–Liquid Extraction

The more common type of procedure, liquid–liquid extraction, is used extensively in the laboratory. It is a very powerful method for the separation and isolation of materials encountered at the microscale level.

In the majority of extractions, a capped centrifuge tube, or a 10 × 75-mm test tube, or a conical vial is used as the container. In any extraction technique, it is essential that complete mixing of the two immiscible solvents be realized.

Let us consider a practical example. Benzanilide, prepared by the in situ rearrangement of benzophenone oxime in acid solution, is separated from the product mixture by extraction with three 1.0-mL portions of methylene chloride solvent.

NOTE. *This wording is the accepted manner of indicating that three successive extractions are performed, each using 1.0 mL of methylene chloride.*

At the microscale level, the extraction process consists of two parts: (1) mixing of the two immiscible solutions, and (2) separation of the two layers after the mixing process.

1. *Mixing.* In the experimental procedure for the isolation of the benzanilide product, methylene chloride solvent (1.0 mL) is added to the aqueous reaction mixture contained in a 5.0-mL conical vial. The extraction procedure is outlined in the following steps.

    a. The vial is capped.

    b. The vial is shaken gently to thoroughly mix the two phases.

    c. The vial is carefully vented by loosening the cap to release any pressure that may develop.

    d. The vial is allowed to stand on a level surface to permit the two phases to separate. A sharp phase boundary should be evident.

NOTE. *The mixing stage may be carried out using a Vortex® mixer.*

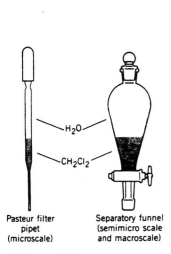

FIGURE 5.23 Extraction devices.

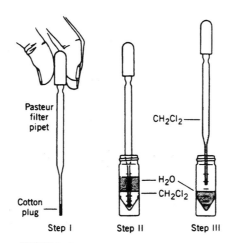

FIGURE 5.24 Pasteur filter pipet separation of two immiscible liquid phases, with the denser layer containing the product.

2. *Separation.* At the microscale level the two phases are separated with a Pasteur filter pipet (a simple Pasteur pipet can be used in some situations), which acts as a miniature separatory funnel. The separation of the phases is shown in Figure 5.23.

A major difference between macro and micro techniques is that at the microscale level, as just discussed, the mixing and separation are done in two parts (1, 2), whereas at the macroscale level with the separatory funnel, the mixing and separation are both done in the funnel in one step. It is important to note that the separatory funnel is an effective device for extractions at the semimicroscale or macroscale level, but at the microscale level it is not practical to use because the volumes are so small. The recommended procedures are diagrammed in Figures 5.24 and 5.25. Continuing the example, it is known that benzanilide is more soluble in methylene chloride than in water. Multiple extractions are performed to ensure complete removal of the benzanilide from the aqueous phase. The methylene chloride solution is the lower layer since it is more dense than water. The following Steps (I–IV) outline the general method (refer to Fig. 5.24).

I. Squeeze the pipet bulb to force air from the pipet.

II. Insert the pipet into the vial until close to the bottom. Be sure to hold the pipet in a vertical position.

III. Carefully allow the bulb to expand, drawing only the lower methylene chloride layer into the pipet. This procedure is done in a smooth, steady manner so as not to disturb the boundary between the layers. With practice, one can judge the amount that the bulb must be squeezed to just separate the layers.

IV. (Step IV is not shown in the figure). Holding the pipet in a vertical position, place it over an empty vial and gently squeeze the bulb to transfer the methylene chloride solution into the vial. A second extraction can now be performed after addition of another portion of methylene chloride to the original vial. The identical procedure is repeated. In this manner, multiple extractions can be performed, with each methylene chloride extract being transferred to the same vial; that is, the extracts are combined. The reaction product has now been transferred from the aqueous layer to the methylene chloride layer, and the phases have been separated.

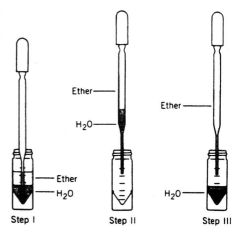

FIGURE 5.25 Pasteur filter pipet separation of two immiscible liquid phases, with the less dense layer containing the product.

In a diethyl ether–water extraction, the ether layer is less dense and thus is the top phase. Generally, the reaction product dissolves in the ether layer and is thus separated from byproducts and other impurities. The procedure followed to separate the water–ether phases is identical to that outlined earlier, except that it is the top layer that is transferred to the new container. The Steps (I–III) are shown in Figure 5.25.

I. Draw both phases into the pipet as outlined before in Steps I and II. Try not to allow air to be sucked into the pipet, since this will tend to mix the phases in the pipet. If mixing does occur, allow time for the boundary to reform.

II. Return the bottom aqueous layer to the original container by gently squeezing the pipet bulb.

III. Transfer the separated ether layer to the new vial.

Separatory Funnel Extraction

As previously mentioned, the separatory funnel (Fig. 5.23) is an effective device for extractions carried out at the semimicroscale and macroscale levels. With the use of this funnel, the mixing and separation are done in the funnel itself in one step. Many of you may be familiar with this device from your work in the general chemistry laboratory.

The solution to be extracted is added to the funnel, after first making sure that the stopcock is closed. The funnel is generally supported in an iron ring attached to a ring stand or the lab bench. The proper amount of extraction solvent is now added (about one third of the volume of the solution to be extracted is a good rule of thumb) and the stopper placed on the funnel.

NOTE.   *The size of the funnel should be such that the total volume of solution is less than three fourths the total volume of the funnel. If the funnel is constructed with a ground-glass stopcock and/or stopper, the ground-glass surfaces must be lightly greased to prevent sticking, leaking, or freezing. If Teflon® stoppers and stopcocks are used, grease is not necessary since they are self-lubricating.*

The funnel is removed from the ring stand, the stopper rested against the index finger of one hand, and the funnel held in the other with the fingers positioned so as to operate the stopcock (Fig. 5.26a). The funnel is carefully inverted, the liquid is allowed to drain away from the stopcock,

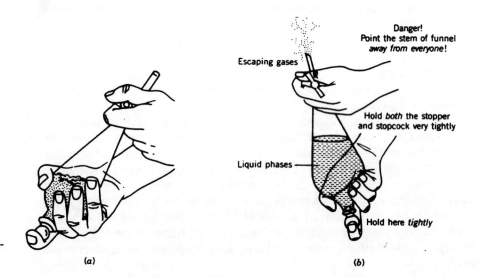

FIGURE 5.26   (a) Correct position for holding a separatory funnel while shaking. (b) Correct method for venting a separatory funnel.

and then the stopcock is opened slowly to release any built-up pressure (Fig. 5.26b).

NOTE. *Make sure the stem of the funnel is pointing up and that it does not point at anyone.*

The stopcock is closed, the funnel shaken for several seconds, the funnel positioned for venting, and the stopcock opened to release built-up pressure. This process is repeated several more times. After the final sequence, the stopcock is closed and the funnel returned upright to the iron ring.

The layers are allowed to separate, the stopper is removed, the stopcock is opened gradually, and the bottom layer is drained into a suitable container; the upper layer is removed by pouring from the top of the funnel.

When aqueous solutions are extracted with a *less dense solvent*, such as ether, the bottom, aqueous layer is drained *into the original container* from which it was poured into the funnel. Once the top ether layer is removed from the funnel, the aqueous layer can then be returned for further extraction. Losses can be minimized by rinsing this original container with a small portion of the extraction solvent, which is then added to the funnel. When the extraction solvent is denser than the aqueous phase (e.g., methylene chloride) the aqueous phase is the top layer, and therefore is retained in the funnel for subsequent extractions.

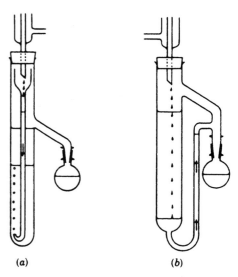

FIGURE 5.27 Early designs for single stage extractors. (*a*) Kutscher–Steudel extractor. (*b*) Wehrli extractor.

Continuous Liquid–Liquid Extraction

Continuous extraction of liquid–liquid systems is also possible. Figure 5.27a illustrates a single-stage type of extractor developed originally by Kutscher and Steudel for use with less-dense extraction solvents, and Figure 5.27b, one developed by Wehrli for use with more-dense solvents. A modification of these early designs, which combines the utility of both, is now commercially available (Fig. 5.28).

By using this device (Fig. 5.28), it is possible to extract various species from aqueous solutions using a less-dense or more-dense immiscible organic solvent. In both cases, the important aspect is that the extraction can be carried out with a limited amount of solvent. Furthermore, the number of individual extractions that would have to be performed to accomplish the same task would be prohibitive.

When one uses the convertible liquid–liquid continuous extraction apparatus (Fig. 5.28) with an extraction solvent that is heavier than water, the stopcock is open and the insert A is not used. The apparatus is fitted with a condenser at B and a distilling pot at C. The extraction solvent is distilled from the pot at C and the condensate from the condenser is allowed to pass down through the aqueous solution containing the desired compound as shown in Figure 5.27b. The more-dense extraction solution eventually returns to the distillation pot. In this manner the removed material is concentrated in the pot and fresh extraction solvent is continually passed through the aqueous solution.

When extraction solvents lighter than water are used, the stopcock is closed and the insert, A, is placed in the apparatus (Fig. 5.28). The extraction is carried out by allowing the condensate of the extraction solvent, as it forms on the condenser on continuous distillation, to drop through the inner tube and to percolate up through the solution containing the material to be extracted (see Fig. 5.27a). This inner tube usually contains a sintered glass plug on its end, which generates smaller droplets of the solvent and thus increases the efficiency of the procedure. The extraction solution is

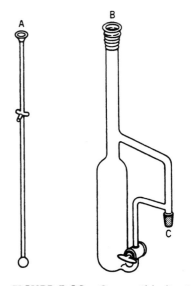

FIGURE 5.28 Convertible liquid–liquid continuous extractors. *(Courtesy of Aldrich Chemical Co., Inc., Milwaukee, WI.)*

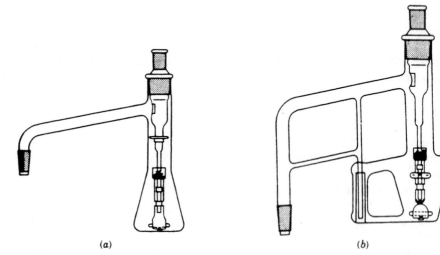

FIGURE 5.29 Normag liquid–liquid extractors. (a) For extraction with solvents of lower density. (b) For extraction with solvents of higher density. *(Courtesy of Aldrich Chemical Co., Inc., Milwaukee, WI.)*

then returned to the original distilling flask. Eventually, in this manner, the desired material, extracted in small increments, is collected in the boiling flask and can then be isolated by concentration of the collected solution. This method works on the premise that fresh portions of the less-dense phase are continuously introduced into the system and is often used in those instances where the organic material to be isolated has an appreciable solubility in water. Continuous liquid–liquid extraction is useful for removal of extractable components from those having partition ratios that approach zero. It should be realized that this is a method that requires a long period of time.

Extractors have been developed to further increase the efficiency of the extraction process. One such technique is to insert a mechanical or magnetic rotating distributor in the extractor vessel. The latter type are commercially available. One, the "Normag" (Fig. 5.29), is arranged so that the extraction solvent is presented to the solution being extracted as fine droplets.

This results in optimum conditions for the extraction and thus the rate of the process is increased dramatically. It is available in models using solvents of both higher and lower density.

An alternate design for a liquid–liquid extractor has recently become available (Fig. 5.30). It is used with a solvent more dense than water, which is placed in flask A. Distillation of the solvent produces a condensate, which drips through a frit in the joint at C. The small droplets from the frit fall through the aqueous phase in the chamber D. The solution of extractant–solvent then returns to the distilling flask through tube E.

Microextractors of the lighter and heavier solvent type have also been developed. Two designs are illustrated in Figure 5.31.

These microextractors work on the same principle that we discussed previously. An alternate design has been reported by Gould in which the Soxhlet apparatus is modified by using various adapters, depending on whether the solvent is heavier or lighter than the aqueous solution to be extracted. A novel technique for removing medium-polar solvents by continuous extraction with water has been reported by Uzar.[7]

Countercurrent multiple fractional extraction, an automated technique, has been developed to allow 200 or more successive extractions to

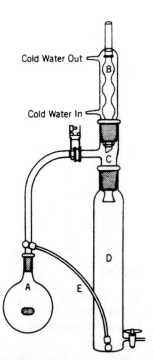

Cold Water Out

Cold Water In

FIGURE 5.30 The Supelco liquid–liquid extractor. *(Courtesy of Supelco Inc., Supelco Park, Bellefonte, PA 16823.)*

[7] Uzar, H. C. *J. Chem Educ.* **1990** 67, 349.

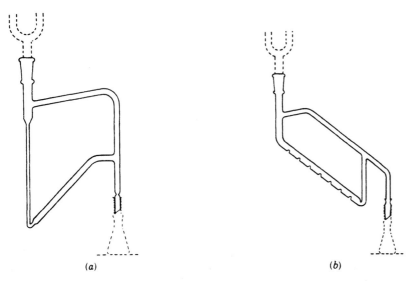

FIGURE 5.31 Micro liquid—liquid extractors. (a) For extraction with solvents of lower density. (b) For extraction with solvents of higher density.

be performed.[8] The basic type of extractor consists of a series of extraction tubes through which the upper phase is moved. The extraction tubes (Fig. 5.32) are shaken to equilibrate the phases. After each equilibration, the less-dense phase is transferred to the next tube by a reservoir; the more-dense phase remains in the original tube. Fresh extraction solvent is added after each extraction. The material to be extracted is placed in the first tube at the start of the extraction. As the process proceeds, the different components being extracted progress through the series of extraction tubes at

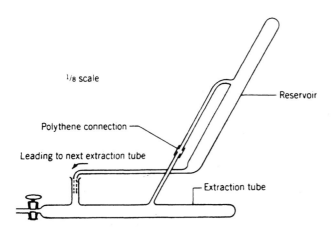

FIGURE 5.32 A single unit of the multiple extraction apparatus. *From Elvidge, J. A.; Summer, P. G. A Course in Modern Techniques of Organic Chemistry 2nd ed., 1966. (By permission of the publishers, Butterworth & Co. (Publishers) Ltd. ©, London, England).*

[8] For a complete discussion of the continuous liquid—liquid extraction method, see Craig, L. C.; Craig, D. in *Technique of Organic Chemistry*, 2nd ed., A. Weissberger, Ed.; Interscience: New York, 1956; Vol. III, pp. 149–332. A shorter presentation is given in Elvidge, J. A.; Sammes, P. G. *A Course in Modern Techniques of Organic Chemistry*, 2nd. ed.; Butterworths: London, 1966; Chapter 7, p. 57.

different rates, depending on their partition coefficients. This technique permits separation of various species having nearly the same partition coefficients. Craig has shown that a series of 10 amino acids which have partition coefficients that differ by less than 0.1, can be separated by this approach.

Drying of the Wet Organic Layer

It is important to realize that organic extracts separated from aqueous phases usually contain traces of water. Before evaporation of the solvent to isolate the desired species, or before further purification steps can be taken, the organic extract must be dried to remove any residual water. This condition is conveniently achieved with an inorganic anhydrous salt, such as magnesium, sodium, or calcium sulfate. These materials readily form insoluble hydrates, thus removing the water from the wet organic phase. The hydrated solid can then be removed from the dried solution by filtration or decantation. An ideal drying agent should have a short drying time, high capacity for water, and a high degree of absorption. Table 5.4 summarizes the properties of some of the more common drying agents used in the laboratory.

There are two basic requirements for an effective solid drying agent: (1) it should not react with the material in the system, and (2) it must be easily and completely separated from the dried liquid phase. The amount of drying agent used depends on the amount of water present, on the capacity of the solid desiccant to absorb water, and on its particle size. If the solution is wet, the first amount of drying agent will clump (molecular

TABLE 5.4 Properties of Common Drying Agents

Drying Agent	Formula of Hydrate	Comments
Sodium sulfate	$Na_2SO_4 \cdot 10\ H_2O$	Slow in absorbing water and is inefficient but is inexpensive and has a high capacity. Loses water above 32 °C. Granular form available
Magnesium sulfate	$MgSO_4 \cdot 7\ H_2O$	One of the best. Can be used with nearly all organic solvents. Usually in powder form
Calcium chloride	$CaCl_2 \cdot 6\ H_2O$	Relatively fast drying agent. However, it reacts with many oxygen and nitrogen containing compounds. Usually in granular form
Calcium sulfate	$CaSO_4 \cdot \frac{1}{2}\ H_2O$	Very fast and efficient. However, notice that it has a low dehydration capacity
Silica gel	$(SiO_2)_m \cdot n\ H_2O$	High capacity and efficient. Commercially available t.h.e.® SiO_2 drying agent is excellent[a]
Molecular sieves	$[Na_{12}(Al_{12}Si_{12}O_{48})] \cdot 27\ H_2O$	High capacity and efficient. Use the 4-Å size[b]

[a] Available from EM Science, Cherry Hill, NJ 08034.
[b] Available from Aldrich Chemical Co. Inc, 940 West Saint Paul Ave., Milwaukee, WI 53233.

sieves and t.h.e.® SiO$_2$ are exceptions). In this case, additional drying agent is added until the agent appears mobile on swirling the container. Swirling the contents of the container increases the rate of drying, since it aids in establishment of the equilibrium for hydration.

$$\text{Drying agent} + n\,\text{H}_2\text{O} = \text{Drying agent} \cdot n\,\text{H}_2\text{O}$$
(anhydrous solid)   (solid hydrate)

Most drying agents attain approximately 80% of their drying capacity within 15 min, so longer drying times are generally not required.

As mentioned above, particle size plays a role in the effectiveness of the drying agent used. Magnesium sulfate is a good all-around drying agent. However, it is supplied as a fine powder and thus has a high surface area. The disadvantage is that the desired product can become trapped on the surface of the magnesium sulfate particles. If the drying agent, after separation, is not thoroughly washed, precious product may be lost. Furthermore, removal of a finely powdered solid agent is generally more difficult since it may pass through the filter paper (if used) or clog the pores of a fine porous filter. It is advisable to use a drying agent that is available in a granular form. Anhydrous sodium sulfate is a good example. A smaller surface area translates into less adsorption of product on the surface and easier separation from the dried solution.

The drying agent may be added directly to the container containing the organic extract or the extract may be passed through a Pasteur filter pipet packed with the drying agent. A funnel fitted with a cotton, glass wool, or polyester plug to hold the drying agent may also be used.

Separation of Acids and Bases

The separation of organic acids and bases constitutes another important and extensive use of the extraction method. An organic acid reacts with dilute aqueous sodium hydroxide solution to form a salt. The salt, having an ionic charge, dissolves in the more polar aqueous phase (e.g. Experiment [7]).

The reaction reverses the solubility characteristics of a water insoluble acid. The water phase may then be extracted with an immiscible organic solvent to remove any impurities, leaving the acid salt in the water phase. Neutralization of the soluble salt with hydrochloric acid causes precipitation of the insoluble organic acid in a relatively pure state. In a similar fashion, organic bases, such as amines, can be rendered completely water soluble by treatment with dilute hydrochloric acid to form hydrochloride salts (e.g. Experiment [23]).

Extraction procedures are also used in the separation of mixtures of solids. For example, the separation of a mixture made up of an aromatic (Ar) organic acid (ArCO$_2$H), base (ArNH$_2$), and neutral compound (ArH). A flow chart is given below that diagrams the sequence.

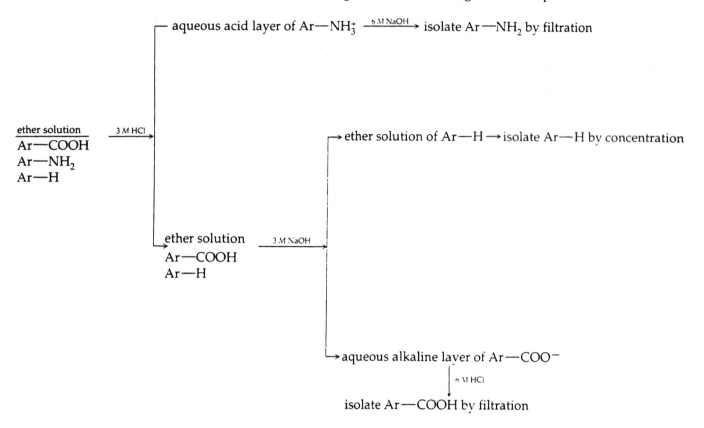

In this example, we assume the organic acid and base to be solid compounds. If either is a liquid, an additional extraction of the final acidic aqueous or alkaline solution with ether, followed by drying and concentration, would be required to isolate the acid or base component.

SALTING OUT

It was emphasized in the solubility section that organic compounds with fewer than 5 carbon atoms, and also those with one or more polar groups, tend to be water soluble. In these cases, the partition coefficient for the species would generally be equal to, or less than, 1. Transfer of this type of compound into an organic phase by extraction from water is thus quite difficult. A technique often used to overcome this problem is the addition of an inorganic salt, such as sodium chloride, to the water phase. As a result of this addition, the attraction of the polar water molecules for the inorganic ions is much stronger than that for the organic species. The organic compound is then free to be extracted into an organic solvent. This approach is often referred to as *salting out*.

SOLID-PHASE EXTRACTION

In the modern research laboratory, the traditional liquid–liquid extraction technique may be replaced by the **solid-phase extraction** method.[9] The advantage of this new approach is that it is rapid, small volumes of solvent

[9] For a description of this method see Zief, M.; Kiser, R. *Am. Lab.* **1990**, 70 and Zief, M. *NEACT J.* **1990**, *8*, 38.

are used, emulsion formation is avoided, isolated solvent extracts do not require a further drying stage, and it is ideal for working at the microscale level. This technique is finding wide acceptance in the food industry and in the environmental and clinical area, and it is becoming the accepted procedure for the rapid isolation of drugs of abuse and their metabolites from urine.

Solid-phase extraction is accomplished using prepackaged, disposable, extraction columns. A typical column is shown in Figure 5.33. The columns are available from several commercial sources.[10]

The polypropylene columns can be obtained packed with 100, 200, 500, or 1000 mg of 40-μm sorbent sandwiched between two 20-μm polyethylene frits. The columns are typically 57 mm long. Sample volumes generally average 1–6 mL.

The adsorbents used in the columns are silica-gel based with a chemically bonded nonpolar stationary phase. In fact, they are the same nonpolar adsorbents used extensively in the reversed-phase high performance liquid chromatography (HPLC) technique. More specifically, the adsorbents are derivatized silica gel where the —OH groups of the silica gel have been replaced with siloxane units by treatment with the appropriate organochlorosilanes.

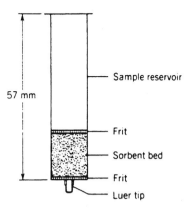

FIGURE 5.33 Polyethylene solid-phase extraction column.

Si—OH   Si—O—Si(CH$_3$)$_3$

Si—OH   Si—O   CH$_3$
                        Si
Si—OH   Si—O   R

Silica surface   Chemically bonded silica surface

Two of the most popular nonpolar packings are those containing R groups consisting of octadecyl (C$_{18}$H$_{37}$—) or phenyl (C$_6$H$_5$—) units. These systems can adsorb nonpolar (like attracts like) organic material from aqueous solutions. This material is then eluted from the column, using a solvent strong enough to displace it. Solvents such as methylene chloride or hexane are used extensively. In many instances, methanol appears to be an effective solvent for eluting analytes from the octadecyl bonded-phase columns. The analyte capacity of bonded silica gels has been estimated to be 10–20 mg of analyte per gram of packing.

It is imperative to understand that for this extraction technique to be effective, information on the structure of the material to be separated, the number and type of functional groups present, the polarity, the molecular weight, the solubility characteristics, and so on, is essential, if good separation is to be obtained. Furthermore, the elution solvent must be evaluated, and it must be established that adsorption of the desired species will occur on the column and that it also can be removed.

An example of a typical solid-phase extraction is the determination of the amount of caffeine in coffee. A 1-mL capacity column is used containing 100 mg of octadecyl-bonded silica. The column is conditioned by aspirating 2 mL of methanol followed by 2 mL of water through the column. We then draw 1 mL of a coffee solution containing approximately 0.75 mg

---

[10] These columns are available from Analytichem International, J. T. Baker, Inc., Supelco, Inc., and Waters Associates.

of caffeine/mL through the sorbent at a flow rate of 1 mL/min. The column is washed with 1 mL of water and air dried under vacuum for 10 min. The adsorbed caffeine is eluted using two 500-μL portions of chloroform. High-performance liquid chromatographic analysis indicates that 94% of the caffeine was isolated from the coffee sample.

BIBLIOGRAPHY

For overviews on extraction methods see the following general references:

Blount, B. *Mikrochemie* **1936**, *19*, 162.

Colegrave, E. B. *Analyst* **1935**, *60*, 90.

Craig, L. C. *Anal. Chem.* **1950**, *22*, 1346.

Craig, L. C.; Craig, D. In *Technique of Organic Chemistry*, 2nd ed., A. Weissberger, Ed.; Interscience: New York, 1956; Vol. III, Part I, Chapter 2.

Garner, W. *Ind. Chem.* **1928**, *4*, 332.

Gould, B. S. *Science* **1943**, *98*, 546.

Hanson, C., Ed., *Recent Advances in Liquid–Liquid Extraction*; Pergamon: Oxford, 1971.

Hartland, S. *Countercurrent Extraction*; Pergamon: Oxford, 1970.

Jubermann, O. in *Houben–Weyl Methoden der Organischen Chemie*, 4th ed.; Verlag: Stuttgart, 1958, Vol. I, p. 223.

Kirk–Othmer Encyclopedia of Chemical Technology 3rd ed.; Wiley: New York, 1980; Vol. 9, p. 672.

Kutscher, K; Steudel, H. *Z. Physiol. Chem.* **1903**, *39*, 474.

Schneider, Frank L. *Qualitative Organic Microanalysis*; Vol. II of *Monographien aus dem Gebiete der qualitativen Mikroanalysis*, A. A. Benedetti-Pichler, Ed.; Springer-Verlag: Vienna, Austria, 1964; p. 61.

Soxhlet, F; Szombathy *Dinglers Polytech. J.* **1879**, *232*, 461.

Thorpe, J. F.; Whiteley, M. A. *Thorpe's Dictionary of Applied Chemistry*, 4th ed.; Longman: New York, 1940; Vol. IV, p. 575.

Wehrli, S. *Helv. Chim. Acta* **1937**, *20*, 927.

References to Solid-Phase Extractions:

Baker-10 spe Applications Guide, Vol. 1, p 182; J. T. Baker Chemical Co., Phillipsburg, NJ.

Cooke, N. H. C.; Olsen, K. *Amer. Lab.* **1979**, *11*, 45.

Dorsey, J.; Dill, K. A. *Chem. Rev.* **1989**, *89*, 331.

Nawrocki, J.; Baszewski, B. *J. Chromatogr.* **1988**, *559*, 1.

NOTE.   *The following list of experiments utilize Technique 4: Experiments [4A], [4B], [5A], [5B], [7], [8A], [8B], [8C], [11A], [11B], [11C], [12], [13], [16], [17], [19A], [19B], [19C], [19D], [22A], [22B], [23], [27], [30], [32], [34A], [34B], [3A$_{adv}$], [4$_{adv}$], [6$_{adv}$], [A1$_b$], [D3], [E3], [F1], [F2], [F3], and [F4].*

TECHNIQUE 5

Crystallization

This discussion introduces the basic strategy involved in achieving the purification of solid organic substances by crystallization. The technique of crystallizing an organic compound is one of fundamental importance, and one that must be mastered in order to deal successfully with the purification of these materials. *It is not an easy art to acquire.* Organic solids tend not to crystallize with the ease of inorganic substances.

Indeed, in earlier times, an organic chemist occasionally would resist an invitation to leave a well-worn laboratory for new quarters. This concern arose from the suspicion that the older facility (in which many crystallizations had been carried out) harbored seed crystals for a large variety of substances in which the resident investigator had an interest. Carried by dust from the earlier work, this trace of material presumably aided the successful initiation of crystallization of reluctant materials. Further support for this argument/legend was gained by the often quoted (but not substantiated) observation that after a material was first crystallized in a particular laboratory, subsequent crystallizations of the material, regardless of its purity or origin, were always easier to carry out.

A reaction could very often have been viewed as a failure if an amorphous sludge could not be enticed to become a collection of beautiful white crystals. The melting point of an amorphous substance is ill-defined, and if this material is mixed with a crystalline reference compound, large melting point depressions usually result.

In several areas of organic chemistry, particularly those dealing with natural products, the success or failure of an investigation can depend to a large extent on the ability of the research chemist to isolate tiny quantities of crystalline substances. Often, the compounds of interest must be extracted from enormous amounts of extraneous material. In one of the more spectacular examples, Reed et al. in 1953 isolated 30 mg of the crystalline coenzyme, lipoic acid, from 10 tons of beef liver residue.[11]

S—S CH₂CH₂CH₂CH₂CO₂H
H

Lipoic acid

PROCEDURE

The essentials of this purification technique are outlined as follows: (1) dissolve the material (primarily made up of the compound of interest along with smaller quantities of contaminating substances) in a warm solvent; (2) once the solid mixture is fully dissolved, filter the heated solution, and then bring it to the point of saturation by evaporating a portion of the solvent; (3) cool the warm saturated solution to cause a drop in solubility of the dissolved substance. This results in precipitation of the solid material; and (4) isolate the precipitate by filtration, and then remove the last traces of solvent.

The technique is considered successful if the solid is recovered in good yield and is obtained in a higher state of purity than that before the procedure. This cycle, from the solid state to solution and back to the solid state, is termed *recrystallization*, if both the initial and final solid materials are crystalline.

Although the technique sounds fairly simple, in reality it is demanding. The successful purification of microscale quantities of solids will require your utmost attention.

The first major problem to be faced is the choice of solvent system. To achieve high recoveries, the compound to be crystallized would ideally be very soluble in the solvent of choice at elevated temperatures, but nearly insoluble when it is cold. If the crystallization is to increase the purity of the

[11] Reed, L. J.; Gunsalus, I. C.; Schnakenberg, G. H. F.; Soper, Q. F.; Boaz, H. E.; Kem, S. F.; Parke, T. V. *J. Am. Chem. Soc.* **1953**, *75*, 1267.

compound, however, the impurities should be either very soluble in the solvent at all temperatures, or not soluble at any temperature. In addition, the solvent should possess as low a boiling point as possible so that traces can be easily removed from the crystals after filtration.

Thus, the choice of solvent is critical to a good crystallization. Table 5.5 is a list of common solvents used in the purification of most organic solids. (The list has contracted significantly in the past few years as health concerns about these very volatile compounds have arisen.)

TABLE 5.5   Common Solvents

Solvent	bp (°C)
Water	100
Methanol	65
Ethanol, 95%	78
Ligroin	60–90
Acetone	56
Diethyl ether	35
Methylene chloride	41
Petroleum ether	30–60

Seldom are the solubility relationships ideal for crystallization and most often a compromise is made. If there is no suitable single solvent available, it is possible to employ a mixture of two solvents, termed a solvent pair. In this situation, a solvent is chosen that will readily dissolve the solid. After dissolution, the system is filtered. A second solvent, miscible with the first, in which the solute has a lower solubility, is then added dropwise to the hot solution to achieve saturation. In general, polar organic molecules have higher solubilities in polar solvents, and nonpolar materials are more soluble in nonpolar solvents (like dissolves like). Considerable time can be spent in the laboratory working out an appropriate solvent system for a particular reaction product. In most instances, with known compounds, the optimum solvent system has been established.

Because many impurities have solubilities similar to those of the compounds of interest, most crystallizations are not very efficient. Recoveries of 50–70% are not uncommon. It is important that the purest possible material be isolated prior to recrystallization.

A number of microscale crystallization routines are available.

SIMPLE CRYSTALLIZATION

Simple crystallization works well with large quantities of material (100 mg and up), and it is essentially identical to that of the macroscale technique.

1. Place the solid in a small Erlenmeyer flask or test tube.
2. Add a minimum of solvent and heat the mixture to the solvent's boiling point in a sand bath.
3. Stir, and add solvent dropwise with continued heating, until all of the material has dissolved.
4. Add a decolorizing agent, if necessary (powdered charcoal, or better, charcoal pellets), to remove colored minor impurities and resinous byproducts.

5. Filter the hot solution into a second Erlenmeyer flask (preheat the funnel with hot solvent). This operation removes the decolorizing agent and any insoluble material initially present in the sample.
6. Evaporate enough solvent to reach saturation.
7. Cool to allow crystallization (crystal formation will be better if this step takes place slowly).
8. Collect the crystals by filtration.
9. Wash (rinse) the crystals.
10. Dry the crystals.

FILTRATION TECHNIQUES

Use of the Hirsch Funnel

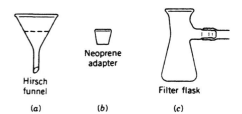

FIGURE 5.34 Component parts for vacuum filtration (see parts a–c).

The standard filtration system for collecting products purified by recrystallization in the microscale laboratory is vacuum filtration with an 11-mm Hirsch funnel. In addition, many reaction products that do not require recrystallization are collected directly by this technique. The Hirsch funnel, as shown in Figure 5.34*a*, is composed of a ceramic cone with a circular flat bed perforated with small holes. The diameter of the bed is covered by a flat piece of filter paper of the same diameter. The funnel is sealed into a filter flask with a Neoprene adapter (see Fig. 5.34*b*).

The filter flask, which is heavy walled and especially designed to operate under vacuum, is constructed with a side arm (they are often called "side-arm pressure flasks"; see Fig. 5.34*c*).

The side arm is connected with heavy-walled rubber vacuum tubing to a water aspirator, or water pump. The water pump utilizes a very simple and inexpensive aspirator. The system is based on the Venturi effect in which water is forced through a constricted throat in the pump (see Fig. 5.35).

If water, as an incompressible liquid, completely fills the water pump at all points, the same volume of liquid must pass every cross section in any given time as it is discharged out of the aspirator. Hence,

$$Q = Av$$

where Q = the discharge rate (cm³/s)
A = the cross section of the discharge
v = the velocity of the discharge

and the *equation of continuity* follows

$$Q = Av = A_1 v_1 = \text{constant}$$

where A_1 = the cross section of the throat
v_1 = the velocity in the throat

FIGURE 5.35 Aspirator pump.

A consequence of this relationship is that the velocity is greatest at points where the cross section is least, and vice versa. Hence, the water velocity through the throat of the aspirator is much faster than the discharge velocity. Air is drawn into the low-pressure water rushing through the constricted portion (Bernoulli's principle).

Two pressure effects are involved in the operation of this type of pump. First, the pressure is limited to the vapor pressure of water at the temperature of the water supply reservoir. Second, a drop in water pressure (caused by a laboratory neighbor turning on a tap directly connected to your water line) will often result in a backup of water through the hose connection and into the filter flask, as the pressure momentarily is lowest on that side of the system. It is, therefore, essential that safety traps (see Fig. 5.39) be mounted between the aspirator and the filtration apparatus.

When water is running through the aspirator, a partial vacuum is formed, which creates a flow of air down the vacuum tubing from the filter flask. With the rubber adapter in place, the entering air is forced through the filter paper, which is held flat by suction. The mother liquors of the crystallization are rapidly forced into the filter flask, while the crystals retained by the filter are quickly dried by the stream of air passing through them (Fig. 5.36).

In some situations, the substance collected on the Hirsch funnel is not highly crystalline. If this is true, the compact filter cake may be difficult to dry using the method outlined above. In these situations, a thin, flexible rubber sheet or a piece of plastic food wrap is placed over the mouth of the funnel such that the suction generated from the aspirator (or vacuum pump) pulls the sheeting down onto the filter cake. This process creates pressure on the cake. This pressure assists in forcing a large portion of the remaining solvent from the collected material and thus further drying is achieved. It is advisable to use a section of sheeting large enough that, when it is placed over the funnel, the entire filter cake is covered. If this is not done, a vacuum will not be created and thus drying will not occur.

In some instances, substances may retain water or other solvents with great tenacity. To dry these materials, a **desiccator** is often used. A desiccator is generally a glass or plastic container in which a material (desiccant) having the capacity to absorb water is placed. The substance to be dried, held in a suitable open container, is then placed on a support above the desiccant layer. This technique is widely used in the quantitative analysis laboratory for drying collected precipitates. Vacuum desiccators are available if required (see Fig. 5.37a). If this method of drying is still insufficient, a **drying pistol** is then employed. These pistols (Abderhalden vacuum-drying apparatus, see Fig. 5.37b) are commercially available from most supply houses. The sample, in an open container (vial) is placed in the apparatus, which is then evacuated. The pistol has a pocket in which a strong absorbing agent, such as P_4O_{10} (for water), NaOH or KOH (for acidic gases), or paraffin wax (for organic solvents) is placed. The temperature of the pistol is controlled by refluxing vapors that surround the barrel. A simple alternative to this method is the use of a side-armed test tube as shown in Figure 5.38.

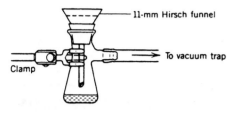

FIGURE 5.36 Vacuum filtration apparatus.

(a)

FIGURE 5.37a Vacuum desiccator

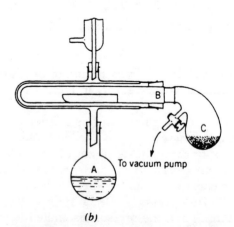

(b)

FIGURE 5.37b Abderhalden vacuum drying apparatus. A, refluxing heating liquid; B, vacuum drying chamber; C, desiccant.

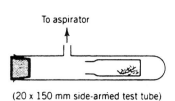

FIGURE 5.38 Side arm test tube as a vacuum drying apparatus.

(20 x 150 mm side-armed test tube)

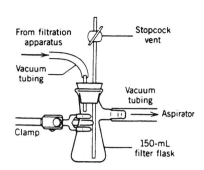

FIGURE 5.39 Vacuum trap.

As mentioned above, when you are using a water pump, it is very important to have a safety trap mounted in the vacuum line leading from the filter flask. Any drop in water pressure (easily created by one or two other students on the same water line turning on their aspirators at the same time) can result in the backup of water into the system as the flow through the aspirator decreases (see Fig. 5.39).

Craig Tube Crystallizations

The Craig tube is commonly used for microscale crystallizations in the range of 10–100 mg of material (see Fig. 5.40). The process consists of the following steps.

1. The sample is placed in a small test tube (10 x 75 mm).

2. The solvent (0.5–2 mL) of choice is added, and the sample dissolved by heating in the sand bath. Rapid stirring with a microspatula (roll the spatula rod between your fingers) greatly aids the dissolution and protects against boil-over. A modest excess of solvent is added after the sample is completely dissolved. It will be easy to remove this excess at a later stage, as the volumes involved are very small. The additional solvent ensures that the solute will stay in solution during the hot transfer.

3. The heated solution is transferred to the Craig tube by Pasteur filter pipet (the pipet is preheated with hot solvent). This transfer automatically filters the solution (if decolorizing charcoal powder has been added, two filtrations by the pipet may be required. The second filtration can almost always be avoided by the use of charcoal pellets.)

4. The hot, filtered solution is then concentrated to saturation by gentle boiling in the sand bath. Constant agitation of the solution with a microspatula during this short period will avoid the use of a boiling stone, and guarantees that a boil-over will not occur. Ready crystallization on the microspatula, just above the solvent surface, serves as a good indication that saturation is close at hand.

5. The upper section of the Craig tube is set in place, and the system is allowed to cool in a safe place. As cooling commences, seed crystals, if necessary, may be added by crushing them against the side of the Craig tube with a microspatula just above the solvent line. A good routine, if the time is available, is to place the assembly in a small Erlenmeyer, then place the Erlenmeyer in a beaker, and finally cover the first beaker with a second inverted beaker. This procedure will ensure slow cooling, which will enhance good crystal growth (Fig. 5.41). A Dewar flask may be used when very slow cooling and/or larger crystals are required (as in X-ray crystallography).

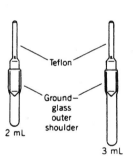

FIGURE 5.40 Craig tubes.

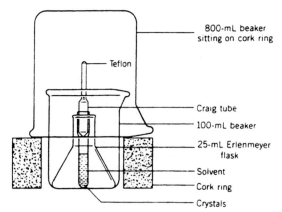

FIGURE 5.41 Apparatus for slow crystallization.

6. After the system reaches room temperature, cooling in an ice bath will further improve the yield.

7. The solvent is now removed by inverting the Craig tube assembly into a centrifuge tube and spinning the mother liquors away from the crystals (Fig. 5.42). This operation takes the place of the usual filtration step in simple crystallizations. It avoids another transfer of material and also avoids product contact with filter paper.

8. After removal from the centrifuge, the Craig tube is disassembled and any crystalline product clinging to the upper section is scraped into the lower section. If the lower section is tared, it can be left to air-dry to constant weight, or it can be placed in a warm vacuum oven (wrap a piece of filter paper over the open end secured by a rubber band to prevent dust from collecting on the product while drying). The yield can then be directly calculated.

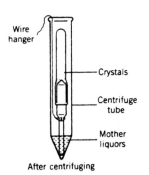

FIGURE 5.42 Crystal collection with a Craig tube.

The cardinal rule in carrying out the purification of small quantities of solids is: *Keep the number of transfers to an absolute minimum!* The Craig tube is very helpful in this regard.

The preceding routine will maximize the crystallization yield. If time is important, the process can be shortened considerably. Shortcuts, however, invariably lead to a corresponding drop in yield.

RECRYSTALLIZATION PIPET

Landgrebe has recently described an alternative to the Craig tube method.[12] This approach utilizes a modified Pasteur pipet as a recrystallization tube. The method works well for 10–100-mg quantities, as long as the volume of solvent used in the recrystallization does not exceed 1.5 mL, the capacity of a Pasteur pipet. A description of the sequence follows:

1. Prepare a recrystallization tube (Fig. 5.43) by pushing a plug of cotton (copper wire is used) into the Pasteur pipet so that the cotton resides 1–2 cm below the wider bore of the pipet.

2. Seal the (lower) part of the tube below the cotton plug with a microburner. Pull the glass so that a very narrow tip is formed. This procedure allows the tip to be broken easily at a later stage of the operation.

3. Place the solid into the tared tube, reweigh to determine the weight of solid, and then clamp the tube near the top in a vertical position.

[12] Landgrebe, J. A. *J. Chem. Educ.* **1988**, *65*, 460.

FIGURE 5.43 Recrystallization tube.

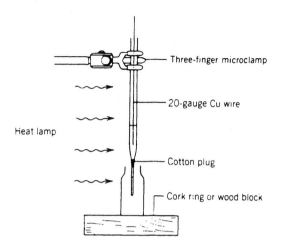

Three-finger microclamp

20-gauge Cu wire

Heat lamp

Cotton plug

Cork ring or wood block

FIGURE 5.44 Dissolution of sample in hot solvent.

Arrange a tared vial so that the bottom tip of the recrystallization tube protrudes about 1 cm into it. (Fig. 5.44).

4. Add an appropriate amount of solvent to the tube using a Pasteur pipet. Stir the suspension with a copper wire, and arrange a heating lamp approximately 6–8 cm from the tube.

5. When the solid has dissolved, remove the vial, snap the tip off the tube, and quickly replace the vial under it. Continue to warm the solution being filtered (do not boil). If the filtration is too slow, gently apply pressure using a pipet bulb.

6. After crystallization is complete, the mother liquor may be removed using a Pasteur filter pipet. Cold, fresh solvent may be added to wash the crystals, and the wash solvent then can be removed by using the Pasteur filter pipet as before. Dry the crystals as discussed above (see Fig. 5.37 or 5.38).

NOTE. *The following list of experiments utilize Technique 5: Experiments [6], [7], [15], [16], [18], [19A], [19B], [19C], [19D], [20], [23A], [23B], [24A], [24B], [25A], [25B], [26], [28], [29A], [29B], [29C], [29D], [30], [31], [33A], [33B], [34A], [34B], [2_{adv}], [3A_{adv}], [3B_{adv}], [5_{adv}], [6_{adv}], [7_{adv}], [A1_{a}], [A2_{a}], [A3_{a}], [A1_{b}], [A2_{b}], [A3_{b}], [A4_{ab}], [B1], [C2], [C3], [D1], [D2], [E1], [E2], [F1], [F2], and [F4].*

Chromatography   **TECHNIQUE 6**

Technique 6A   Column, High Performance Liquid, and Thin-Layer Chromatography

The theory of chromatography is defined in Technique 1 during the development of gas-phase separations. The term is derived from the Greek word for color, *chromatos*. Tswett discovered the technique (1903) during studies that were centered on the separation of mixtures of natural plant pigments.[13] The chromatographic zones were detected simply by observing the color bands. Thus, as originally applied, the name was not an inconsistent use of terminology. Today, however, most mixtures that are chromatographed are colorless. The separated zones in these cases are established by other methods. Coincidentally, "tswett" means "color" in Russian (the discoverer's nationality).

In this section, two additional chromatographic techniques are explored. Both of these procedures depend on adsorption and distribution between a stationary solid phase and a moving liquid phase. The first to be discussed is "column chromatography," a very powerful technique that is used extensively throughout organic chemistry. It was one of the earliest of the modern chromatographic methods to be applied to the separation of organic mixtures by Tswett. The second procedure, thin-layer chromatography (TLC), was developed in the late 1950s. Thin-layer chromatography is particularly effective in rapid assays of sample purity. It is also effective when employed as a preparative technique for obtaining high-quality material for analytical data (ideal conditions for the microscale laboratory).

COLUMN CHROMATOGRAPHY

The term *column chromatography* is derived from the use of a column packed with a solid stationary phase, a relationship similar to the liquid phase of GC. The mobile liquid phase descends, by gravity or applied pressure, through the column.

A wide variety of substances have been employed as the stationary phase in this technique. In practice, however, two materials have become dominant in this type of separation chemistry. Finely ground (100–200 mesh) alumina (aluminum oxide, Al_2O_3) and silica gel (silicic acid) are by far the most useful of the known adsorbents. The liquids, which act as the moving phase and elute (wash) sample materials through the column, are many of the common organic solvents. Table 5.6 lists the better known column packings and elution solvents.

TABLE 5.6   Column Chromatography Materials

Stationary Phase		Moving Phase	
Alumina	↑ *Increasing*	Water	↑ *Increasing*
Silica gel	*adsorption*	Methanol	*solvation*
Magnesium sulfate	*of polar*	Ethanol	*of polar*
Cellulose paper	*materials*	Acetone	*materials*
		Ethyl acetate	
		Diethyl ether	
		Methylene chloride	
		Cyclohexane	
		Pentane	

Silica gel impregnated with silver nitrate, $AgNO_3$, (usually 5–10%) is an attractive solid-phase adsorbent. The silver salt selectively binds to un-

[13] Tswett, M. *Ber. Deut. Botan. Ges.* **1906**, *24*, 235.

saturated sites via a silver ion π complex. Traces of alkene materials are easily removed from saturated reaction products by chromatography with this system (see also Experiment [12]). This adsorbent, however, must be protected from light until used, or the mixture will rapidly darken and become ineffective (photooxidation).

Column chromatography is usually carried out according to the procedures discussed in the following five sections.

Packing the Column

The quantity of stationary phase required is determined by the sample size. A common rule of thumb is to use a weight of packing material 30–100 times the weight of the sample to be chromatographed. The size of the column is chosen to give roughly a 10:1 ratio of height to diameter, appropriately sized for the amount of adsorbent required.

In the microscale laboratory, two standard chromatographic columns are employed.

1. A Pasteur pipet, modified by shortening the capillary tip, is used for the separation of smaller mixtures (10–100 mg). Approximately 0.5–2.0 g of packing is used in the pipet column (Fig. 5.45a).

2. A 50-mL titration buret modified by reducing the length of the column (to 10 cm above the stopcock) is used for the larger sample mixtures (50–200 mg) and for the difficult-to-separate mixtures. Approximately 5–20 g of packing is employed in the buret column (Fig. 5.45b).

Both columns are prepared by first clamping the empty column in a vertical position, and then seating a small cotton, or glass wool, plug at the bottom. The cotton is covered with a thin layer of sand, in the case of the buret. The Pasteur pipets are loaded by adding the adsorbent with gentle tapping, "dry packing." The column is then premoistened just prior to use. The burets are packed by a slurry technique. In this procedure the column is filled part way with solvent; then the stopcock is opened slightly, and as the solvent slowly drains from the column, a slurry of the adsorbent–solvent is poured into the top of the column. The column should be gently tapped while the slurry is added. The solvent is then

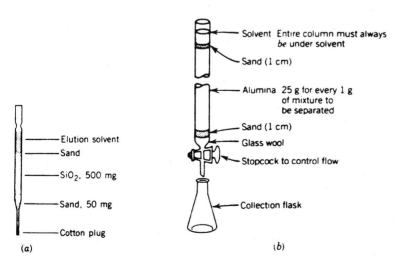

FIGURE 5.45 (a & b) Chromatographic columns. (b) From Zubric, James W. The Organic Chem Lab Survival Manual, 3rd ed.; Wiley: New York, 1992. (Reprinted by permission of John Wiley & Sons, Inc., New York.)

drained to the top of the adsorbent level, and held at that level until used. Alternatively, the wet-packed column can be loaded by sedimentation techniques rather than using a slurry. One such routine is to initially fill the column with the least-polar solvent to be employed in the intended chromatographic separation. Then the solid phase is slowly added with gentle tapping, which helps to avoid subsequent channeling. As the solid phase is added, the solvent is slowly drained from the buret at the same time. After the adsorbent has been fully loaded, the solvent level is then lowered to the top of the packing as in the slurry technique.

Sample Application

The sample is applied in a minimum amount of solvent (usually the least-polar solvent in which the material is readily soluble) to the top of the column by Pasteur pipet. The pipet is rinsed, and the rinses are added to the column just as the sample solution drains to the top of the adsorbent layer.

Elution of the Column

The critical step in resolving the sample mixture is eluting the column. Once the sample has been applied to the top of the column, the elution begins (a small layer of sand can be added to the top of the buret column after addition of the first portion of elution solvent).

NOTE.   *It is very important not to let the column run dry because instant cavitation can occur, which leads to extensive channeling of the column.*

The Pasteur pipet is free flowing (the flow rate is controlled by the size of the capillary tip), and once the sample is on the column, the chromatography will require constant attention. Buret column flow is controlled by the stopcock. The flow rate should be set to allow time for equilibrium to be established between the two phases. The choice of solvent is dictated by a number of factors. A balance between the adsorption power of the stationary phase and the solvation power of the elution solvent will govern the rate of travel of the material descending through the stationary phase. If the material travels rapidly down the column, then too few adsorption–elution cycles will occur and the materials will elute together in one fraction. If the sample travels too slowly, diffusion broadening takes over, and resolution is degraded. In the latter situation, samples then elute over many fractions with overlapping broad bands. Ideal solvent and elution rates strike a balance between these two situations and maximizes the separation. It can take considerable time to develop a solvent or mixture of solvents that produces a satisfactory separation of a particular mixture.

Fraction Collection

As the solvent elutes from the column, it is collected in a series of "fractions" using small Erlenmeyer flasks or vials. Under ideal conditions, as the mixture of material travels down the column, it will separate into several individual bands of pure substances. By careful collection of the fractions, these bands can be separated as they sequentially elute from the column (similar to the collection of GC fractions in the example described in Technique 1). The bands of material being eluted can be detected by a number of techniques (weighing fraction residues, visible absorption bands, TLC, etc.).

Column chromatography is a powerful technique for the purification of organic materials. In general, it is significantly more efficient than crystallization procedures. Thus, this technique is used extensively in micro-scale laboratory experiments. Recrystallization is avoided until the last stages of purification, where it will be most efficient, relying upon chromatography to do most of the separation.

NOTE.   *One major advantage of working with small amounts of product is that the chromatographic times are shortened dramatically.*

Column chromatography of a few milligrams of product usually takes no more than 30 min, but to chromatograph 10 g of product might take a whole afternoon, or even the better part of a day. Large scale chromatography (50–100 g) may even take several days to complete using this type of equipment.

Flash chromatography, first described by Still, Kahn, and Mitra in 1978,[14] has rapidly developed as a standard method for the separation and purification of nonvolatile mixtures of organic compounds. The technique is rapid, easy to perform, and relatively inexpensive. Recovery of material is high, since band-tailing is minimized. At present, many laboratories routinely use the technique to separate mixtures weighing 0.01–10 g in 10–15 min.

This moderate-resolution, preparative technique was originally developed using silica gel, with an optimum particle size of 40–63 μm. More recently, it has been demonstrated that bonded-phase silica gel of a larger particle size can also be used effectively. The columns are generally packed dry, using approximately 6 in. of the silica. Thin-layer chromatography is an efficient technique to employ as an aid in establishing experimental parameters for flash chromatography. It was found that a solvent resulting in TLC differential retardation factor (DR_f) values greater than or equal to 0.15 between the mixture components gives effective separation with flash chromatography. Table 5.7 lists typical experimental parameters for various sample sizes, as a guide to separations using flash chromatography. In general, a mixture of organic compounds that can be separated by TLC can be separated preparatively using flash chromatography.

Flash Chromatography

TABLE 5.7   Typical Experimental Parameters[a]

Column Diameter (mm)	Total Volume of Eluent (mL)[b]	Typical Sample Loading (mg)		Typical Fraction (mL)
		$DR_{f>0.2}$	$DR_{f>0.1}$	
10	100–150	100	40	5
20	200–250	400	160	10
30	400–450	900	360	20
40	500–650	1600	600	30
50	1000–1200	2500	1000	50

[a] Data from Majors, R. E.; Enzweiler, T. *LC, GC* **1988**, *6*, 1046.
[b] Required for both packing and elution.

[14] Still, W. C.; Kahn, M.; Mitra, A. *J. Org. Chem.* **1978**, *43*, 2923.

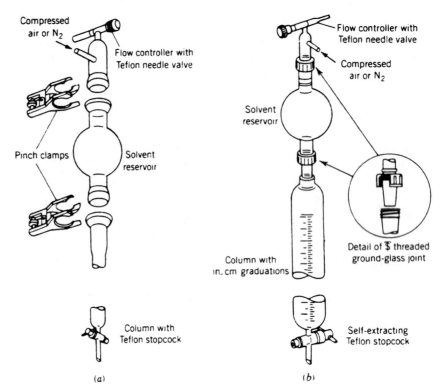

FIGURE 5.46 (a) Conventional column and (b) screw-threaded column.

The chromatographic apparatus generally consists of a 20-mm i.d. glass column, modified so that a positive pressure of compressed air or nitrogen can be applied to the top of the column. A typical arrangement, which is commercially available, is shown in Figure 5.46.[15]

Generally, a 20–25% solution of the sample in the elution solvent is recommended, as is a flow rate of about 2 in./min. It is important that the column be conditioned before the sample is applied. This process is accomplished by flushing the column with the mobile phase (under pressure) to drive out all the air that may be trapped in the stationary phase, and to also equilibrate the packing material and solvent.

Several modifications of the basic arrangement have been reported, especially in regard to the adaptation of the technique to the instructional laboratory. These involve inexpensive pressure control valves, use of a "vibrator" air pump, the adaptation of a balloon reservoir as a supply of pressurized gas and, at the microscale level, the adaptation of a pipet bulb or pump to supply pressure on the column.

A recent method, utilizing a capillary Pasteur pipet for introducing the sample onto the chromatographic column, has been reported that approximately doubles the effectiveness of the column in terms of theoretical plates.[16]

[15] A complete line of glass columns, reservoirs, clamps, and packing materials for flash chromatography is offered by Aldrich Chemical Co., 1001 St. Paul Ave., Milwaukee, WI. Silica gels for use in this technique are also available from Amicon, Danvers, MA; J. T. Baker, Phillipsburg, NJ; EM Science/Merck, Gibbstown, NJ; ICN Biomedicals, Inc., Cleveland, OH; Universal Solvents, Atlanta, GA; Whatman, Clifton, NJ.

[16] Pivnitsky, K. K. *Aldrichimica Acta* **1989,** 22, 30.

Thin-layer chromatography (TLC) is another solid–liquid partition technique of more recent development. It is a close relative to column chromatography, in that the phases used in both techniques are essentially identical. That is, alumina and silica gel are typically used as stationary phases, and the mobile phases are the usual solvents. There are, however, some distinct operational differences between TLC and column chromatography. While the mobile phase *descends* in column chromatography; in TLC, the mobile phase *ascends*. The column of stationary-phase material used in column chromatography is replaced, in TLC, by a very thin layer (100 μm) of the material spread over a flat surface. The technique has some distinct advantages at the microscale level. It is very rapid (2–10 min), and it employs *very* small quantities of material (2–20 μg). The chief disadvantage of this type of chromatography is that it is not very amenable to preparative scale work. Even when large surfaces and thicker layers are used, separations are most often restricted to the 5–10-mg level unless sophisticated research equipment is available.

The sequence of operations for TLC is as follows:

1. A piece of window glass, a microscope slide, or a sheet of plastic can be used as a support for a thin layer of adsorbent spread over the surface. It is possible to locally prepare the glass plates, but plastic-backed thin-layer plates are only commercially available. The plastic-backed plates are particularly attractive because they possess very uniform coatings and are highly reproducible in operation. Another convenient feature of the plastic-backed plates is that they can be cut with scissors into very economical 1 × 3-in. strips (even smaller sizes can be satisfactory). The latter style is used extensively in the microscale laboratory.

2. A pencil line is drawn parallel to the short side of the plate, 1.0 cm from the edge. One or two points, evenly spaced, are marked on the line. The sample to be analyzed (1 mg or less) is placed in a 100-μL conical vial and a few drops of solvent are added. A micropipet (prepared by the same technique used for constructing the capillary insert in the ultramicro-boiling point determination; see Chapter 4) is used to apply a small fraction of the solution from the vial to the plate (Fig. 5.47).

3. The chromatography is carried out by placing the spotted thin-layer plate in a screw-capped, wide-mouth jar, or in a beaker with a watch glass cover, containing a small amount of elution solvent (Fig. 5.48). The material spot on the TLC plate must initially be positioned above the solvent level. The jar is quickly recapped, or the watch glass replaced, to maintain an atmosphere saturated with the elution solvent. The elution solvent rapidly ascends the plate by capillary action. The choice of solvent

THIN-LAYER CHROMATOGRAPHY

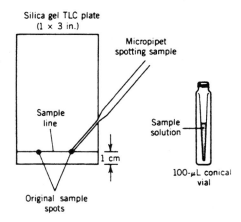

FIGURE 5.47 Sample application to a TLC plate.

FIGURE 5.48 Development of a TLC plate. *From Zubric, James W.* The Organic Chem Lab Survival Manual, *3rd ed.; Wiley: New York, 1992. (Reprinted by permission of John Wiley & Sons, Inc., New York.)*

will be similar to that used in column chromatography, but need not be identical. The spotted material is eluted vertically up the plate. Resolution of mixtures into individual spots along the vertical axis occurs by precisely the same mechanism as in column chromatography. Elution is stopped, when the solvent line nears the top of the plate, by removing the plate from the jar or beaker, and the position of the solvent front should be quickly marked on the plate (before the solvent evaporates) when the chromatography is terminated.

4. Visualization of colorless, separated components can be achieved by placing the plate in an iodine-vapor chamber (a sealed jar containing solid I_2) for several seconds. Iodine forms a reversible complex with most organic substances. Thus, dark spots will develop in those areas containing sample material. On removal from the iodine chamber, the spots should be marked by pencil, because they may fade rather rapidly. TLC plates are commonly prepared with an ultraviolet (UV) activated fluorescent indicator mixed in with the silica gel. Sample spots can be detected with a hand-held UV lamp as the sample quenches the fluorescence induced by the lamp.

5. The elution characteristics are reported as R_f values. The R_f value is a measure of the travel of a substance up the plate relative to the solvent movement. This value is defined as the distance traveled by the substance divided by the distance traveled by the solvent front (the position of the solvent front should be quickly marked on the plate when the chromatogram is terminated; see Fig. 5.49).

Thin-layer chromatography is used in a number of applications. The speed of the technique makes it quite useful for monitoring large scale column chromatography. Analysis of fractions can guide decisions on the solvent elution sequence. The TLC analysis of column-derived fractions can also give an indication of how best to combine collected fractions. Following the progress of a reaction by periodically removing small aliquots for TLC analysis is an extremely useful application of thin-layer chromatography.

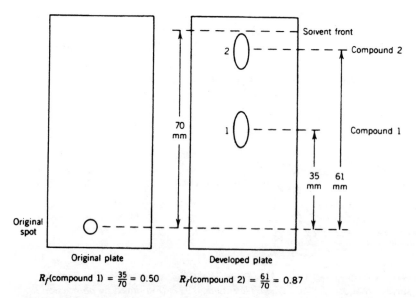

R_f(compound 1) $= \frac{35}{70} = 0.50$ R_f(compound 2) $= \frac{61}{70} = 0.87$

FIGURE 5.49   A sample calculation of R_f values.

Although GC is the chromatographic method of choice in many instances, it is limited to compounds that have a significant vapor pressure at temperatures up to about 200 °C. Thus, compounds of high molecular weight and/or polarity are not amenable to separation by GC, and high-performance liquid chromatography (HPLC) becomes an attractive chromatographic method.

Both GC and HPLC are somewhat similar, in the instrumental sense, in that the analyte is partitioned between a stationary and a mobile phase that travels down a column. Whereas the mobile phase in GC is a gas, the mobile phase in HPLC is a liquid. As shown schematically in Figure 5.50, the mobile phase, or solvent, is delivered to the system by a pump capable of pressures up to about 6000 psi. The sample is introduced by the injection of a solution into an injection loop. The injection loop is brought in line between the pump and the column by turning a switch, and the sample then flows down the column, is partitioned, and then flows into a detector.

The solid phase in HPLC columns used for organic monomers is usually based on silica gel. "Normal" HPLC refers to chromatography using a solid phase (usually silica gel) which is more polar than the liquid phase, or solvent, so that less polar compounds elute earlier. Typical solvents include ethyl acetate, hexane, acetone, low molecular weight alcohols, chloroform, and acetonitrile. For extremely polar compounds, such as amino acids, "reversed-phase" HPLC is used. Here, the liquid phase is more polar than the stationary phase, and the more polar compounds elute more quickly. The mobile phase is usually a mixture of water and some water-miscible organic solvent, such as acetonitrile, dioxane, methanol, 2-propanol, or acetone. The stationary phase is usually a derivatized silica gel where the —OH groups of the silica gel have been replaced by —OSiOR groups where R is typically a linear C_{18} alkyl chain. These so-called bonded-phase columns are not capable of handling as much analyte as normal silica gel columns, and are thus easily overloaded and are less useful for preparative work. For further discussion see the section on Solid-Phase Extraction in Technique 4.

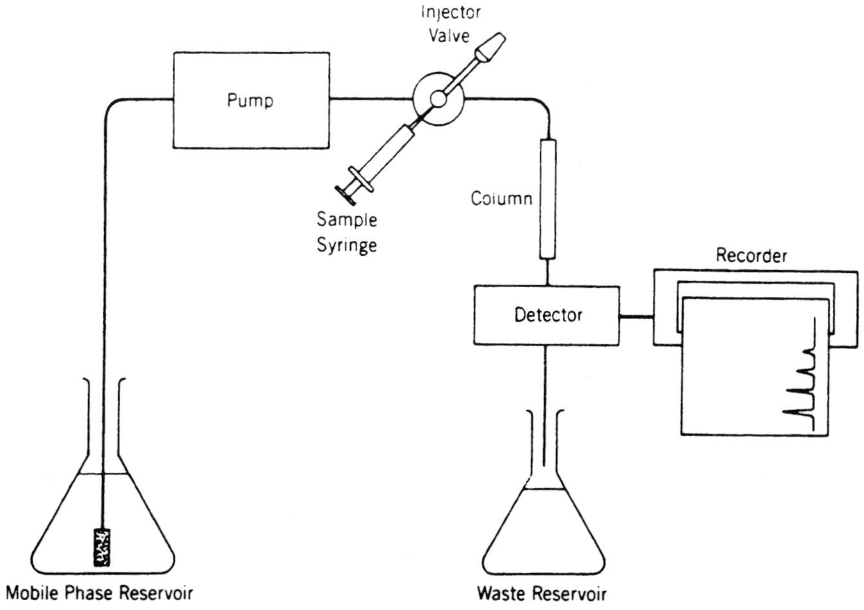

HIGH-PERFORMANCE LIQUID CHROMATOGRAPHY

FIGURE 5.50 High-Performance Liquid Chromatography system block diagram. *(Courtesy of the Perkin-Elmer Corp., Norwalk, CT.)*

A wide variety of detection systems are available for HPLC. A common, inexpensive and sensitive system is UV detection. The solvent flowing off the column is sent through a small cell, and the UV absorbance is recorded with respect to time. Many detectors are capable of variable wavelength operation so the detector can be set to the wavelength most suitable to the compound or compounds being analyzed. Photodiode array detectors are available that can obtain a full UV spectrum in a fraction of a second, so that more information can be obtained on each component of a mixture. For compounds that absorb light in the visible (vis) spectrum, many UV detectors can also be tuned to visible wavelengths. The principal shortcoming of UV–vis detection is that the compounds being studied must possess a chromophore, such as an aromatic ring or other conjugated π system.

For compounds that lack a UV–vis chromophore, refractive index (RI) detection is a common substitute. An RI detector measures the difference in refractive index between the eluant and a reference cell filled with the elution solvent. Refractive index detection suffers in that it is significantly less sensitive than UV–vis detection, and the detector is quite sensitive to temperature changes during the chromatographic run.

More sophisticated HPLC instruments offer the ability to mix two or three different solvents and to use solvent gradients by changing the solvent composition as the chromatographic run progresses. This procedure allows the simultaneous analysis of compounds that differ greatly in their polarity. For example, a silica gel column might begin elution with a very nonpolar solvent, such as hexane, while the solvent is continuously delivered with an increasing solvent polarity by adding in ethyl acetate until the run is ended by eluting with pure ethyl acetate. This effect is directly analogous to temperature programming in GC.

For analytical work, typical HPLC columns are about 5 mm in diameter and about 25 cm in length. The maximum amount of analyte for columns such as this is generally less than 1 mg, and the minimum amount is determined by the detection system. High-performance liquid chromatography can thus be used to obtain small amounts of purified compounds for infrared (IR), nuclear magnetic resonance (NMR) or mass spectrometric (MS) analysis. Larger "semipreparative columns" that can handle up to about 20 mg of material without significant overloading, are available and are useful for obtaining material for ^{13}C NMR spectroscopy or for further synthetic work.

NOTE. *The following experiments utilize Technique 6A: Experiments [8A], [8B], [8C], [11C], [12], [13], [16], [17], [19A], [19B], [19C], [19D], [22A], [22B], [27], [29A], [29B], [29C], [29D], [30], [33A], [33B], [35], [1A$_{adv}$], [1B$_{adv}$], [4$_{adv}$], [7$_{adv}$], [A2$_a$], [A1$_b$], [E1], and [E3].*

Technique 6B   Concentration of Solutions

The solvent can be removed from the chromatographic fractions by a number of different methods.

DISTILLATION

Concentration of solvent by distillation is straightforward, and the standard routine is described in Technique 2. This approach allows for high recovery of volatile solvents and often can be done outside a hood. The Hickman still head and the 5- or 10-mL round-bottom flask are useful for this purpose. Distillation should be used primarily for concentration of the solution, followed by transfer of the concentrate with a Pasteur filter pipet to a vial for final isolation.

EVAPORATION WITH NITROGEN GAS

A very convenient method for removal of final solvent traces is the concentration of the last 0.5 mL of solution by evaporation with a gentle stream of nitrogen gas while the sample is warmed in a sand bath. This process is usually done at a hood station where several Pasteur pipets can be attached to a manifold leading to a tank of the compressed gas. Gas flow to the individual pipets is controlled by needle valves. *Always test the gas flow with a blank vial of solvent.* This evaporation technique is a hand-held operation. The sample vial will cool rapidly on evaporation of the solvent, and gentle warming of the vial with agitation will thus aid removal of the last traces of the volatile material. This procedure avoids possible moisture condensation on the sample residue. *Do not leave the heated vial in the gas flow after the solvent is removed!* This precaution is particularly important in the isolation of liquids. Remember to tare the vial before loading the solution to be concentrated, because achievement of constant weight is the best indication of total solvent removal.

REMOVAL OF SOLVENT UNDER REDUCED PRESSURE

Concentration of solvent under reduced pressure is very efficient. It reduces the time of solvent removal in microscale experiments to a few seconds, or at most, a few minutes. In contrast, distillation or evaporation procedures require many minutes for even relatively small volumes. Vacuum-concentration techniques, however, can be tricky and should be practiced prior to committing a hard-won reaction product to this test. The procedure is most beneficial when applied to fairly large chromatographic fractions (5–10 mL).

The sequence of operations is as follows (see also Fig. 5.51):

1. Transfer the chromatographic fraction to the 25-mL filter flask.

2. Insert the 11-mm Hirsch funnel and rubber adapter into the flask.

3. Turn on the water pump (with trap) and connect the vacuum tubing to the pressure flask side arm while holding the flask in one hand.

4. Place the thumb of the hand holding the filter flask over the Hirsch funnel filter bed to shut off the air flow through the system (Fig. 5.51). This step will result in an immediate drop in pressure. The volatile solvent will rapidly come to a boil at room temperature. Thumb pressure adjusts air leakage through the Hirsch funnel and thereby controls the pressure in the system. It is also good practice to learn to manipulate the pressure so that the liquid does not foam up into the side arm of the filter flask.

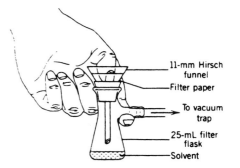

FIGURE 5.51   Removal of solvent under reduced pressure.

It is essential that the filter flask be warmed by the sand bath during this operation, for rapid evaporation of the solvent will quickly cool the solution. The air leak used to control the pressure results in a stream of moist laboratory air being rapidly drawn over the surface of the solution. If the evaporating liquid becomes cold, water will condense over the interior of the filter flask and eventually will contaminate the isolated residue. Warming the flask while the evaporation process is being carried out will avoid this problem and help to speed solvent removal. The temperature of the flask should be checked from time to time by touching it with the palm of the free hand. The flask is kept slightly above room temperature by

Removing Solvent Under Reduced Pressure

Rotary Evaporator. This laboratory uses, as much as possible, evaporation under reduced pressure with condensation using Dry Ice/isopropanol (-78°C) in the condenser.

The rotary evaporator is a motor-driven device that rotates the flask containing the solution to be concentrated under reduced pressure. The rotation continuously exposes a thin film of the solution for evaporation. This process is very rapid, even well below the boiling point of the solvent being removed. Since the walls of the rotating flask are constantly rewetted by the solution, bumping and superheating are minimized. The rotating flask may be warmed in a water bath or other suitable device that controls the rate of evaporation. A suitable adapter (a "bump bulb", **not** shown in the diagram below) should be used on the rotary evaporator to guard against splashing and sudden boiling, which may lead to lost or contaminated products.

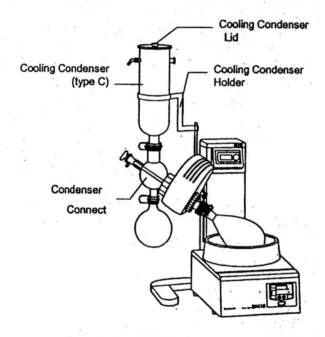

A rotatory evaporator with condenser and receiving flask.

Place the liquid in a flask with a joint compatible with the adapter of the rota-vap. Make sure the joint is clean. Before attaching your flask to the rota-vap adapter, make sure that the pump is turned on and is pulling a vacuum. Check to see that there is enough Dry Ice and Isopropanol to in the cooling condenser to form a slurry (if not, add more). Also check to see that the water bath is about half full (if not, add **distilled** water). When attaching your flask to the adapter use a clip to ensure that your flask does not fall into the water bath. After attaching your flask, turn on the rota-vap motor to make the flask spin. Close the screw clamp in the vacuum trap to obtain maximum vacuum, now carefully lower the flask into the water bath. If bubbling in the flask becomes too intense, raise your flask out of the water bath. The spinning of the flask distributes the liquid in a large area and makes the evaporation fast and smooth. Boiling chips should not be added to the liquid. Once the solvent has evaporated, remove the flask from the water bath. Stop the motor and, *while holding the flask with your hand*, release the vacuum by opening the screw clamp in the vacuum trap. Remove the flask from the rota-vap.

Collection or Control of Gaseous Products

Numerous organic reactions lead to the formation of gaseous products. If the gas is insoluble in water, collection is easily accomplished by the displacement of water from a collection tube. A typical experimental setup for the collection of gases is shown in Figure 5.53.

As illustrated, the glass capillary efficiently transfers the evolved gas to the collection tube. The delivery system need not be glass, as small diameter polyethylene or polypropylene tubing may also serve this purpose. In this latter arrangement, a syringe needle is inserted through a septum to accommodate the plastic tubing as shown in Figure 5.54. An alternative to the use of this connector is to employ a shortened Pasteur pipet inserted through a thermometer adapter (also shown in Fig. 5.54)

An example of a reaction leading to gaseous products that can utilize this collection technique is the dehydration of 2-butanol with an acid catalyst as described in Experiment [9]. The products of this reaction are a mixture of the alkenes, 1-butene, *trans*-2-butene, and *cis*-2-butene having boiling points of −6.3, 0.9, and 3.7 °C, respectively.

In Figure 5.53, the gas collection tube is capped with a rubber septum. This arrangement allows for convenient removal of the collected gaseous butenes using a gas-tight syringe as shown in Figure 5.55.

In this particular reaction, the mixture of gaseous products is conveniently analyzed by ambient temperature GC (see Technique 1).

Some organic reactions release poisonous or irritating gases as byproducts. For example, hydrogen chloride, ammonia, or sulfur dioxide are typical byproducts in organic reactions. In these cases, the reaction is generally run in a **hood**. In addition, a **gas trap** may or may not be employed to prevent the gases from being released into the laboratory atmosphere. If the volatile material evolved is water soluble, the trap technique is convenient at the microscale level. The evolved gas is directed from the reaction

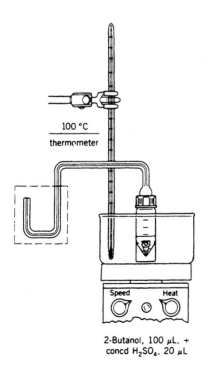

100 °C
thermometer

Speed   Heat

2-Butanol, 100 μL, +
concd H_2SO_4, 20 μL

3 mL
4 mL

FIGURE 5.53   Microscale gas collection apparatus.

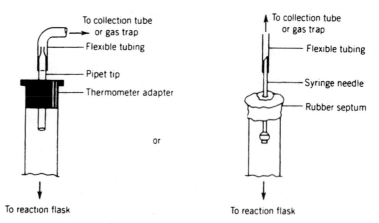

FIGURE 5.54 Alternative arrangements for controlled gas collection.

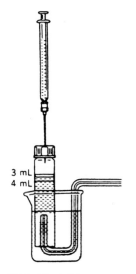

FIGURE 5.55 Removal of collected gases.

vessel to a container of water or other aqueous solution, wherein it dissolves (reacts). For example, a dilute solution of sodium or ammonium hydroxide is suitable for acidic gases (such as HCl) or a dilute solution of sulfuric or hydrochloric acid for basic gases (such as NH_3 or low molecular weight amines).

Various designs are available for the gas trap arrangement. A simple one that is easily assembled is shown in Figure 5.56.

This arrangement is used for a gas that is very soluble in water. Note that the funnel is not immersed in the water. If the funnel is held below the surface of the water and a large quantity of gas is absorbed or dissolved, the water easily could be drawn back into the reaction assembly. If the gas to be collected is *not* very soluble, the funnel may be immersed just below the surface of the water.

When working at the microscale level, small volumes of these gases are evolved, and the funnel may not be necessary. Three alternatives are available in this situation.

1. In the first situation, the beaker (100 mL) in Figure 5.56 is filled with fine, moistened, glass wool and the gas delivery tube is led directly into the wool.

2. The second approach is to place moistened glass wool in a drying tube, which is then attached to the reaction apparatus as shown in Figures 3.23 or 3.26. However, be careful that the added moisture is not allowed to drip into the reaction vessel. It is advisable to place a small section of **dry** glass wool in the tube before the moist section is added.

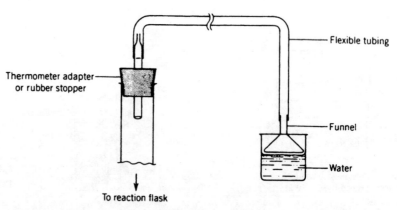

FIGURE 5.56 Trapping of a water-soluble gas.

3. The third alternative is to use a water aspirator. An inverted funnel is placed over the apparatus opening where the evolved gas is escaping (usually the top of a condenser) and connected with flexible tubing to a water trap, and hence to the aspirator. In some cases, a Pasteur pipet can be substituted for the funnel when the volume of evolved gas is relatively small.

NOTE. *The following experiments utilize Technique 7: Experiments [9], [10], [14], [A2ₐ], and [B2].*

Measurement of Specific Rotation TECHNIQUE 8

Solutions of optically active substances, when placed in the path of a beam of polarized light, may rotate the plane of the polarized light clockwise or counterclockwise. The observed optical rotation is measured using a *polarimeter*. This technique is one of the oldest instrumental procedures used to characterize chemical compounds. It is a technique applicable to a wide range of analytical problems that vary from purity control to the analysis of natural and synthetic products in the medicinal and biological fields. The results obtained from the measurement of the observed angle of rotation, α, are generally expressed in terms of *specific rotation* $[\alpha]$.

Ordinary light behaves as though it is composed of electromagnetic waves in which the oscillating electric field vectors may take up all possible orientations around the direction of propagation (see Fig. 5.57).

OPTICAL ROTATION THEORY

NOTE. *A beam of light behaves as though it is composed of two, mutually perpendicular, oscillating fields: an electrical field and a magnetic field. The oscillating magnetic field is not considered in the following discussion.*

The planes in which the electrical fields oscillate are perpendicular to the direction of propagation of the light beam. If one separates one particular plane of oscillation from all other planes by passing the beam of light through a polarizer, the resulting radiation is said to be plane-polarized (see Fig. 5.58).

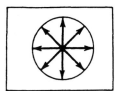

FIGURE 5.57 Oscillation of the electric field of ordinary light occurs in all possible planes perpendicular to the direction of propagation. *From Solomons, T. W. Graham Organic Chemistry, 5th ed., Wiley: New York, 1992. (Reprinted by permission of John Wiley & Sons, Inc. New York.)*

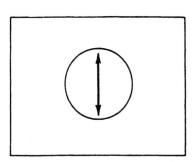

FIGURE 5.58 The plane of oscillation of the electric field of plane polarized light. In this example the plane of polarization is vertical. *From Solomons, T. W. Graham Organic Chemistry, 5th ed., Wiley: New York, 1992. (Reprinted by permission of John Wiley & Sons, Inc. New York.)*

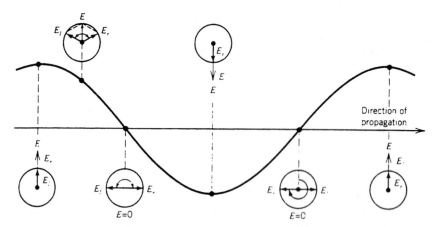

FIGURE 5.59 A beam of plane-polarized light viewed from the side (sine wave) and along the direction of propagation at specific times (circles) where the resultant vector E and the circularly polarized components E_l and E_r are shown. *From Douglas, Bodie; McDaniel, Darl H.; Alexander, John J. Concepts and Models of Inorganic Chemistry. 2nd ed., Wiley: New York, 1983. (Reprinted by permission of John Wiley & Sons, Inc., New York.)*

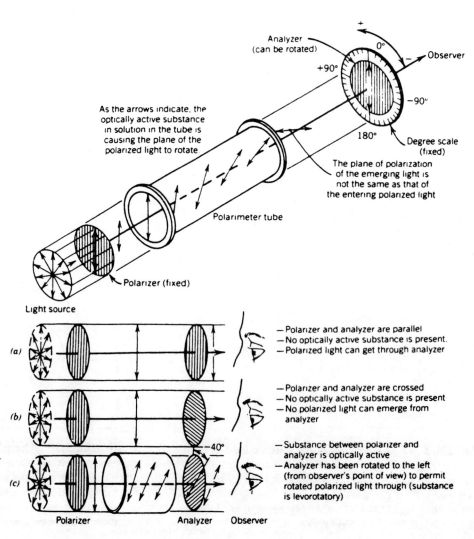

FIGURE 5.60 Operation of a polarimeter. *From Solomons, T. W. Graham Organic Chemistry, 5th ed., Wiley: New York, 1992. (Reprinted by permission of John Wiley & Sons, Inc. New York.)*

In the interaction of light with matter, this plane-polarized radiation is represented as the vector sum of two circularly polarized waves. The electric vector of one of the waves moves in a clockwise direction, whereas the other moves in a counterclockwise direction, both waves having the same amplitude (see Fig. 5.59). These two components add vectorially to produce plane-polarized light.

If the passage of plane-polarized light through a material results in the velocity of one of the circularly polarized components being decreased more than the other by interaction with bonding and nonbonding electrons, the transmitted beam of radiation has the plane of polarization rotated from its *original* position (Figs. 5.60 and 5.61). A **polarimeter** is used to measure this angle of rotation.

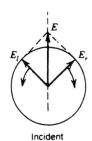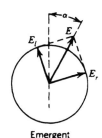

Incident   Emergent

FIGURE 5.61   Plane-polarized light before entering and after emerging from an optically active substance. *From Douglas, Bodie; McDaniel, Darl H.; Alexander, John J. Concepts and Models of Inorganic Chemistry, 2nd ed., Wiley: New York, 1983. (Reprinted by permission of John Wiley & Sons, Inc., New York.)*

THE POLARIMETER

The *polarimeter* measures the amount of rotation caused by an optically active compound (in solution) placed in the beam of the plane-polarized light. The principal parts of the instrument are diagrammed in Figure 5.60. Two Nicol prisms are used in the instrument. The first prism, which polarizes the original light source, is called the polarizer. The second prism, called the analyzer, is used to examine the polarized light after it passes through a solution of the optically active species.

When the axes of the analyzer and polarizer prisms are parallel and no optically active substance is present, the maximum amount of light is transmitted and the instrument dial is set to 0°. However, if the axes of the analyzer and polarizer are at right angles to each other, no transmission of light is observed and the field is dark. The introduction of a solution of a nonracemic chiral substance into the path of the plane-polarized light causes one of the circularly polarized components, through dissymmetric interaction, to be slowed more than the other. The refractive indexes are, therefore, different in the two circularly polarized beams. Figure 5.60 represents a case in which the left-hand component has been affected the most.

NOTE.   *In this simplified figure, the effect on only one of the circularly polarized waves is diagrammed. See Figure 5.61 for a more accurate description (view from behind the figure).*

As seen, this results in a tilt of the plane of polarization. The analyzer prism must be rotated to the left to maximize the transmission of radiation. If rotation is counterclockwise, the angle of rotation is defined as (−) and the enantiomer that caused the effect is termed levorotatory (*l*). Conversely, clockwise rotation is defined as (+), and the enantiomer is said to be dextrorotatory (*d*). It is important to note that if a solution of equal amounts of a *d* and an *l* enantiomeric pair is placed in the beam path of the polarimeter, no rotation is observed. Such a solution is said to be *racemic* if, as in this case, it is an equimolar mixture of enantiomers.

The magnitude of optical rotation depends on several factors: (1) the nature of the substance, (2) the path length through which the light passes, (3) the wavelength of light used as a source, and (4) the temperature. It also depends on the concentration and the solvent of the solution of the optically active material.

The results obtained from the measurement of the observed angle of rotation, α_{obs}, are generally expressed in terms of *specific rotation* $[\alpha]$.[17] The sign and magnitude of $[\alpha]$ are dependent on the specific molecule and are determined by complex features of molecular structure and conformation, and thus cannot be easily explained or predicted. The relationship of $[\alpha]$ to α_{obs} is as follows:

$$[\alpha]_\lambda^T = \frac{\alpha_{obs}}{l \cdot c}$$

where T = the temperature of the sample **in degrees Celsius** (°C),
l = the length of the polarimeter cell **in decimeters** (1 dm = 0.1 m = 10 cm)
c = the concentration of the sample **in grams per milliliter** (g/mL)
λ = the wavelength of the light **in nanometers** (nm) used in the polarimeter.

These units are traditional, though most are esoteric by contemporary standards. The specific rotation for a given compound is dependent on both the concentration and the solvent, and thus both the solvent and concentration used must be specified. For example: $[\alpha]_D^{25}$ (c = 0.4, $CHCl_3$) = 12.3° implies that the measurement was recorded in a $CHCl_3$ solution of 0.4 g/mL at 25 °C using the sodium D line (589 nm) as the light source.

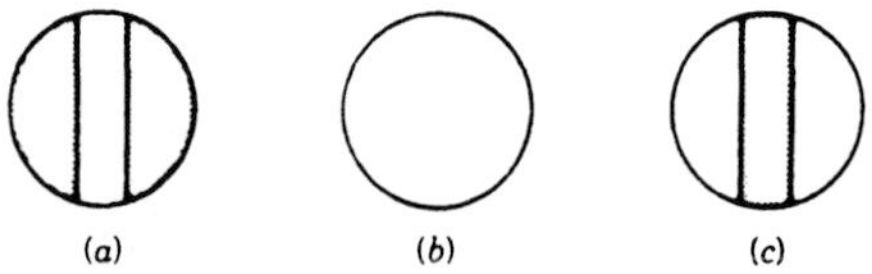

For increased sensitivity, most lower cost polarimeters are equipped with an optical device that divides the viewed field into three adjacent parts (triple-shadow polarimeter; Fig. 5.62). A very slight rotation of the analyzer will cause one portion to become dimmer and the other lighter (Figs. 5.62a and 5.62c). The angle of rotation reading (α) is recorded when the sections of the fields all have the same intensity. An accuracy of ±0.1° is easily obtained using this technique.

High-performance polarimeters are now available with a digital readout and an accuracy of ± 0.001°. These instruments are based on an automatic optical-null balance principle that operates within a rotary range of ±80°. The schematic diagram for two such polarimeters is shown in Figure 5.63. Model 241 (Fig. 5.63a) has two spectral line sources (Hg and Na) and a filter wheel (F) containing five optical filters. A rotatable mirror (M) is coupled to this shaft so that when a desired wavelength is selected, the beam of the corresponding lamp is automatically reflected along the optical path.

The Model 241 MC, (Fig. 5.63b) is equipped with a high-resolution grating monochromer (M) plus deuterium (D_2) and quartz–iodine lamps (continuous sources). The desired wavelength(s) can be selected by the monochromer.

In both instruments, the monochromatic light passes through the polarizer (P), the sample cell (K), the analyzer (A), on to the photomultiplier tube detector (PM). The polarizer and analyzer are rotatable Glan prisms of calcite. The polarizer (and thus the plane of the plane-polarized light) oscillates at an amplitude of about ±0.7° at the line frequency about the optical longitudinal axis. In an unbalanced condition, the photomultiplier tube receives a frequency signal that is amplified and fed to the servomotor (SM) with the corresponding polarity (the latter gives the direction of rotation). The servomotor drives the analyzer until this signal is

FIGURE 5.62 View through the eyepiece of the polarimeter. The analyzer should be set so that the intensity in all parts of the field is the same (*b*). When the analyzer is displaced to one side or the other, the field will appear as in (*a*) or (*c*).

---

[17] The following discussion is also contained in Experiment [11A]. It is repeated here for the sake of continuity.

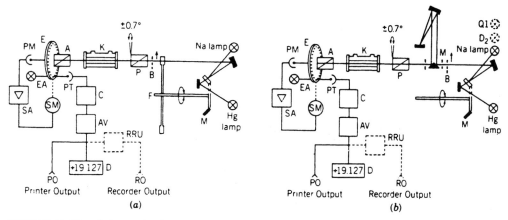

FIGURE 5.63 Schematic diagrams of Perkin-Elmer polarimeters: (*a*) Model 241, (*b*) Model 241 MC. (*Courtesy of the Perkin-Elmer Corp., Newton Centre, MA.*)

reduced to null (this gives the magnitude of the rotation). This condition constitutes a balanced system (optical null).

When an optically active substance is placed in the sample cell (K), the plane of the polarized light is changed based on the optical rotation of the sample. The analyzer is rotated by the servomotor to the new null balance position. The difference between the original and new balance position corresponds to the optical rotation of the sample.

Optical rotary dispersion, the dependence of the rotation of an optically active species versus wavelength, is a natural extension of the basic polarimetric method. The newer instruments (Fig. 5.63*b*, Model 241 MC) are readily adapted to this technique. Information on the degree of coiling of protein helices and the establishment of the configurations of chiral molecules indicate the wide utility of this approach.

An interesting area for measuring optical activity is in the case of natural products. An excellent example is the lichen metabolite, usnic acid, which can be easily isolated from its native source, "Old Man's Beard," as golden yellow crystals, see Experiment [11A].

Usnic acid

Usnic acid contains a single chiral center and, therefore, has the possibility of existing as an enantiomeric pair of isomers. Generally, in a given lichen, only one of the isomers (*R* or *S*) is present. Usnic acid has a very high specific rotation (~ ±460°), and for this reason is an ideal candidate to measure rotation at the microscale level.

NOTE.   *The following experiment utilizes Technique 8: Experiment [11A].*

TECHNIQUE 9 **Sublimation**

Sublimation is a technique that is especially suitable for the purification of solid substances at the microscale level. It is particularly advantageous when the impurities present in the sample are nonvolatile under the conditions employed. Sublimation is a relatively straightforward method in that the impure solid need only be heated and mechanical losses are easily kept to a minimum.

The technique has additional advantages: (1) it can be the technique of choice for purifying sensitive materials, as it can be carried out under very high vacuum and thus it is effective at low temperatures; (2) solvents are not involved and indeed, final traces of solvents are effectively removed (see point 4); (3) impurities most likely to be separated are those having lower vapor pressures than the desired substance and, often therefore, lower solubilities, exactly those materials very likely to be contaminants in attempts at recrystallization; (4) solvated materials tend to desolvate during the process; and (5) in the specific case of water of solvation, it is very effective even with those substances that are deliquescent. The main disadvantage of the technique is that it may not be as selective as recrystallization. This nonselectivity occurs when the vapor pressure of the materials being sublimed are similar.

Materials sublime when heated below their melting points under reduced pressure. Substances that are candidates for purification by sublimation are those that do not have strong intermolecular attractive forces. Naphthalene, ferrocene, and *p*-dichlorobenzene are examples of compounds that meet these requirements.

SUBLIMATION THEORY

The processes of *sublimation* and *distillation* are closely related. Crystals of a solid substance that sublimes, when placed in an evacuated container, will gradually generate molecules in the vapor state by the process of *evaporation* (i.e., the solid exhibits a vapor pressure). Occasionally, one of the vaporized molecules will strike the crystal surface or the walls of the container and be held by attractive forces. This latter process is the reverse of evaporation and is termed *condensation*.

Sublimation is the complete process of *evaporation* from the solid phase to *condensation* from the gas phase to form crystals *directly* without passing through the liquid state.

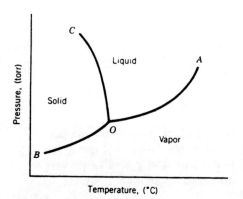

FIGURE 5.64 Single-component phase diagram.

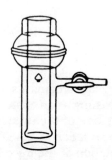

FIGURE 5.65 Vacuum sublimator. *(Courtesy of ACE Glass Inc., Vineland, NJ)*

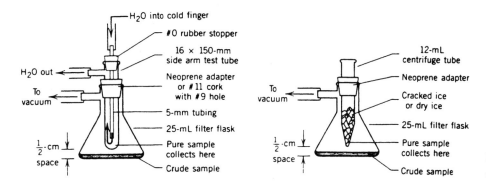

FIGURE 5.66 Various sublimation apparatus.

A typical single-component phase diagram is shown in Figure 5.64, which relates the solid, liquid, and vapor phases of a substance to temperature and pressure. Where two of the areas (solid, liquid, or vapor) touch, there is a line, and along each line, the two phases exist in *equilibrium*. Line BO is the sublimation–vapor pressure curve of the substance in question, and only along line BO can solid and vapor exist together in equilibrium. At temperatures and pressures along the BO curve, the liquid state is thermodynamically unstable. Where the three lines representing pairs of phases intersect, all three phases exist together in equilibrium. This point is called the *triple point.*

Many solid substances have a sufficiently high vapor pressure near their melting point and they thus can be sublimed easily *under reduced pressure* in the laboratory. Sublimation occurs when the vapor pressure of the solid equals the applied pressure.

Heating the sample with a microburner or a sand bath to just below the melting point of the solid causes sublimation to occur. The vapors condense on the cold-finger surface, whereas any less volatile residue will remain at the bottom of the flask. Apparatus suitable for sublimation of small quantities are now commercially available (Fig. 5.65).

A simple apparatus suitable for sublimation of small quantities of material in the microscale organic laboratory are shown in Figure 5.66.

An example of the purification of a natural product, where the sublimation technique at the microscale level is effective, is in the case of the alkaloid caffeine. This substance can be isolated by extraction from tea (see Experiment [11B]).

NOTE. *The following experiments utilize Technique 9: Experiments [11B], [25A], and [25B].*

ex 7-9 on our own

Molecular Model Exercises
Chemistry 112A Laboratory

These exercises will be done during the first lab period of Chemistry 112A following check-in and the orientation lecture given by your TA. You will do each exercise with your TA. **Learning how to effectively manipulate molecular models will help you considerably in the visualization of the shapes of organic molecules.**

Exercise No. 1

a. Assemble a molecular model of methane, CH_4. Note that the hydrogen atoms describe the corners of a regular tetrahedron with the carbon atom at the center of the tetrahedron. Demonstrate by attempted superposition that two models of methane are identical.

b. Replace any one hydrogen atom in each of the two methane models with a halogen to form two molecules of CH_3X. Are the two structures identical? Does it make a difference which of the four hydrogen atoms on a methane molecule you replace?

c. Repeat these steps for two disubstituted methanes with two identical substituents (CH_2X_2), and then with two different substituents (CH_2XY). Use two different colored atoms for this.

Exercise No. 2

a. Construct a model of a trisubstituted methane molecule (CHXYZ). Four different colored atom-centers are attached to a central tetrahedral atom center. Note that the carbon now has four different substituents. Compare this model with a second model of CHXYZ. Are the two structures identical (superimposable)?

b. Interchange any two substituents on <u>one</u> of the carbon atoms. Are the two CHXYZ molecules identical now?

c. Compare the two models that were not identical. What is the relationship between them? Do they have a mirror-image relationship? That is, are they related as an object and its mirror reflection? These two models are called *stereoisomers* and they will be discussed in McMurry in Chapter 9.

Exercise No. 3

a. Make a model of ethane, CH$_3$CH$_3$. Does each of the carbon atoms retain a tetrahedral configuration? Can the carbon atoms be rotated with respect to each other without breaking the carbon-carbon bond?

b. Rotate about the carbon-carbon bond until the carbon-hydrogen bonds of one carbon atom are aligned with those of the other carbon atom. This is called the *eclipsed* conformation. When the C-H bond of one carbon atom bisects the H-C-H angle of the other carbon atom the conformation is called *staggered*. These conformations are arrangements of atoms in a molecule that can be interconverted by bond rotations.

c. In which of these two conformations of ethane are the hydrogen atoms of one carbon closest to those of the other carbon?

Exercise No. 4

Prepare a second model of ethane. Replace any one hydrogen on each ethane model with a substituent such as halogen (a green atom-center), to form two models of CH_3CH_2X. Are the structures identical? If not, can they be made identical by rotation about the C-C bond? With one of the models demonstrate that there are three equivalent staggered conformations (see Exercise No. 3) of CH_3CH_2X. How many equivalent eclipsed conformations are possible?

Exercise No. 5

Assemble a model of a 1,2-disubstituted ethane molecule, CH_2XCH_2X. Note how the orientation of and the distance between the X groups changes with rotation of the carbon-carbon bond. The arrangement in which the X substituents are at maximum separation is called the *anti* conformation. The other staggered conformations are called *gauche* conformations. How many *gauche* conformations are possible? Are they energetically equivalent? Are they identical?

Exercise No. 6

Construct two models of butane, $CH_3CH_2CH_2CH_3$. Note that the structures can be viewed as dimethyl substituted ethanes. Show that rotations of the C-2, C-3 bond of butane produce eclipsed, *anti*, and the *gauche* conformations. Measure the distance between C-1 and C-4 in the conformations just mentioned. How many eclipsed conformations are possible? In which eclipsed conformation are the C-1 and C-4 carbon atoms closest to each other?

Exercise No. 7

Cyclopentane is a more flexible ring system than cyclobutane or cyclopropane. A model of cyclopentane in a conformation with all the ring carbon atoms coplanar exhibits minimal deviation of the C-C-C bond angles from the normal tetrahedral bond angle. How many eclipsed hydrogen interactions are there in this planar conformation? If one of the ring carbon atoms is pushed slightly above (or below) the plane of the other carbon atoms a model of the envelope conformation is obtained. Does the envelope conformation relieve some of the eclipsing interactions?

Exercise No. 8

a. Assemble the six-membered ring compound cyclohexane. Is the ring flat or puckered? Place the ring in a chair conformation and then in a boat conformation. Demonstrate that the chair and boat are indeed conformations of cyclohexane -- that is, they may be interconverted by rotations about the carbon-carbon bonds of the ring.

b. Note that in the chair conformation carbon atoms 2, 3, 5 and 6 are in the same plane and carbon atoms 1 and 4 are above and below the plane, respectively. In the boat conformation carbon atoms 1 and 4 are both above (they could also both be below) the plane described by carbon atoms 2, 3, 5 and 6. Are the hydrogen atoms in the chair conformation staggered or eclipsed? Are any hydrogen atoms eclipsed in the boat conformation? Do carbon atoms 1 and 4 have an *anti* or a *gauche* relationship in the chair conformation? (**Hint**: Look down the C-2, C-3 bond).

c. A twist conformation of cyclohexane may be obtained by slightly twisting carbon atoms 2 and 5 of the boat conformation. Note that the C-2, C-3 and the C-5, C-6 bonds no longer retain their parallel orientation in the twist conformation. If the ring system is twisted too far, another boat conformation results. Compare the number of eclipsed interactions present in the boat, twist, and chair conformations of cyclohexane. Is it apparent why the relative order of thermodynamic stabilities is chair>twist>boat?

Exercise No. 9

a. Now consider a ring of 6 carbons such as occurs in graphite (the form of carbon in soot or pencil lead). Put together a gray bent unit (V shaped) with a gray hairpin unit (U shaped) to make a piece that looks like >= and connect a pair of them to make a piece that looks like >==<. Assemble three >==< pieces to make a ring. Is the ring as nonplanar as the six-membered ring you assembled in Exercise No. 8? In fact, this type of 6-membered ring (called a benzene ring) prefers to be completely flat. All the experiments you will perform this quarter involve molecules that contain benzene rings. The reason for this is that the flatness of the benzene rings makes many of the compounds that contain them easy to crystallize.

b. Put two identical substituents (red atom centers) onto the flat 6-membered ring that you have constructed from gray units. How many distinguishable ways are there to attach two identical substituents?

c. Put two different substituents (one red and one green) onto the flat 6-membered ring. How many distinguishable ways are there to attach these two substituents?

d. Put three identical substituents (red atom centers) onto the flat 6-membered ring. How many different ways are there to attach these three red substituents?

e. Put two identical substituents (2 red atom centers) and one different (1 green substituent) onto the flat 6-membered ring. How many distinguishable ways are there to attach these 3 substituents?

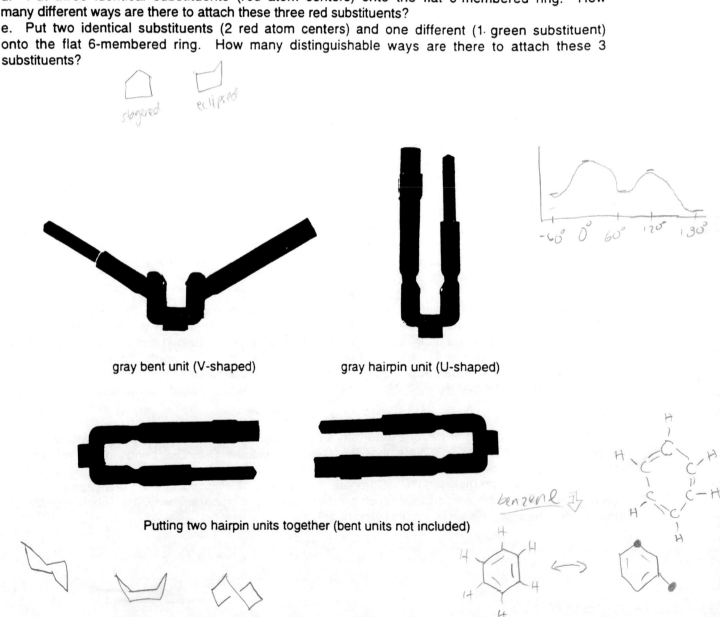

gray bent unit (V-shaped)   gray hairpin unit (U-shaped)

Putting two hairpin units together (bent units not included)

CHEM 112A
Laboratory Experiments

Synthesis of Tetraphenylporphyrin and its Purification by Column Chromatography

In this lab you will synthesize tetraphenylporphyrin, as drawn below in Scheme 1, and explore the effect of placing a copper ion in the middle of the ring. This copper complex is related to the red pigment found in the feathers of some species of birds (to see an example of this, go to *http://wwwchem.uwimona.edu.jm:1104/gifs/touraco.gif*)

Introduction

Porphyrins constitute an important class of compounds in chemistry and biology. The parent molecule for porphyrins is *porphine*, the ring system within the dashed circle in Scheme 1 below. Porphyrins and their derivatives form stable complexes with a variety of metal ions. The complexes with iron are called hemes and play a vital role in living cells.

Scheme 1

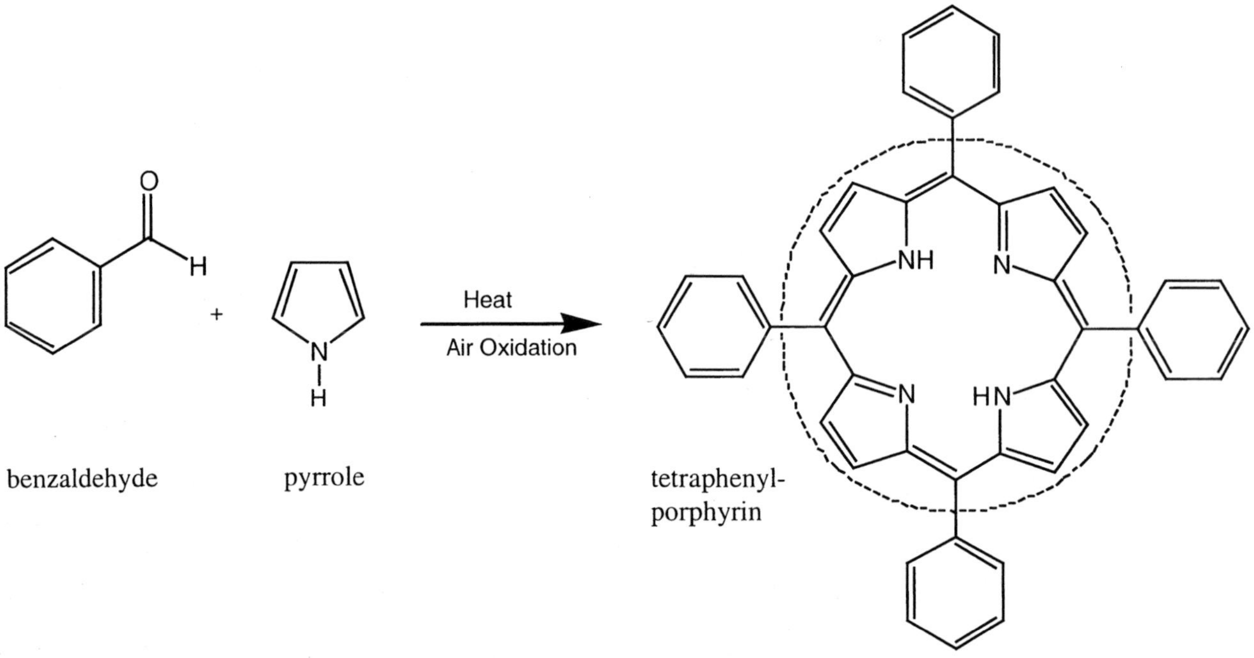

benzaldehyde   pyrrole   tetraphenyl-
                                          porphyrin

In the reaction drawn in Scheme 1, 8 carbon-carbon bonds are formed. The synthesis takes place in the vapor phase rather than in solution. This gas phase experiment illustrates how to minimize solvent use in the preparation of organic compounds and provides an example of how to avoid corrosive reagents and utilize air as an oxidizer.

The porphyrin numbering system is shown for porphine in Scheme 2. The molecule to be prepared in the present synthesis is 5,10,15,20-tetraphenylporphyrin. Spontaneous assembly of this compound from 4 molecules of benzaldehyde and 4 molecules of pyrrole involves air oxidation, but some incompletely oxidized material (tetraphenylchlorin) forms as an impurity. The *chlorin* ring is found in chlorophyll. Porphyrins occur in hemoglobin, cytochromes, and many enzymes. They also form the basis of molecular memory devices being created by ZettaCore, which have been developed from discoveries made at UCR.

The product will be deposited on the walls of the reaction flask. You will then perform thin-layer chromatography (TLC) to visualize the product and use column chromatography to separate tetraphenylporphyrin from its chlorin impurity. These products contain highly

Scheme 2

porphine

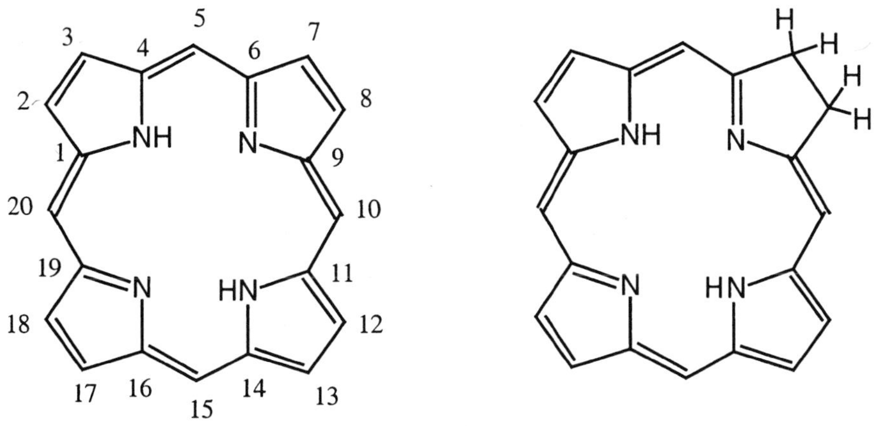

chlorin

conjugated π-electron systems (alternating double and single bonds), which cause them to be brightly colored. After purification the porphyrin and chlorin electronic absorption spectra will be compared. Then a sample of tetraphenylporphyrin is to be reacted with a divalent metal ion to make a complex, whose polarity will be gauged using TLC.

Prelab Exercises:

(1) Build a molecular model of porphine and make sure that it is completely planar. Be sure to use only sp^2 (gray) units for the carbon atoms, green trigonal units for the NH's, and green "hairpin" with green bent units for the double-bonded nitrogens. Measure the distances between the NH's that are kitty-corner from one another. Then replace one C=C double bond with two sp^3 carbons (black units) to build a model of chlorin. If you make the chlorin model completely flat, how does the nitrogen-nitrogen distance change relative to the distance in porphine? [You will want to repeat that comparison a few times to double check, since the difference is subtle.]

(2) Scheme 2 illustrates one way of making a Lewis dot structure for porphine. Draw another Lewis dot structure of porphine in which you rearrange nine of the double bonds. These two dot structures should be energetically equivalent.

(3) The fact that there are two equivalent Lewis dot structures means that the porphine molecule has symmetry (for instance, positions 2 & 3 are not only chemically equivalent to one another but are also chemically equivalent to positions 12 & 13). Suppose both hydrogens are removed from the two NH groups. The result will be a dianion of porphine (that is, the molecule will have 2 negative charges). Draw 4 different, equivalent Lewis dot structures for this dianion. Which other positions become chemically equivalent to positions 2,3,12, & 13?

(4) If a divalent metal ion is inserted in the center of the porphine ring, its charge will exactly balance the two negative charges of the dianion. Write a balanced equation for the reaction of tetraphenylporphyrin (which you can abbreviate as TPP) with cupric acetate [$Cu(CH_3COO)_2$] to give acetic acid [CH_3COOH] and a copper(II) ion in the center of the TPP dianion.

(5) It turns out that the dimensions of the copper(II) ion are just right so that it fits into the exact center of the porphine ring of the TPP dianion. Do you predict that this metal salt should be more polar or less polar than TPP itself? In your final writeup of the experiment, compare this prediction with what you observe in the thin layer chromatogram of the copper(II) complex of TPP.

[Prelab questions continued on page E-5]

Background

Read the sections on Column Chromatography (pp. E-7–E-11 of the lab text) and on Thin Layer Chromatography (pp 103-104 of the lab text) before coming to lab. Also read the section on ultraviolet-visible spectoscopy and the Beer-Lambert equation on pp. E-19 – E21 of the lab text). Make a flow chart showing the sequence of operations you will be performing. Note the points at which you will be taking spectra and running TLC's.

This experiment has several objectives. Two of the most important are as follows:

(*a*)   To learn about working up an experiment (that is, to understand how to purify and recover a product from a chemical reaction). For this you will use column chromatography.

(*b*)   To test the prediction you have made in question 5 of the prelab exercises above (that is, to use thin layer chromatography not only to analyze purity but also to assess the relative polarities of tetraphenylporphyrin and its copper complex).

Chromatography is a technique for separating mixtures. Chromatography is used both for isolating products from a reaction (in this case, for purifying tetraphenylporphyrin away from its tetraphenylchlorin impurity) and for analyzing the purity of a sample.

The fundamental principle of chromatography is that different compounds pass through a medium at different rates. In this experiment you can see the different colors – red-purple for tetraphenylporphyrin and green for tetraphenylchlorin (hence, the name *chromatography*). There are many sorts of chromatography. All forms of chromatography employ a stationary phase (in this case, silica gel, which is a porous form of silicon dioxide) and a mobile phase (in this case, the solvent or *eluent*).

The types of chromatography used in this experiment use a solvent mixture, hexanes plus ethyl acetate, as the mobile phase. Hexanes (a mixture of *n*-hexane and its isomers) by themselves are too *nonpolar* to move the mixture rapidly through the stationary phase. In other words, a pure hydrocarbon solvent would *elute* the products too slowly. Consequently, a small amount of a more polar solvent (ethyl acetate) is added to the eluent. Note that the solvent mixture that you are using for column chromatography will contain a higher percentage of ethyl acetate than the solvent mixture you are using for thin layer chromatography (TLC).

The mobile phase in this experiment is much less polar than the stationary phase. The rate with which two compounds pass through silica gel provides a qualitative measure of relative polarity: the more polar a compound, the slower the rate with which it travels. Thus, you are expected to look at the relative rates of migration to assess relative polarity.

Assessing Purity of Tetraphenylporphyrin (TPP)

Once TPP has been separated by chromatography, it is necessary to assess its purity. The colors of porphyrins and chlorins result from four distinct absorptions in the visible spectrum (the so-called Q-bands). For TPP, the longest wavelength Q-band (at 650 nm) corresponds to the weakest absorption, while for tetraphenylchlorin the 650 nm absorption is the strongest of the Q-bands. [The absorption spectra have been reported by Russell H. Ball, G.D. Dorough, and Melvin Calvin "Further study of the porphine-like products of the reaction of benzaldehyde and pyrrole." *Journal of the American Chemical Society* (1946) **68**, 2278-2281].

The next longest wavelength Q-band occurs around 590 nm. Tetraphenylporphyrin and tetraphenylchlorin both have the same extinction coefficient at 590 nm. The intensity ratio of the two longest wavelength Q-bands is 0.45 for pure tetraphenylporphyrin and 7 for tetraphenylchlorin. You are to measure the 650 nm/590 nm intensity ratio for the tetra-phenylporphyrin from your column chromatography, in order to assay its purity.

Prelab Exercises [continued from page E-3]

(6) The hydrocarbon solvent used in this experiment, hexanes, is a mixture of C_6H_{14} isomers. Draw the structures of the 4 branched, constitutional isomers of *n*-hexane and circle the ones that should be chiral (that is, draw circles around the structures that cannot be super-imposed on their mirror images).

(7) Which of the two products, tetraphenylporphyrin or its impurity tetraphenyl-chlorin, should have a dipole moment? Which compound do you expect to travel faster through silica gel, the red-purple porphyrin or the green chlorin?

(8) The 650 nm/590 nm intensity ratio for tetraphenylchlorin is 7, while the ratio for tetraphenyl porphyrin is 0.45. Predict the 650 nm/590 nm intensity ratio for a sample that contains 98% tetraphenylporphyrin and 2% tetraphenylchlorin.

SAFETY PRECAUTIONS: Ethyl acetate and hexanes are flammable, so avoid exposure to heat sources. Place all waste in the appropriate containers in the hood. Avoid inhalation of silica gel. Benzaldehyde and pyrrole can be irritants.

Experimental Procedure

Reaction

Place a 3 mL conical vial with a sealed septum cap on your aluminum block. Heat the vial to 170°C. Now inject benzaldehyde (10µL, 0.1 mmol) via syringe and allow it to vaporize. Raise the temperature to 180°C and then inject pyrrole (7µL, 0.1 mmol) via syringe. Raise the temperature to about 250°C and heat for 15 min. Turn off the hot plate, carefully remove the vial from the hot plate and allow to cool to room temperature.

Workup

After the vial is cool, add 0.3 mL of methylene chloride to the vial. Cap the vial and carefully swirl the liquid to dissolve the product from the walls of the vial.

Thin Layer Chromatography (TLC)

With the assistance of your TA, perform thin layer chromatography of the product mixture on silica TLC plates using a 14:1 hexanes:ethyl acetate mobile phase. Draw the starting line in pencil on the plate before spotting. Let the plate sit for a minute after spotting to allow the solvent to evaporate completely. Run the TLC in a closed solvent chamber. Mark the solvent front with a pencil as soon as the plate is removed from the solvent chamber. The tetraphenylporphyrin appears as the leading spot on the silica plate, while polymeric impurities (sometimes called *schlunz*) remain at the starting line. Determine the R_f value of tetraphenylporphyrin. Draw a copy of the TLC plate in your lab notebook.

Column Chromatography

Prepare a silica gel column in a Pasteur pipette. Insert a small cotton plug, then a layer of sand, then the silica gel, and finally a thin layer of sand on top. Make sure each layer of the column is flat. Add your column solvent (7:1 hexanes:ethyl acetate) and continue to add until solvent drips out of the bottom of the column into your collection flask. Allow the solvent to drain down to just the top of the topmost sand layer. Now carefully add your crude product that has been dissolved in methylene chloride to the top of the sand. Allow this to be absorbed by the sand layer and then carefully add more column solvent, being careful not to disturb the bed of sand. Position your collection tubes underneath the column and begin collection. Continue to add column solvent as the solvent layer goes down. Never let the column go dry. You should observe the products passing through the column and being collected. After collecting the product in the first tube (about 1 mL= 20 drops), position the second tube under the column. Collect the same amount of solvent as you did in the first tube. Repeat for the third and fourth tube. After collecting, you may allow the column to go dry. Write down careful observations of each fraction you have collected.

Purity of Tetraphenylporphyrin Measured using Electronic Absorption Spectra

Using a screw cap vial, dilute a sample of the red-purple band that you purified by column chromatography (using 7:1 hexane:ethyl acetate) to give a pink solution. Using the Spectronic 20 absorption instruments (one of which is set at 650 nm and the other at 590 nm) measure the absorbances of this solution (it should have an absorbance of at least 0.15 at 590 nm, but no more than 0.5). Calculate the percentage of tetraphenylchlorin impurity in your purified TPP. Label this vial and turn it in to your TA at the end of the lab period. Be sure to wipe the insides of cuvette you used for this measurement, rinse it with water, and again wipe it dry, so that another student can use it afterwards.

Metallation of Tetraphenylporphyrin

Take the collection tube containing your porphyrin product. Remove half of the solution and place it into a clean test tube. Now add 10 drops of the cupric acetate solution to this test tube. Gently shake the test tube and heat it to a gentle reflux in the fume hood for about 10 minutes. Note any color change. Now perform a TLC using 14:1 hexanes:ethyl acetate mobile phase, spotting (side by side) a sample both from your tetraphenylporphyrin product tube and from the test tube to which you added the Cu(II) solution. Determine the R_f values of both spots.

Place the fractions and the silica column into the waste containers provided.

Optional Experiment (if you have time)

Run the above TLC using the 7:1 hexanes:ethyl acetate mobile phase instead of the 14:1 hexanes:ethyl acetate mobile phase. Compare the R_f values for the different eluents.

Writeup and Post-lab Question

Your writeup should include your interpretation of the experimental results, as they pertain to the following questions:

(1) Based on the TLC R_f values, is the copper complex of tetraphenylporphyrin more polar or less polar than tetraphenylporphyrin itself? Compare your conclusion with the prediction you made in Prelab exercise 5.

(2) The 650 nm/590 nm intensity ratio measured for pure tetraphenylporphyrin has a value of 0.454 ± 0.035, while the 650 nm absorption for tetraphenylchlorin is 7 times as intense at the 590 nm absorption. Does the value you measured for the sample you purified by column chromatography lie within the stated error limits for pure tetraphenylporphyrin? If not, calculate the percentage of tetraphenylchlorin that remains in your purified sample.

In addition to writing up your results, please also answer the following:

If the TLC solvent is changed to 20:1 Hexanes:ethyl acetate, how should the R_f values be affected?

References: Green Chemistry in Education Workshop, University of Oregon, 2002.
C.M. Drain and X. Gong, *Chemical Communications* (1997) 2117-2118.

Column Chromatography

9.1 OVERVIEW

In this unit we will study the separation of chemicals by **column chromatography**. In column chromatography the stationary phase is packed inside a glass tube, the sample is loaded into the top of the column, and the mobile phase is allowed to flow down. The sample components separate by their differential interactions with the stationary phase producing well-defined bands (Fig. 9.1). These bands are collected in separate containers as they come out of the column. Traditionally, column chromatography was performed in open tubes at atmospheric pressure. In the last 20 years, high-performance liquid chromatography (HPLC, where the mobile phase is pumped through the column at high pressure, has displaced open-column chromatography in many of its applications. However, the technique is still commonly used in the organic chemistry laboratory because it is rather inexpensive.

Separation by column chromatography depends on the type of stationary phase used and can take place by different mechanisms, such as adsorption, partition, reversed phase, ion-exchange, affinity, and size exclusion. Except for affinity chromatography, all the other types are commonly used in the organic chemistry lab, with adsorption being the most widely employed. In this unit the emphasis will be on adsorption column chromatography.

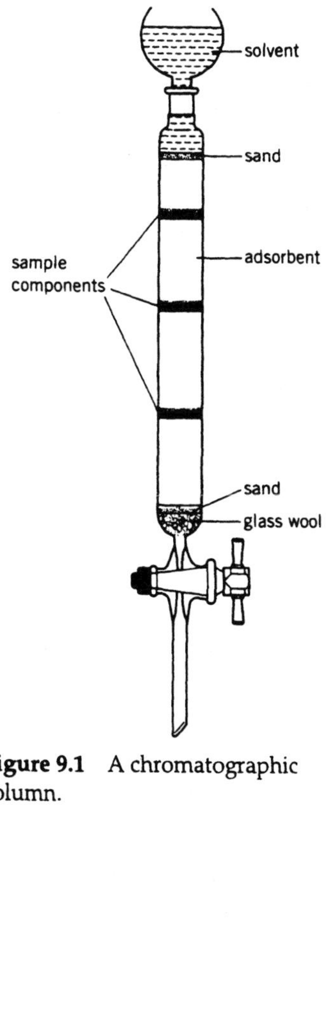

Figure 9.1 A chromatographic column.

9.2 PRACTICAL ASPECTS

Packing the Column

Before the separation is attempted, the sample should be analyzed by TLC to determine the mobility of the components with different solvents. The selection of the adsorbent and mobile phase is made following the guidelines outlined in **pp 98-102**. For column chromatography, as for TLC, the most common adsorbents are silica gel and alumina. **Calcium phosphate** (hydroxyapatite), a stationary phase of limited adsorptivity, is used in the purification of proteins and other biological macromolecules; **activated charcoal** and **starch** are used for special applications.

There are two main methods for packing a regular chromatographic column: **dry** and **wet**. The wet method is the most commonly used, and we will discuss it here. Dry columns afford separation in less time than conventional columns, and are used to separate complex mixtures; a disadvantage of dry columns, however, is that larger amounts of adsorbent are required to accomplish the separation. For more information about dry columns see Reference 3.

The quality of the separation obtained by column chromatography depends on the adsorption equilibrium in the column. Although equilibrium is actually never reached because the solvent is constantly flowing, experimental conditions can be set so that the column operates under near-equilibrium conditions. The **amount of adsorbent**, its **particle size**, the **dimensions of the column**, and the **flow rate** are all important parameters that determine the success of the separation.

To carry out a separation by the wet method, the amount of stationary phase needed is approximately 20–50 times the weight of the sample. For difficult separations involving compounds of similar polarity, this ratio can be increased to 100–200. Normal particle size for column chromatography is 0.15–0.5 mm. Particle size smaller than 0.1 mm results in very low flow rates. Larger particle size implies less surface area per mass unit of adsorbent, and therefore, less adsorptivity. The dimension of the column should be such that the ratio between its length and its diameter is in the range 10–20. In general, the longer the column, the better the separation. However, there is a practical limit to this imposed by the slow flow rate obtained with very long columns.

The flow rate plays an important role in the separation. Fast flow rates usually do not give good separations because the column operates under conditions far from equilibrium. On the other hand, very slow flow rates not only lead to lengthy analyses but also give poor separations as the solutes tend to remix by diffusion in the column. The optimal flow rate depends on the specific separation, the type of adsorbent used, and the geometry of the column. Normally, flow rates in the range 1–60 mL per hour are employed.

To pack a chromatographic column, the adsorbent of choice is mixed with about five volumes of the mobile phase and the slurry is poured into a dry glass column that is fitted with a sintered glass plate or a plug of glass wool and a layer of sand to support the stationary phase. The column should be clamped in a vertical position. Usually the glass tube is equipped with a stopcock to control the solvent flow through the column. As the solid stationary phase settles down, the column is gently tapped with a wooden rod or a spatula. This avoids the formation of channels and air bubbles inside the adsorbent. The stopcock is opened and the solvent allowed to run before more slurry is added to the column. To avoid the formation of boundaries in the stationary phase, the new portion of adsorbent should be added before the previous portion has settled down completely. At no point should the solvent level be allowed to run below the level of the adsorbent. If this happens, the column should be emptied and repacked. Once the column has been filled to the desired height, a circle of filter paper or a 0.5-cm layer of sand is placed on top of the stationary phase; this prevents disturbances in the adsorbent as the sample and solvent are added to the column. The solvent is drained so its meniscus is just above the surface of the sand. The column is now ready to be loaded (Fig. 9.2a).

Loading the Sample

A solution of the sample, typically in the same solvent as the one used to pack the column, is loaded at the top of the column with the aid of a Pasteur pipet (Fig. 9.2b). The volume of the sample solution should be kept to a minimum; for a column about 40 cm long and 2 cm in diameter, a sample volume of 1–2 mL is ideal. Very large sample volumes result in poor separations. The stopcock at the outlet end of the column is opened and the sample allowed to penetrate the adsorbent (Fig. 9.2c). Once the sample has been completely loaded and the meniscus of the sample solution is just above the surface of the sand, a small aliquot of fresh solvent is added to wash the walls of the column (Fig. 9.2d); this volume is allowed to penetrate the column (Fig. 9.2e) and then more solvent is added to fill the column (Fig. 9.2f). Allowing the sample to penetrate the column before the solvent is added prevents unwanted dilution of the sample and leads to better results. A solvent reservoir is attached to the top of the column. Solvent flow should not be stopped once the column is running because it results in broadening of the bands due to diffusion.

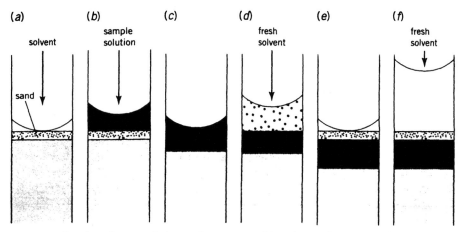

Figure 9.2 Loading the sample into a chromatographic column. See text for details.

Sometimes the sample is not totally soluble in the solvent used to run the column but it dissolves in more polar solvents. Loading a partially soluble sample directly on top of the column is unacceptable, because it leads to very poor separations. Loading the sample in a solvent more polar than the solvent used to run the column leads to poor separations as well, as we will discuss in the next section. The problem can be circumvented by dissolving the sample in the polar solvent, adding a small amount of adsorbent to the solution (2–10 times the weight of the sample), and evaporating the solvent in a rota-vap. As the solvent evaporates the sample gets adsorbed to the stationary phase. The solid mixture of sample and adsorbent, called a **pellet**, is then placed on top of the column and the solvent allowed to run as usual.

Development and Elution

The rules that govern the separation in adsorption column chromatography are the same as in adsorption TLC   Nonpolar compounds have weaker interactions with the adsorbent, move faster than polar compounds and come out first. Similar to TLC, the process of running solvent through the stationary phase is called *development*. However, there is a big difference between TLC and column chromatography. While TLC development is always done with a pure solvent or a single mixture of solvents, column chromatography development can be done in three different ways: **isocratic**, **stepwise**, or **gradient development**. In **isocratic development** (from the Greek; *isokratos*, equal strength) only one solvent is used throughout the development. In a way, this is similar to TLC. Isocratic development is useful in separating components of similar polarity; for example, a mixture of chlorophyll a and b can be separated by using a single solvent of medium polarity such as ethyl acetate or a mixture of toluene-methanol. Isocratic development is also employed when we want to isolate only the least polar compound of a mixture. The complex mixture is loaded into the column filled with a solvent of similar polarity to that of the desired compound. The solvent is run through the column, and only the compound (or compounds) with polarity similar to that of the solvent moves; the more polar compounds remain adsorbed at the top of the column.

After removal of the nonpolar compounds, if we want to remove compounds that are strongly adsorbed to the stationary phase, solvents of higher polarity are needed. We can do this in a **stepwise** manner by adding successive aliquots of solvents of increasing polarity. A series of *solvents of increasing polarity* is called an **eluotropic series**. For example: pentane, toluene, diethyl ether, acetone, and methanol constitute an eluotropic series.

In using the eluotropic series mentioned above, for example, mixtures of pentane with an increasing concentration of toluene (such as 10, 50, and 70%) should be run sequentially after pure pentane and before pure toluene. When changing from aprotic to protic solvents, for example, from acetone to methanol, the concentration of the protic solvent should be increased even more gradually than in the case of aprotic solvents (such as pentane and toluene). For example, a gradual increase of methanol in methanol-acetone mixtures would be 1, 2, 5, 10, 20, 30, 40, 70, and 100% methanol.

Sometimes it is convenient to increase the polarity of the mobile phase more gradually than in a stepwise manner. We can achieve this with a **gradient development** generated by mixing two solvents of different polarity. The solvent of high polarity is allowed to flow, at a flow rate R_1, into a mixing chamber that contains the less-polar solvent connected to the column with a flow rate R_2 (Fig. 9.3). Different gradients can be generated depending on the relative flow rates of both solvents. When $R_2 = 2R_1$ the concentration of the more-polar solvent in the mixing chamber increases linearly with time; this is called a **linear gradient**. Gradient development in column chromatography is the equivalent of temperature programming in GC. It makes it possible to separate in a single chromatographic run mixtures of compounds with a wide variety of polarities.

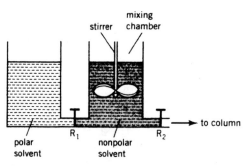

Figure 9.3 A gradient formation system.

Summarizing the types of column development we can say that in **adsorption chromatography, the polarity of the mobile phase is either kept constant, as in isocratic development, or increased during the development, *but never decreased*.**

The removal of the compounds from the column is normally done by allowing the solvent to flow through and collecting different fractions as the components come out of the column. This process is called **elution** and the liquid coming out of the column is called the **eluent**.

Colorless compounds must be detected by indirect methods. Unlike TLC, it is not customary to run chromatographic columns using adsorbents with fluorescent indicators because these indicators may leach into the elution solvent and contaminate the sample. TLC, GC, and UV-visible spectroscopy are all very useful ways to follow the development of a chromatographic column. Fractions of equal volume can be collected with the aid of an automatic fraction collector (Fig. 9.4) and analyzed by GC, TLC, or UV; those fractions that show similar compositions are pooled together and the solvent is evaporated. Automatic UV-visible detectors are also available. The detector is connected at the end of the column and monitors the absorbance of the eluent, at a given wavelength, as it comes out of the column. If the sample absorbs in the UV-visible region of the spectrum, peaks are observed as the compounds elute from the column. The use of this method is limited to mobile phases with little or no absorption in the UV-visible region.

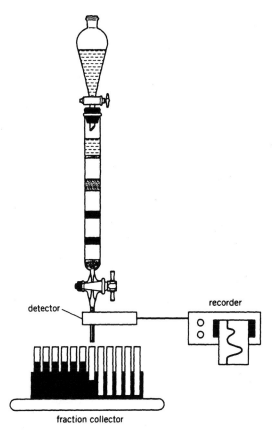

Figure 9.4   A chromatographic column with fraction collector, detector, and recorder.

A less frequently used elution method consists of extruding the stationary phase from the column and cutting the bands. The column is first allowed to run dry, then the stationary phase is removed by extrusion by forcing compressed air through the column. The bands of interest are cut with a spatula and the compounds are eluted from the adsorbent with acetone or other suitable solvents.

COLUMN CHROMATOGRAPHY DO'S AND DON'TS

Follow these recommendations to obtain good results with chromatographic columns.

Do's
- Clamp the column in a vertical position.
- The column should be free of air bubbles.
- Avoid sudden changes in the composition of the mobile phase.
- Load small sample volumes.

Don'ts
- Do not let the column run dry.
- Do not use extreme flow rates.
- Do not stop solvent flow once the sample has been loaded.

BIBLIOGRAPHY

1. Chromatographic Methods. A. Braithwaite and F.J. Smith. 4th ed. Chapman and Hall, London, 1990.
2. Chromatography. E. Heftmann, ed. Reinhold, New York, 1967.
3. Vogel's Textbook of Practical Organic Chemistry. A.I. Vogel, B.S. Furniss, A.J. Hannaford, P.W.G. Smith, and A.R. Tatchell. 5th ed. Longman, Harlow, UK. 1989.

Isolation of Caffeine from Tea and Purification by Sublimation

Product

Common names: Caffeine, 1,3,7-trimethyl-2,6-dioxopurine
CA number: [58-08-2]
CA name as indexed: 1*H*-Purine-2,6-dione, 3,7-dihydro-1,3,7-trimethyl-

Purpose

To extract the active principle, an alkaloid, caffeine, from a native source, tea leaves. Caffeine is a metabolite (a product of the living system's biochemistry) found in a variety of plants. We will use ordinary tea bags as our source of raw material. This experiment illustrates an extraction technique often employed to isolate water-soluble, weakly basic natural products from their biological source (see also Experiment [11A] for another extraction strategy). The isolation of caffeine will also give you the opportunity to use sublimation as a purification technique, as caffeine is a crystalline alkaloid that possesses sufficient vapor pressure to make it a good candidate for this procedure.

Prelab

Before coming to laboratory, you have to complete a Lab Preparation Write-up, as described on pp 1-2. There are no prelab questions for this experiment, but you should include a flow chart in your outline of procedure, indicating what is to be kept and what is to be discarded.

ALKALOIDS

Caffeine belongs to a rather amorphous class of natural products called alkaloids. This collection of substances is unmatched in its variety of structures, biological response on nonhost organisms, and the biogenetic pathways to their formation.

The history of these fascinating organic substances begins at least 4000 years ago. While their therapeutic activity was incorporated into poultices, potions, poisons, and medicines, no attempt was made to isolate and identify the substances responsible for the physiological response until the very early 1800s.

The first alkaloid to be obtained in the pure crystalline state was morphine; isolated by Friedrich Wilhelm Sertürner (1783–1841) in 1805. He recognized that the material possessed basic character and he, therefore, classified it as a vegetable alkali (that is a base with its origin in the plant kingdom). Thus, compounds with similar properties ultimately became known as alkaloids. The term "alkaloid" was introduced for the first time by an apothecary, Meissner, in Halle in 1819.

Sertürner, also a pharmacist, lived in Hamelin, another city in Prussia. He isolated morphine from opium, the dried sap of the poppy. As the analgesic and narcotic effects of the crude resin had been known for centuries, it is not surprising that, with the emerging understanding of chemistry, the interest of Sertürner became focused on this drug, which is still medicine's major therapy for intolerable pain. He published his studies in detail in 1816 and very quickly two French professors, Pierre Joseph Pelletier (1788–1842) and Joseph Caventou (1795–1877) at the Ecole de Pharmacie in Paris recognized the enormous importance of Sertürner's work.

In the period from 1817–1820, these two men and their students isolated many of the alkaloids, which continue to be of major importance.

Included in that avalanche of purified natural products was caffeine, which they obtained from the coffee bean. This substance is the target compound that you will be isolating directly from the raw plant in this experiment. A little more than 75 years later, caffeine was first synthesized by Fischer in 1895 from dimethylurea and malonic acid.

THE CLASSIFICATION OF ALKALOIDS

These compounds are separated into three general classes of materials.

1. True alkaloids: these compounds contain nitrogen in a heterocyclic ring; are almost always basic (the lone-pair of the nitrogen is responsible for this basic character); are derived from amino acids in the biogenesis of the alkaloid; invariably are toxic and possess a broad spectrum of pharmacological activity; are found in a rather limited number of plants (of the 10,000 known genera only 8.7% possess at least one alkaloid); and normally occur in a complex with an organic acid (this helps to make them rather soluble in aqueous media). As we will see, there are numerous exceptions to these rules. For example, there are several very well-known quaternary alkaloids. These are compounds in which the nitrogen has become tetravalent and positively charged (as in the ammonium ion). Thus, they are not actually basic.

2. Protoalkaloids: These compounds are simple amines, derived from amino acids, in which the basic nitrogen atom is not incorporated into a ring system; and they are often referred to as *biological amines*. An example of a protoalkaloid is mescaline.

3. Pseudoalkaloids: These compounds contain nitrogen atoms usually *not* derived from amino acids. There are two main classes into which pseudoalkaloids are divided, the steroidal alkaloids and the *purines*. Caffeine has been assigned to this latter class of alkaloids.

Morphine

Mescaline

Caffeine

Prior Reading
Technique 4: Solvent Extraction
        Solid–Liquid extraction (see pp. 78–80).
        Liquid–Liquid Extraction (see pp. 80–82).
Technique 9: Sublimation
        Sublimation Theory (see pp. 116–117).

DISCUSSION

Caffeine (1,3,7-trimethylxanthine) and its close relative theobromine (3,7-dimethylxanthine) both possess the oxidized purine skeleton (xanthine). These compounds are classified as pseudoalkaloids, as only the nitrogen atom at the 7 position can be traced to an amino group originally derived from an amino acid (in this case glycine). This classification emphasizes the rather murky problem of deciding just what naturally occurring nitrogen bases are *true* alkaloids. We will simply treat caffeine as an alkaloid.

Xanthine   Purine   Pyrimidine

It should be noted that although the pyrimidine ring (present in caffeine's purine system) is a significant building block of nucleic acids it is rare elsewhere in nature.

These two methylated xanthines are found in quite a number of plants and have been extracted and widely used for centuries. Indeed, they very likely have been, and remain today, the predominant stimulant consumed by humans. Every time you make a cup of tea or coffee, you perform an aqueous extraction of plant material (tea leaves, *Camellia sinenis*, 1–4%, or coffee beans, *Coffea* spp., 1–2%) to obtain a dose of between 25–100 mg of caffeine. Caffeine is also the active substance (~2%) in maté (used in Paraguay as a tea) made from the leaves of *Ilex paraguensis*. In coffee and tea, caffeine is the dominant member of the pair, whereas in *Theobroma cacao*, from which we obtain cocoa, theobromine (1–3%) is the primary source of the biological response. Caffeine acts to stimulate the central nervous system with its main impact on the cerebral cortex, and as it makes one more alert, it is no surprise that it is the chief constituent in No-Doz® pills.

Caffeine is readily soluble in hot water (because the alkaloid is often bound in thermally labile, partially ionic complexes with naturally occurring organic acids, such as with 3-caffeoylquinic acid in the coffee bean), which allows for relatively easy separation from black tea leaves by aqueous extraction.

Other substances, mainly tannic acids, are also present in the tea leaves and they are also water soluble. The addition of sodium carbonate, a base, during the aqueous extraction helps to increase the water solubility of these acidic substances by forming ionic sodium salts and liberating the free base.

Subsequent extraction of the aqueous phase with methylene chloride, in which free caffeine has a moderate solubility, allows the transfer of the caffeine from the aqueous extract to the organic phase. At the same time, methylene chloride extraction leaves the water-soluble sodium salts of the organic acids behind in the aqueous phase.

Extraction of the tea leaves directly with nonpolar solvents (methylene chloride) to remove the caffeine gives very poor results—since, as we have seen, the caffeine is bound in the plant in a partially ionic complex that will not be very soluble in nonpolar solvents. Thus, water is the superior extraction solvent for this alkaloid. The water also swells the tea leaves and allows for easier transport across the solid–liquid interface.

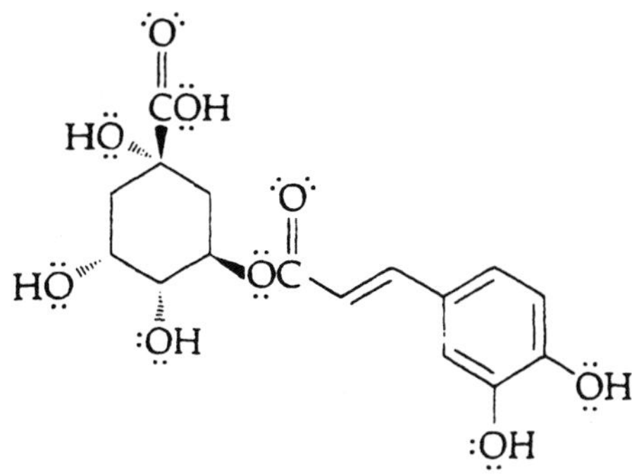

3-Caffeoylquinic acid

Following extraction and removal of the solvent, sublimation techniques are applied to the crude solid residues in order to purify the caffeine. This technique is especially suitable for the purification of solid substances at the microscale level, if they possess sufficient vapor pressure. Sublimation techniques are particularly advantageous when the impurities present in the sample are nonvolatile under the conditions employed.

Sublimation occurs when a substance goes directly from the solid phase to the gas phase upon heating, bypassing the liquid phase. Sublimation is technically a straightforward method for purification in that the materials need only be heated and therefore, mechanical losses can be kept to a minimum (the target substance must, of course, be thermally stable at the required temperatures). Materials sublime only when heated *below* their melting points, and reduced pressure is usually required to achieve acceptable sublimation rates. Obviously, substances that lend themselves best to purification by sublimation are those that do not possess strong intermolecular attractive forces. Caffeine, and ferrocene (the latter is used as a reactant in Experiment [27]) meet these criteria as they present large flat surfaces occupied predominantly with repulsive π electrons. For other isolations, see the discussion of *solid-phase* extraction methods in Technique 4 for an example of the extraction of caffeine from coffee beans (see pp. 89–90).

Estimated time to complete the experiment: 2.5 hours.

EXPERIMENTAL PROCEDURE

Physical Properties of Constituents

Compound	MW	Amount	mmol	mp(°C)
Tea		1.0 g		
Water		10 mL		
Sodium carbonate	105.99	1.1 g	10	851

Read the section on Liquid-Liquid extractions, pp 80-82.

Anhydrous Na₂CO₃, 1.1 g
+ H₂O, 10 mL + tea bag

Reagents and Equipment. Carefully open a commercial tea bag (2.0–2.5 g of tea leaves) and empty the contents. Weigh out 1.0 g of tea leaves and place them back in the empty tea bag. Close and secure the bag with staples.

Weigh, and add to a 50mL beaker, 1.1 g (10 mmol) of anhydrous sodium carbonate followed by 15 mL of water. The mixture is heated on a hot plate with occasional swirling to dissolve the solid. Now add the tea bag to the solution. Place the bag in the beaker so that it lies flat across the bottom.

Reaction Conditions

GENTLY Place a small watch glass over the mouth of the Erlenmeyer flask and then heat the aqueous suspension to boiling [GENTLY] for 30 min on a hot plate

Isolation of Product

Cool the flask and contents to room temperature. Transfer the aqueous extract from the Erlenmeyer flask to a 12- or 15-mL centrifuge tube using a Pasteur filter pipet. In addition, gently squeeze the tea bag by pressing it against the side of the Erlenmeyer flask to recover as much of the basic extract as possible. Set aside the tea bag and its contents.

Extract the aqueous solution with 2.0 mL of methylene chloride.

NOTE. *The tea solution contains some constituents that may cause an emulsion. If you find that during the mixing of the aqueous and organic solvent layers (by shaking or using a Vortex mixer) an emulsion is obtained, it can be broken readily by centrifugation.*

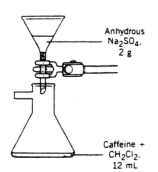

Anhydrous Na₂SO₄, 2 g

Caffeine + CH₂Cl₂, 12 mL

Separate the lower (methylene chloride) layer (check to make sure that the lower layer is, indeed, the organic layer by testing the solubility of a few drops of it in a test tube with distilled water) using a 9-in. Pasteur pipet. Drain the wet extracts through a filter funnel containing a small plug of cotton that is covered with about 2.0 g of anhydrous sodium sulfate, previously "moistened" with a small amount of methylene chloride. (■) (The organic phase will be saturated with water following the extraction, therefore it is referred to as "wet." It also may contain a few droplets of the aqueous phase, which become entrained during the phase separation; this can be particularly troublesome if an emulsion forms during the mixing.)

Collect the dried filtrate in a 25-mL filter flask. Extract the remaining aqueous phase with four additional 2.0-mL portions of methylene chloride (4 × 2 mL). Each extraction (an extraction is often referred to as a washing) is separated, and then dried as above, and transferred to the same filter flask. Finally, rinse the sodium sulfate with an additional 2.0 mL of methylene chloride and combine this wash with the earlier organic extracts.

HOOD Transfer the methylene chloride extract into a sublimation flask. Carefully take your sublimation flask to the rotary evaporator and concentrate the solution to an off-white solid.

Purification and Characterization

Purify the crude solid caffeine by sublimation.

Assemble a sublimation apparatus as shown in Figure 5.66; either arrangement is satisfactory. Using an aspirator, apply a vacuum to the system through the filter flask (remember to install a water-trap bottle between the side-arm flask and the aspirator). After the system is evacuated, run cold water gently through the cold finger or add ice to the centrifuge tube. By cooling the surface of the cold finger *after* the system has been evacuated, you will minimize the condensation of moisture on the area where the sublimed sample will collect.

Once the apparatus is evacuated and cooled, begin the sublimation by gently heating the flask with a microburner or sand bath. If you use a gas burner, always keep moving the flame back and forth around the bottom and sides of the flask.

BE CAREFUL. *Do not MELT the caffeine. If the sample does begin to melt, remove the flame for a few seconds before heating is resumed. Overheating the crude sample will lead to decomposition and the deposition of impurities on the cold finger. High temperatures are not necessary since the sublimation temperature of caffeine (and of all solids that sublime) is below the melting point. It is generally worthwhile to carry out sublimations as slowly as possible, as the purity of the material collected will be enhanced.*

When no more caffeine will sublime onto the cold finger, remove the heat, shut off the aspirator and the cooling water to the cold finger, and allow the apparatus to cool to room temperature under reduced pressure. Once cooled, carefully vent the vacuum and return the system to atmospheric pressure. *Carefully*, remove the cold finger from the apparatus.

NOTE. *If the removal of the cold finger is done carelessly, the sublimed crystals may be dislodged from the sides and bottom of the tube and drop back onto the residue left in the filter flask.*

Scrape the caffeine from the cold finger onto weighing paper using a microspatula and a sample brush. Weigh the purified caffeine and calculate its percent by weight in the original tea leaves. Determine the melting point and compare your value to that in the literature.

If your melting point apparatus uses capillary tubes to determine the melting point, an evacuated sealed tube is necessary since caffeine sublimes; the melting point is above the sublimation temperature (see Chapter 4). The melting point may be obtained using the Fisher-Johns apparatus without this precaution.

Writeup. In the conclusions section of your report answer the following questions:
1. Build a molecular model of caffeine, using planar green trigonal pieces for 3 of the nitrogens and an ordinary gray double bond for the C=N double bond. Make the C=O double bonds using half of an ordinary gray double bond with a red U-shaped endpiece for the other half, to represent the oxygen. Is the skeleton of caffeine (the carbons, nitrogens, and oxygens) flat? Discuss how this might account for the fact that caffeine sublimes at atmospheric pressure instead of melting.

2. If you dissolve caffeine in acid a proton goes onto one of the nitrogens to give the conjugate acid of caffeine, **caffeineH$^+$**. The acid dissociation constant (K$_a$)of **caffeineH$^+$** is K$_a$= 0.25 $\underline{M}$. If a cup of tea has a pH of 7.6, what should be the ratio of concentrations of **caffeineH$^+$** to unprotonated caffeine in the tea?

If you are scheduled to run the fullerene experiment next week, be sure to perform the extraction described on the back of this page before you leave the laboratory.

Procedure for the week before the C$_{60}$ isolation

The procedure below is to be performed the week prior to the C$_{60}$ chromatography experiment, once you have completed the regularly scheduled laboratory.

Equipment and Reagents
Vacuum filtration setup with Hirsch funnel and filter paper (see pp 93-94)
One 5 mL shell vial with a small magnetic stirring bar and one screw cap vial
0.1 g fullerene soot; 4 mL of toluene; 0.1 g freshly activated alumina

Extraction of Fullerenes and Preparation of Pellet

Into a perfectly dry 5 mL shell vial weigh 0.10 g of "fullerene soot." Do this operation carefully to avoid spattering the solid. Add 3 mL of toluene and a small magnetic stirring bar, then stir on a magnetic stirrer for about 10 minutes. In the meantime prepare a vacuum filtration setup by using a small filter flask and a Hirsch funnel fitted with a circle of Whatman #1 paper. Make sure that the paper covers all the holes but does not touch the conical wall of the funnel. Wet the paper with a small amount of toluene and make sure the vacuum sucks down the filter paper efficiently. Then filter the suspension. Wash the shell vial with 1 mL more toluene and use this to rinse through the filter cake. Carefully wipe out the shell vial with a piece of paper towel and weigh 0.10 g of activated alumina into it. Write your name and student number legibly on the outside of the vial. After your vacuum filtration is complete take a 0.25 mL aliquot of the colored filtrate and dilute it to 3 mL in a graduated cylinder. Keep this diluted solution in a screw cap vial for running UV-visible absorption spectroscopy later on. Carefully pipette the remainder of the colored filtrate into the shell vial and set the open shell vial into a specially designated rack in the fume hood in order for the solvent to evaporate over the coming week, so that you can perform the column chromatography the following laboratory meeting.

ULTRAVIOLET–VISIBLE SPECTROSCOPY: INTRODUCTION TO ABSORPTION SPECTROSCOPY

In an atom, molecule, or ion, a limited number of electronic energy states are available to the system because of the quantized nature of the energies involved. The absorption of a photon by the system can be interpreted as corresponding to the occupation of a new energy state by an electron. The difference in energy between these two states may be expressed as ΔE:

_____ Upper state (excited electronic state, E_1)

$\uparrow\downarrow \Delta E$

_____ Lower state (ground electronic state, E_0)

where the energy of the photon, E, is related to the frequency of the radiation by the Planck equation,

$$E = h\nu_i$$

where h is Planck's constant, 6.626×10^{-34} J s, and ν_i is the frequency in hertz. In the case above, $\Delta E = E_1 - E_0 = h(\nu_1 - \nu_0) = h\nu_i$.

Thus, when a frequency match between the radiation and an energy gap (ΔE) in the substance occurs, a transition between the two states involved may be induced. The system can either absorb or emit a photon corresponding to ΔE, depending on the state currently occupied (emission would occur if the system relaxed from an upper-level excited state to a lower state). All organic molecules absorb photons with energies corresponding to the visible or ultraviolet regions of the electromagnetic spectrum, but to be absorbed, the incident energy in this frequency range must correspond to an available energy gap between an electronic ground state and an upper-level electronic excited state. The electronic transitions of principal interest to the organic chemist are those that correspond to the excitation of a single electron from the highest occupied molecular orbital (HOMO) to the lowest unoccupied molecular orbital (LUMO). As we will see, this will be the molecule's absorption occurring at the longest wavelength in the electronic absorption spectrum; it is, therefore, the most easily observed.

Electromagnetic radiation can be defined in terms of a frequency ν, which is inversely proportional to a wavelength λ times a velocity c ($\nu = c/\lambda$, where c is the velocity of light in a vacuum, 2.998×10^8 m/s, and $c = \nu\lambda$ is the wave velocity). Thus,

$$\Delta E = h\nu = \frac{hc}{\lambda} = hc\tilde{\nu}$$

where $\tilde{\nu}$ is the wavenumber, defined as the reciprocal of the wavelength ($1/\lambda$) $\times$ the velocity of light.

Most ultraviolet and visible (UV and vis) spectra are recorded linearly in wavelength, rather than linearly in frequency or in units proportional to frequency (the wavenumber) or in energy values. Wavelength in this spectral region is currently expressed in nanometers (nm, where 1 nm = 10^{-9} m) or angstrom units (Å, where 1 Å = 10^{-10} m). The older literature is full of UV–vis spectra in which wavelength is plotted in millimicrons (mμ), which are also equivalent to 10^{-9} m. For a further discussion of the relationship between frequency, wavelength, wavenumber, and refractive index, see the discussion on infrared spectroscopy.

It is unfortunate that because of instrumentation advantages this region of the spectrum is most often plotted in units that are nonlinear in energy (note the inverse

Table 9.27 Spectroscopic Wavelength Ranges

Region	Wavelength (m)	Energy (kJ/mol)	Change Excited
Gamma ray	Less than 10^{-10}	$> 10^6$	Nuclear transformation
X-ray	10^{-8}–10^{-10}	10^4–10^6	Inner shell electron transitions
Ultraviolet (UV)	4×10^{-7}–1×10^{-8}	10^3–10^4	Valence shell electrons
Visible (vis)	8×10^{-7}–4×10^{-7}	10^2–10^3	Electronic transitions
Infrared (IR)	10^{-4}–2.5×10^{-6}	1–50	Bond vibrations
Microwave	10^{-2}–10^{-4}	10–1000	Molecular rotations
ESR	10^{-2}	10	Electron spin transitions
NMR	0.5–5	0.02–0.2	Nuclear spin transitions

relationship of E to λ). A convenient formula for expressing the relationship of wavelength and energy in useful values is

$$E = 28{,}635/\lambda \text{ kcal/mol} \qquad (\lambda \text{ in nm})$$

or in terms of wavenumbers

$$E = (28.635 \times 10^{-4})\tilde{\nu} \qquad (\tilde{\nu} \text{ in cm}^{-1})$$

The electromagnetic spectrum and the wavelength ranges corresponding to a variety of energy-state transitions are listed in Table 9.27. Infrared, UV–vis, and rf are of particular interest to the organic chemist because the excitation of organic substances by radiation from these regions of the spectrum can yield significant structural information about the molecular system being studied.

The absorption of rf energy by organic molecules immersed in strong magnetic fields involves exceedingly small energy transitions ($\sim$0.05 cal/mol), which correspond to nuclear spin excitations and result in NMR spectra. When a molecule absorbs microwave radiation, the energy states available for excitation correspond to molecular rotations and involve energies of roughly 1 cal/mol. With relatively simple molecules (in the gas phase) possessing a dipole moment (required for the absorption process) the analysis of the microwave spectrum can yield highly precise measurements of the molecular dimensions (bond lengths and angles). Unfortunately, relatively few organic systems exhibit pure rotational spectra that can be rigorously interpreted.

Absorption of radiation in the infrared region of the spectrum involves the excitation of vibrational energy levels and corresponds to energies in the range of about 1–12 kcal/mol. The excitation of electronic states requires considerably higher energies, from a little below 40 to nearly 300 kcal/mol. The corresponding radiation wavelengths would fall across the visible (400–800 nm), the near-UV (200–400 nm), and the far- (or vacuum) UV (100–200 nm) regions. The long-wavelength visible and near-UV regions of the spectrum hold information of particular value to the organic chemist. Here the energies correspond to the excitation of loosely held bonding (π) or lone-pair electrons. The far-UV region, however, involves high-energy transitions associated with the inner-shell and σ-bond electronic energy transitions. This region is difficult to access because atmospheric oxygen begins to absorb UV radiation below 190 nm, which requires working in evacuated or purged instruments (which is why this region is often referred to as the vacuum UV).

UV–VIS SPECTROSCOPY

As we have seen, the application of electronic absorption spectroscopy in organic chemistry is restricted largely to excitation of ground-state electronic levels in the near-UV and vis regions. When photons of these energies are absorbed, the excited electronic states that result have bond strengths appreciably less than their ground-state values, and the internuclear distances and bond angles will be altered within the region of the molecules where the electronic excitation occurs (see Figure 9.41). It is normally reasonable to assume that nearly all of the molecules are present in the ground vibrational state within the ground electronic state. The upper electronic state also contains a set of vibrational levels and any of these may be open to occupation by the excited electron (see Figure 9.41). Thus, an electronic transition from a particular ground-state level can be to any number of upper-level vibrational states on the excited electronic state.

The shape of an electronic absorption band will be determined to a large extent by the spacing of the vibrational levels and the distribution of band intensity over the vibrational sublevels. In most cases these effects lead to broad absorption bands in the UV–vis region.

The wavelength maximum at which an absorption band occurs in the UV–vis region is generally referred to as the λ_{max} of the sample (where wavelength is determined by the band maximum).

The quantitative relationship of absorbance (the intensity of a band) to concentration is expressed by the Beer–Lambert equation:

$$A = \log \frac{I_0}{I} = \varepsilon c l$$

where

A = absorbance, expressed as I_0/I

I_0 = the intensity of the incident light

I = the intensity of the light transmitted through the sample

ε = molar absorbtivity, or the extinction coefficient (a constant characteristic of the specific molecule being observed); values for conjugated dienes typically range from 10,000 to 25,000

c = concentration (mol/L)

λ = length of sample path (cm)

The calculated extinction coefficient and solvent are usually listed with the wavelength at the band maximum. For example, data for methyl vinyl ketone (3-buten-2-one) would be reported as follows:

$$\lambda_{max} \; 219 \text{ nm} \quad (\varepsilon = 3600, \text{ ethanol})$$
$$\lambda_{max} \; 324 \text{ nm} \quad (\varepsilon = 24, \text{ ethanol})$$

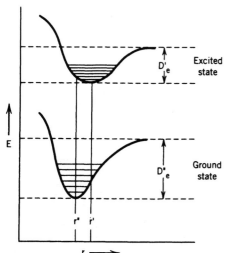

Figure 9.41 Two electronic energy levels in a diatomic molecule.

Isolation of C₆₀ from Fullerene Soot

E9.1 FULLERENES

Since the discovery in the early nineteenth century that diamond was just another form of carbon, it was believed that carbon existed only in two allotropic forms: diamond and graphite. This belief crumbled in 1985 when Harold Kroto, Richard Smalley, Robert Curl, and colleagues reported the production of a new stable form of carbon consisting of a cluster of sixty atoms, C_{60}. They proposed that the high stability of this molecule was due to its unusual shape, similar to a soccer ball. Because of its resemblance to the geodesic domes designed by the American architect Buckminster Fuller, they called this new molecule **buckminsterfullerene** (Fig. 9.6). The nickname **buckyball** was shortly coined.

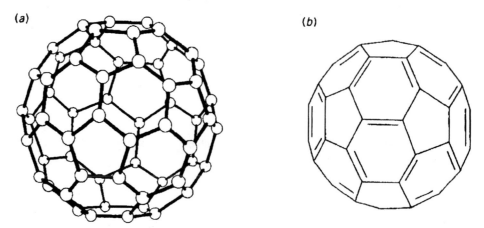

Figure 9.6 Buckminsterfullerene: *a*) stick-and-ball model; *b*) showing single and double bonds.

The study of this new form of carbon did not take off until 1990, when Donald Huffman and Wolfgang Kratschmer reported a method for the production of large quantities of buckminsterfullerene. Vaporization of graphite rods in a helium atmosphere afforded a soot from which C_{60} could be extracted and isolated in bulk amounts.

The carbon atoms in the C_{60} molecule are sp^2 hybridized and each one is bound to three others. They occupy the vertices of a truncated icosahedron, forming a closed structure with 32 faces (20 hexagons and 12 pentagons). Each pentagon is surrounded by hexagons, and no two pentagons share a carbon-carbon bond. All sixty carbon atoms in the buckminsterfullerene molecule are equivalent. This was demonstrated by its ^{13}C-NMR spectra, which shows one single peak in the chemical range typical of sp^2-hybridized carbons (143 ppm).

When it was first discovered, it was believed that C_{60} was some sort of super-aromatic molecule. Single bonds alternate with double bonds and 12,500 resonance forms can be written! However, it was later shown by crystallographic studies that the double and single bonds are rather localized. There are no double bonds on the sides of the pentagons; double bonds are confined only to the sides shared by two hexagons. This is reflected by two different carbon-carbon bond lengths. The bond length between two hexagonal rings is 1.38 Å while the bond length between a hexagon and a pentagon is greater, 1.45 Å. Far from being a superaromatic, nonreactive molecule, C_{60} reacts readily in solution as an electron-deficient polyene. It undergoes cycloadditions, nucleophilic additions, radical additions, hydrogenation and halogenations, just to mention a few transformations.

The excitement created by the discovery of the "roundest of all possible round molecules," as Smalley called the C_{60} molecule, permeated almost all areas of chemistry and physics. Applications to use these remarkable molecules as cages to trap atoms and ions, as molecular containers, as drug-delivery agents, and even as superconductors were rapidly sought. While many applications have been realized, others still remain unfulfilled. In 1991 buckminsterfullerene was named the Molecule of the Year by the *Science* magazine. In the editorial article, Daniel E. Koshland, Jr. wrote: "Part of the exhilaration of the fullerenes is the shock that an old reliable friend, the carbon atom, has for all these years been hiding a secret life-style. We are all familiar with the charming versatility of carbon, the backbone of organic chemistry, and its infinite variation in aromatic and aliphatic chemistry, but when you got it naked, we believed it existed in two well-known forms, diamond and graphite. The finding that it could exist in a shockingly new structure unleashes tantalizing new experimental and theoretical ideas." Kroto, Smalley, and Curl were awarded the 1996 Nobel Prize in Chemistry.

Buckminsterfullerene is not the only round molecule made exclusively of carbon atoms. Other closed molecules with a variable number of carbon atoms have been synthesized and characterized. C_{70} can be isolated along with C_{60} in the soot resulting from the vaporization of graphite (Fig. 9.7). Similar to C_{60}, C_{70} has pentagons surrounded by hexagons; it is an elongated molecule that resembles a football. Other molecules isolated from the same soot include C_{76}, C_{84}, C_{90} and C_{94}. This new family of compounds are called **fullerenes**.

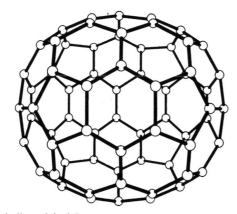

Figure 9.7   Stick-and-ball model of C_{70}.

E9.2 ISOLATION OF FULLERENES

C_{60} and C_{70} can be isolated from fullerene soot by extraction with toluene. Fullerenes are surprisingly soluble in aromatic hydrocarbon solvents such as toluene, benzene, and *o*-dichlorobenzene, and only slightly soluble in alkanes. Solubility values for selected solvents are shown in Table 9.1.

Solutions of C_{60} in toluene have a beautiful magenta color. When the solvent is evaporated and the solid deposits as a thin film it takes on a mustard-yellow color. In contrast, solutions of C_{70} in the same solvent are red-orange. These two fullerenes can be separated by column chromatography on neutral alumina by using mixtures of hexane and toluene as elution solvents. C_{60} has weaker interactions

Table 9.1 Solubility (mg/mL) of C_{60} and C_{70} at 30°C in Selected Solvents (Refs. 2 and 3)

Solvent	C_{60}	C_{70}
acetone	0.001	0.019
n-hexane	0.040	0.013
methylene chloride	0.254	0.080
toluene	2.75	1.40
carbon disulfide	5.16	9.87
o-dichlorobenzene	24.6[a]	36.2

[a] at 25°C.

Table 9.2 Molar Absorptivities (L mol⁻¹ cm⁻¹) for C_{60} and C_{70} at Selected Wavelengths (Hexanes) (Refs. 7, 8, 17)

Wavelength (nm)	C_{60}	C_{70}
470	250	14,500
540	710	6,050

with the stationary phase and elutes first. This can be visualized by a magenta band followed by a red-orange one. C_{60} can be obtained reasonably pure by this method, with a contamination of C_{70} of less than 2%. On the other hand, this method does not afford pure samples of C_{70}, which contain variable amounts of C_{60}.

The fractions eluting from the column can be analyzed by UV-visible spectroscopy to determine their purity. C_{60} and C_{70} have sufficiently different absorptions in the visible portion of the spectrum (400–700 nm) to allow their differentiation. The UV-visible spectra of C_{60} and C_{70} are shown in Figure 9.8. Their molar absorptivities at selected wavelengths are gathered in Table 9.2.

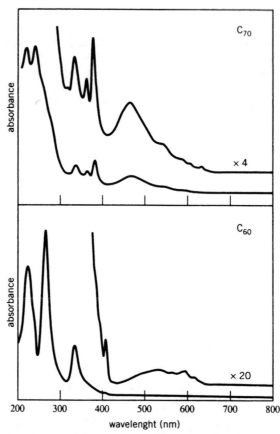

Figure 9.8 UV-visible spectra of C_{70} and C_{60} in hexanes (Ref. 7).

E9.3 A CHEMICAL TEST FOR FULLERENES

Fullerenes behave like electron-deficient alkenes and react easily with nucleophiles, especially amines. The mechanism seems to involve the transient formation of radicals that display a green color. The green color finally disappears and a brown product forms. A variable number of amine molecules, normally between 1 and 12, are added to the skeleton of the fullerene. Additions on C_{70} lead directly to the observation of a brown color.

E9.4 OVERVIEW OF THE EXPERIMENT

In this experiment you will extract fullerenes from fullerene soot by using toluene. The soot contains more than 7% fullerenes, of which buckminsterfullerene is the main component; C$_{70}$ is present in smaller amounts. The extraction of the fullerenes will be performed by stirring with the solvent at room temperature. Extraction at higher temperatures is not recommended because the solubility of fullerenes decreases as the temperature increases in the range 10–50°C.

The mixture of fullerenes will be separated on a microcolumn by using neutral alumina as stationary phase and hexanes-toluene as elution solvent. Because the fullerenes have very limited solubility in hexanes (Table 9.1), the mixture must be loaded into the column as a pellet (see section 9.2). To make the pellet you will mix the fullerene toluene extract with a small amount of alumina and evaporate the solvent in a rota-vap. The powder obtained after evaporation (the pellet) will be loaded on top of the column, the solvent will be added, and the column eluted as usual. For a successful separation, the alumina must be activated at 100°C for at least 12 hours before use.

You will start the separation by using 5% toluene in hexanes as the mobile phase and then you will increase the polarity by using 20% toluene in hexanes. If the separation works you will see a light magenta band coming out of the column, followed by a red-orange band. You will collect several fractions and analyze them by UV-visible spectroscopy (Unit 32). You will also obtain the UV-visible spectrum of the original toluene extract. Using the extinction coefficients listed in Table 9.2, you will calculate the concentration of C$_{60}$ and C$_{70}$ in the fractions, and assess the success of the separation.

You will finally perform a simple chemical test with ethanolamine. Both C$_{60}$ and C$_{70}$ undergo a nucleophilic addition with ethanolamine. The reaction with C$_{60}$ gives an aqua color while C$_{70}$ produces a brown color.

PROCEDURE

Prelab for Separation of C$_{60}$ & C$_{70}$

1. In your lab notebook make a flow chart that diagrams all of the steps you will be following in the course of the chromatographic separation. Carefully note the solutions whose UV-visible absorbances are to be measured (including the sample of the extract that you diluted and stored when you extracted fullerene soot the week before) and how their reaction with ethanolamine will be examined afterwards.

2. Read the discussion of UV-visible absorption spectroscopy on pages **E20-E22**.

"Fullerene soot" is estimated to contain a total of about 7% C$_{60}$ and C$_{70}$ combined. Suppose that all of the C$_{60}$ and C$_{70}$ dissolves in the 4 mL of toluene you used in the extraction procedure. From the molar absorptivities listed in Table 9.2, predict the

> **Safety First**
>
> - Toxicological studies on C$_{60}$ and C$_{70}$ are incomplete. Treat them with caution. Avoid spattering the solid fullerene soot.
> - Toluene and hexanes are flammable solvents.

absorbances at 470 and 540 nm you should observe for the 0.25 mL of the extract that you diluted to 3 mL if: (*a*) The extract contains 100% C$_{60}$; (*b*) The extract contains 100% C$_{70}$; (*c*) The extract contains equal weights of C$_{60}$ & C$_{70}$; and (*d*) The extract contains an 80:20 (by weight) mixture of C$_{60}$ & C$_{70}$.

In-lab and Final Writeup

1. Using Equations 3 and 4 and the absorbance values at 470 and at 540 nm (corrected for light scattering), calculate the molar concentration of C$_{60}$ and C$_{70}$ in each chromatographic fraction and in the original extract.

2. Using the molecular weights of the fullerenes and the total volume of the original extract (4 mL), calculate the total mass of C$_{60}$ & of C$_{70}$ (in milligrams) present in the original extract. How does this compare with Prelab #2 above?

3. From your answer to In-lab #1 above calculate the masses of C$_{60}$ and C$_{70}$ in each of the chromatographic fractions you collected.

4. Calculate the purity of C$_{60}$ in the first magenta fraction.

5. From your answer to In-lab #3 above calculate the total mass of C$_{60}$ obtained in all of your chromatographic fractions combined.

6. From your answer to In-lab #3 above calculate the total mass of C$_{70}$ obtained in all of your chromatographic fractions combined.

7. Make a table listing the fraction number, the volume of each fraction, its color, the recovered masses of C$_{60}$ and C$_{70}$ in that fraction; and the color change seen when the solution was treated with ethanolamine.

Procedure for Separation of C$_{60}$ & C$_{70}$

Packing and Running the Column Using a clamp and a notched stopper, secure a small Pasteur pipet in the vertical position. Insert the tip of the column into a length of Tygon tubing (2 inches long) and position a screw clamp on the tubing (see Fig. 9.5). The clamp will control the flow of liquid. Place a small cotton plug at the end of the column and add a thin layer of sand no more than 2 mm thick. Add 2 mL of 5% toluene in hexanes to the column and open the screw clamp to drain most of the liquid, leaving some above the sand. This operation will get rid of any air bubbles in the cotton. Fill the column completely with solvent.

Using several layers of paper towel to protect your hands, break off the tip of a small Pasteur pipet. To facilitate this operation, *first etch the Pasteur pipet with a file*. Carefully dispose of the broken glass in the broken-glass container. Mix the alumina slurry in the beaker and draw some of it with the wide-mouth Pasteur pipet. Position this pipet on top of the column and watch the alumina settle down while the liquid ascends (Fig. 9.5). You do not need to squeeze the rubber bulb, since the alumina goes down just by gravity. Remove the wide-mouth pipet and add more solvent to refill the column to the rim. Reposition on top of the column the wide-mouth Pasteur pipet with more slurry. Let the alumina flow down. Repeat this operation until the alumina level is about one inch from the top of the column. This method of packing the column avoids the formation of air bubbles inside the column and results in better separations. For this method to work, the solvent should fill the column to the rim before you position the wide-mouth pipet on top. Gently tap the sides of the column with a microspatula. This will compact the alumina inside the column. Add a thin layer of sand on top of the column.

Before you load the column with the sample make sure that you have everything ready. Number eight screw-cap vials Fraction 1 to 8. Get at least 15 mL of 5% toluene in hexanes in an Erlenmeyer flask and 15 mL of 20% toluene in hexanes in another flask. Have these two flasks perfectly labeled and covered.

Open the screw clamp and drain the solvent. Leave a solvent head of about 3–4 mm above the sand and close the clamp. Make a small funnel with a piece of weighing paper and use it to load the alumina pellet on top of the column. Once the pellet is loaded, add solvent to completely wet the pellet and start collecting fractions. Keep adding solvent 0.5 mL at a time, making sure that the column never runs dry and there is always solvent on top of the pellet; keep track of the volume of solvent added. Fraction 1 should be colorless. Once the magenta band of C$_{60}$ starts coming out of the column, change the vial and start collecting Fraction 2. Keep collecting the magenta fraction until about 2.5–3 mL have eluted. Then change to Fraction 3. Collect fractions of about 3 mL each until the red-orange band of C$_{70}$ starts coming out of the column. When the red-orange band is about to come out of the column, change the vial to the next fraction, and start adding 20% toluene in hexanes on top of the column in 0.5 mL portions. Collect fractions of about 3 mL each until most of the fullerenes have eluted from the column as indicated by a pale red-orange color. With a 10-mL graduated pipet or cylinder, measure the volume of the magenta fraction.

Analysis of Fullerenes

Obtain the UV-visible spectrum of the dilute original extract in the range 700–400 nm; use toluene as a blank. Measure the absorbance values at 470, 540, and 700 nm and calculate the concentrations of C$_{60}$ and C$_{70}$ as indicated below. Some light scattering due to the presence of big particles in solution may occur. Light scattering increases the absorbance values but the effect can be corrected in part by subtracting the absorbance value at 700 nm (where absorption is almost exclusively due to light scattering) from the values at 470 and 540 nm. This correction is important in the analysis of the original extract, but it is negligible in the case of the column fractions and will be omitted.

Analyze the fraction with the deepest magenta color by UV-visible spectroscopy in the range 400–700 nm. Measure the absorbance at 470, 540, and 700 nm. Also analyze the fraction with the deepest red-orange color, measuring the absorbance at the same wavelengths. If time permits, also analyze some of the intermediate fractions.

Use the following system of two equations with two unknowns (see section 32.4) to calculate the concentration of C$_{60}$ and C$_{70}$ in each sample. Use the absorbance values (A), corrected for light scattering if necessary, and the molar absorptivity values (ε) at the specified wavelengths (Table 9.2):

$$A^{470} = \varepsilon_{C_{70}}^{470} \times [C_{70}] \times \ell + \varepsilon_{C_{60}}^{470} \times [C_{60}] \times \ell \tag{1}$$

$$A^{540} = \varepsilon_{C_{70}}^{540} \times [C_{70}] \times \ell + \varepsilon_{C_{60}}^{540} \times [C_{60}] \times \ell \tag{2}$$

In Equations 1 and 2, ℓ is the length of the cuvette (1 cm).

Substituting the molar absorptivities with the values given in Table 9.2 and solving for [C$_{60}$] and [C$_{70}$], we obtain the following equations:

$$[C_{60}] = \frac{A^{470} \times 6050 - A^{540} \times 14500}{(6050 \times 250 - 14500 \times 710)} \tag{3}$$

$$[C_{70}] = \frac{A^{540} - 710 \times [C_{60}]}{6050} \tag{4}$$

In Equations 1–4, A^{470} and A^{540} are the absorbances at 470 and 540 nm (in the case of the original extract these values are corrected for light scattering by subtracting the absorbance at 700 nm). [C$_{60}$] and [C$_{70}$] indicate molar concentrations.

Chemical Test Place about 0.5 mL of the fractions analyzed by UV in small test tubes. Add two drops of ethanolamine to each tube, shake, and observe the results. Ethanolamine does not dissolve in the fraction's solvent and any color change will be observed at the interface.

Cleaning Up

- Dispose of the Pasteur pipets in the container labeled "Fullerenes–Solid Waste."
- Dispose of the unused alumina slurry in the container labeled "Recycled Alumina."
- Dispose of the fullerene soot with filter paper in the container labeled "Fullerenes–solid waste."
- Dispose of the liquid fractions in the container labeled "Fullerenes–Liquid Waste."
- Dispose of the ethanolamine test solutions in the container labeled "Fullerenes–Liquid Waste."
- At the end of the section, the instructor will empty the rota-vap traps into the container "Fullerenes–liquid Waste."

Before coming to lab you must work the four prelab problems. While you are doing the experiment measure the refractive index of your starting mixture and of fractions 1 and 3 from your first distillation. You will then *redistill* fraction 1. When you *redistill* fraction 1 you will collect a forerun (1 or 2 drops) and then two more substantial fractions. Measure the refractive index of both fractions from this *redistillation*. Measure the specific rotation of pure alpha-pinene, of your starting mixture, and of fraction 3 from your first distillation,. Report how the refractive index and specific rotation change. Calculate the volume fraction of heptane and alpha-pinene in each of the four distilled liquids for which you measured refractive indices. Calculate the weight fraction of alpha-pinene in the starting mixture and in the distillation fraction for which you measured specific rotation. The flow chart below summarizes what you have to do.

Purpose and Prior Reading

(1) To effect the separation of a binary liquid mixture composed of liquids having boiling points that are relatively far apart (greater than 30°C). To develop the skill to operate a short path distillation apparatus so that purifications required in later experiments can be successfully carried out (pp 61-65).

(2) To make use of two techniques for evaluating the purity of a liquid when compared with an authentic pure sample: (a) Refractive index (pp 48-50); and
(b) Specific rotation of polarized light (for molecules that are not identical to their mirror images - pp 111-115)

DISCUSSION

Heptane and alpha-pinene are liquid hydrocarbons that have boiling points approximately 50°C apart. Typical liquid-vapor composition curves are shown in Figure 5.4-5.6. If you understand these curves, it should be apparent that two successive distillations (a "2-plate" distillation) ought to yield nearly pure components. The procedure to be outlined consists of two distillations and a set of measurements. The first distillation (first plate) separates the liquid mixture into three separate fractions. The *redistillation* further purifies the first fraction (second plate). Exercising careful technique during the first distillation should provide a fraction rich in the lower boiling component, a middle fraction, and a fraction rich in the higher boiling component. Then careful *redistillation* of the top fraction can be expected to give reasonably pure heptane. The measurements assay the purity of fractions 1 and 3 from the first distillation and of the fractions from the *redistillation* of fraction 1. The flow chart below summarizes the sequence of distillations and measurements.

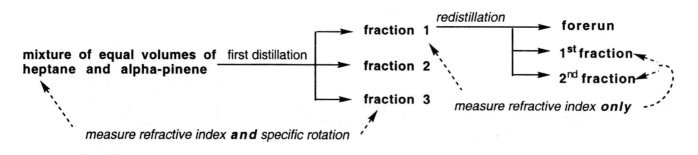

COMPONENTS

$CH_3CH_2CH_2CH_2CH_2CH_2CH_3$

Heptane

density = 0.684 g/mL

$n_D^{20} = 1.3870$

2 views of alpha-pinene

density = 0.857 g/mL

$n_D^{20} = 1.4660$

Equipment

Please sign out a short-path distillation apparatus from the stockroom. At the end of the lab period you must sign this back in. *Breakage of this item is not covered by lab fees.* From your drawer you will need the 10 mL round-bottom flask, the two conical vials, the thermometer adapter, and the thermometer. In the laboratory you will find lengths of gum rubber condenser hose. At your bench you have a hotplate equipped with a heating block (p 20), a digital thermometer, and a 3-finger clamp attached to a vertical bar. You will also require strips of paper towel and aluminum foil to insulate the distillation apparatus.

Reagents

You will need 2-3 boiling stones for each distillation. To make your starting mixture you will mix 2 mL of heptane and 2 mL of alpha-pinene in the round-bottom flask. But first put together the entire assembly (called a *still*) empty so your TA can check it out.

Procedure for the First Distillation

Set up the still without any contents, as shown below to the left. Attach the short-path distillation apparatus to the empty 10 mL round-bottom flask (the *still pot*) using a screw cap. Then connect the thermometer adapter and insert the thermometer as deeply as possible into the *still head* without its touching the wall. Attach the 5 mL conical vial to the receiving end of the short path distillation apparatus. Using the 3-finger clamp fit this assembly snugly into the hemispherical depression in the heating block (clamp the fingers around the short-path distillation apparatus). Then connect the lengths of condenser hose to the inlet and outlet of the water jacket. Once your TA has examined this setup and given the OK, raise the entire still assembly above the heating block, detach the still pot, and load it. Using polyethylene pipettes, measure two 1 mL portions of heptane and two 1 mL portions of alpha-pinene into the still pot. Swirl to mix and then withdraw 0.5 mL into an Eppendorff tube for refractive index and optical rotation measurements. Then add 2-3 boiling stones, reattach the still pot to the assembly, and lower it back into the heating block.

Tear off a strip of paper towel roughly 1 cm wide and wrap it around the lower part of the distillation apparatus up to the condenser sidearm. Then tear off a 1 cm wide strip of aluminum foil and wrap it around the outside of the paper towel. Connect the inlet condenser hose to the water tap and make sure the outlet flows into the sink. Turn on the water slowly so that the water jacket fills up and the outlet flow is a slow steady stream (little faster than a drip). Again, have your TA look at the assembly to make sure it is all right.

After the TA has OK'd the assembled still this second time, (as shown below to the right) turn on the hotplate to a setting of 6. As the temperature rises write in your lab notebook the digital thermometer reading of the heating block when the mixture starts to boil. You will see refluxing vapors rise into the wrapped part on the distillation apparatus, and, a few minutes later, the thermometer temperature in the still head will start to climb. **Make sure that the thermometer bulb is entirely immersed in the refluxing vapors before liquid passes out of the condenser.** In your notebook record the heating block temperature

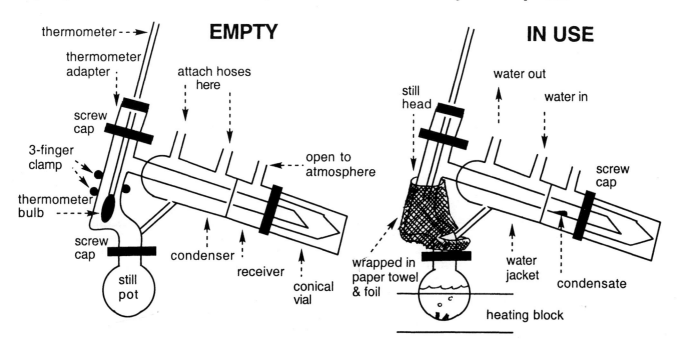

and the thermometer temperature in the still head when the first drop falls into your collection vial. In a short time the head temperature should rise above 90° (if it does not, this means that your thermometer is not properly immersed in vapors in the still head).

Continue the distillation until the head temperature climbs above 110°. If it falls below 90°, raise the setting on your hotplate to 7. When the head temperature exceeds 110° raise the setting of your hotplate to 7, note the block and head temperatures, quickly remove the collection vial, and hold a glass vial to the end of the condenser and collect drops (no more than 0.5 mL) until the head temperature rises above 140°. Then connect the 3 mL conical vial to the receiving end of the condenser, record the block and head temperatures, and continue the distillation until there is so little liquid left in the pot that the boiling stones clearly protrude well above the top of the boiling liquid. Record the block and head temperatures at this point, shut off the heating, and let the hotplate and heating block cool.

Measurements

It will take about 30-40 minutes for your heating block to cool below 50°. In this interval you should perform as many measurements as you can. To measure the optical rotation, first fill a polarimeter cell with ethanol and take a blank reading. The polarimeter used in Chem 112A does not look exactly like the instrument shown in Fig. 5.62 (left-hand column of p. 114). Instead, the view through the eyepiece looks like

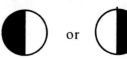

To measure optical rotation you rotate the analyzer to find the darkest disk between these two "half moons". With just ethanol in the cell, your reading on the polarimeter should be close to zero. Write down your reading for the blank. Then take the polarimeter cell out of the instrument, open it, remove about 0.5 mL of the ethanol, add 0.25 mL of pure alpha-pinene, and refill the cell to the top with ethanol. Close the cell and take another reading. Then discard the contents of the cell, refill with ethanol, and take another blank reading. Once more, remove about 0.5 mL of ethanol, add 0.25 mL of your starting mixture, refill the cell to the top with ethanol, and take another reading. Repeat this blank/reading sequence with fraction 3 from your first distillation.

Record the refractive indices of pure heptane and pure alpha-pinene, as well as of your starting mixture and fractions 1 & 3 from your first distillation. When you have completed your redistillation measure the refractive indices of the first and second collected fractions.

Redistillation

When the heating block temperature has dropped to below 50° raise the entire still assembly and carefully remove the still pot. Discard the contents and wipe out the flask with a paper towel. Then remove the thermometer adapter and wipe off the thermometer. Finally wipe out the inside of the still head and condenser with a twisted strip of paper towel. Then transfer your collected fraction 3 to a glass vial and wipe out the 3 mL conical vial so that it is clean. Transfer your collected fraction 1 to the still pot and wipe out the 5 mL conical vial. Then set up the still and redistill your heptane at a heater setting of 5. Do not connect the conical vial until after you have collected 1 or 2 drops of the forerun in an an Eppendorff tube (while the temperature is still rising rapidly). Record the block and head temperatures for the beginning and end of collection of two fractions of heptane in the conical vials. You should start collecting the second fraction once the head temperature has stabilized (it should rise slowly during your collection of the second fraction). If the head temperature starts to fall while a substantial amount of boiling liquid remains in the still pot, turn up the heating temperature to a setting of 6.

Record the boiling point ranges (head temperature at the start and finish of collecting a fraction) of all of the fractions.

Cleanup and lab report

When the redistillation is over, let the heating block cool to <50°. Then raise the still and let it cool to the touch. Transfer the redistilled heptane to glass vials. Diassemble the still and wipe out the glassware with paper towels. Return the short path distillation apparatus to the stockroom (where it will be inspected before you are allowed to sign it back in).

Your lab writeup should report your experimental data (boiling point ranges, optical rotations, refractive indices) and your calculations of the volume fractions of heptane and alpha-pinene in fractions 1 & 3 from your first distillation as well as the two collected fractions from your redistillation. Note that you have two ways (refractive index & optical rotation) to calculate this for Fraction 3. Compare the results of those two methods.

(1) The refractive index (n, also known as the index of refraction) varies with the wavelength of light. That's how a prism refracts white light into individual colors. When atoms are excited, they emit specific colors of light (called spectroscopic lines). The refractive index of organic liquids is usually recorded at the "sodium D line", a very closely spaced pair of spectroscopic lines at 589 nm. For this reason, refractive indices are often reported as n_D. This is the yellow-orange color you see in the flame of a gas stove when water boils over and spills onto the burner (it is also the wavelength emitted from many types of street lamp). Visible light at 589 nm has been selected as the standard wavelength for two reasons. First, the sodium D line is easy to produce, either by putting a piece of salt into a gas flame or by means of a sodium vapor lamp. Secondly, liquids that are discolored by slight impurities are usually yellowish or brown, and they pass 589 nm light without absorbing very much of it.

The refractive index also depends on temperature, and n_D values in the textbook are usually values for room temperature (20°C). Therefore they are more properly written as n_D^{20} .

Most organic liquids expand as temperature goes up and contract as temperature goes down.

Is the density at 25°C greater or smaller than at 20°C?

Do you think the value of n_D^{25} for a liquid should be greater or smaller than its value of n_D^{20} ?

(2) The value of n_D^{20} for a mixture can be **approximated** as the weighted average of the refractive indices of the individual components. For a heptane/alpha-pinene mixture
$$n_D^{20} \text{(mixture)} = V_{heptane}\, n_D^{20} \text{(heptane)} + V_{pinene}\, n_D^{20} \text{(pinene)},$$
where V's stand for volume fractions (for instance, 2 mL heptane mixed with 2 mL alpha-pinene gives $V = 0.5$ for each) Predict n_D^{20} for a mixture of 2 mL heptane and 2 mL alpha-pinene in this way·

(3) Optical rotation (α) is also usually measured at the sodium D line. The α_D of a solution is proportional to the number of grams of solute per mL of solution. 2 mL of heptane plus 2 mL of alpha pinene give 4 mL of solution. How many grams per mL are in that mixture? The *specific rotation* of a compound is the rotation corresponds to the value of α_D for a concentration of 1 gram per mL (which turns out to be greater than the density of most organic liquids). Suppose you diluted 0.25 mL of the 50:50 heptane/alpha-pinene mixture to 5 mL with solvent and measured the optical rotation. How many grams per mL in the solution? By what factor would you have to multiply the value of α_D to get the specific rotation of alpha-pinene?

(4) Make a molecular model of alpha-pinene. You will have to use some of the flexible (silvery) bent units to make the 4-member ring. Make a molecular model of the mirror image of pinene. Is alpha-pinene superimposable on its mirror image? Molecules that are **not** superimposable on their mirror images rotate the plane of polarized light (optical rotation) if there is more of one mirror image than another in a given sample.

Make a model of heptane, where the chain is fully extended. Make a model of the mirror image of heptane. Are these two mirror images superimposable? Should a sample of pure heptane exhibit optical rotation? Make models of ethanol and its mirror image? Should a sample of pure ethanol exhibit optical rotation?

Fractional Semimicroscale Distillation: Separation of Hexane and Toluene

Before coming to lab you must work the four prelab problems. While you are doing the experiment measure the refractive index of your starting mixture, of your first fraction 1 and of your fraction 3. When you redistill fraction 1 measure the refractive index of fraction 1 from this second distillation. Report how the refractive index changes and calculate the mole fraction of hexane and toluene in each of the 4 liquid samples for which you measured refractive indices. In the Conclusions section of your write-up please discuss how the measured mole fractions compare with what you predicted based on the curves in Figure 5.11.

Experiment [3B] Fractional Semimicroscale Distillation: Separation of Hexane and Toluene

Purpose
To effect the separation of a binary liquid mixture composed of liquids having boiling points that are relatively far apart, greater than 30 °C. To develop the skills to operate a semimicrodistillation apparatus so that purifications required in later experiments can be successfully carried out.

Prior Reading
Technique 2: Distillation (see pp. 61–72).
              Distillation Theory (see pp. 61–65).
              Simple Distillation at the Semimicroscale Level (see pp. 65–68).
              Fractional Semimicroscale Distillation (see pp. 68–71).
Chapter 4: Determination of Physical Properties
              Ultramicro-Boiling Point (see pp. 44–47).
              Refractive Index (see pp. 48–50).

DISCUSSION

Hexane and toluene are liquid hydrocarbons that have boiling points approximately 40 °C apart. The liquid–vapor composition curve in Figure 5.11 represents this system; therefore, it is apparent that a two-plate distillation should yield nearly pure components. The procedure to be outlined consists of two parts. The first deals with the initial distillation (first plate), which separates the liquid mixture into three separate fractions. The second deals with *redistillation* of the first and third fractions (second plate). Exercising careful technique during the first distillation should provide a fraction rich in the lower boiling component, a middle fraction, and a fraction rich in the higher boiling component. Then careful *redistillation* of these fractions can be expected to complete the separation of the two components and to produce fractions of relatively pure hexane and toluene. The Hickman still employed in the microscale laboratory is a simple, short-path column, and, therefore, one would not expect complete separation of the hexane and toluene in one cycle.

COMPONENTS

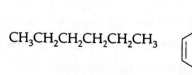

CH₃CH₂CH₂CH₂CH₂CH₃

Hexane   Toluene

Estimated time for the experiment: 2.0 hours.

EXPERIMENTAL PROCEDURE

Physical Properties of Components

Compound	MW	Amount	bp(°C)	d	n_D
Hexane	86.18	1.0 mL	69	0.66	1.3751
Toluene	92.15	1.0 mL	111	0.87	1.4961

Reagents and Equipment

In a clean, dry, stoppered 5-mL conical vial are placed 1.0 mL of hexane and 1.0 mL of toluene by using an automatic delivery pipet.

Place the vial in a small beaker to prevent tipping. A boiling stone is added, the Hickman still is assembled with the thermometer positioned directly down the center of the column (see previous discussion), and the system is mounted in a sand bath (see Fig. 6.3).

Experimental Conditions

The temperature of the sand bath is raised to 80–90 °C, at a maximum rate of 5 °C/min (> 70 °C, at 3 °C/min), using a hot plate.

CAUTION: Do not let the temperature of the still rise too rapidly.

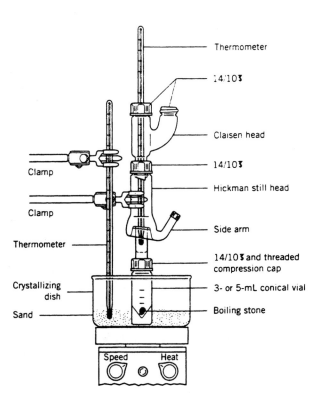

FIGURE 6.3 Hickman still with Claisen head adapter.

Once gentle boiling begins, the heating rate should be lowered to a maximum of 2 °C/min. It is **absolutely crucial** that the distillation rate be kept below 100 μL/3 min to achieve the necessary fraction enrichment that will permit good separation during the second stage of the experiment. The distillate is collected in *three fractions* over the temperature ranges (**1**) 65–85 °C (bath temperature ~95–110 °C); (**2**) 85–105 °C (bath temperature ~140 °C); and (**3**) 105–110 °C (bath temperature ~170 °C) in amounts of approximately 800, 400, and 800 μL, respectively. Remove each fraction from the still with a bent-tip Pasteur pipet. Store the liquid condensate (fractions) in clean, dry, 1-dram, screw-cap vials. *Remember to number the vials in order and use an aluminum foil cap liner.*

Characterization of Crude Fractions

For each of the three fractions, record the refractive index. Fraction 1 has been enriched in one of the two components. Which one? Does the refractive index agree with that found in the literature? Fraction 3 has been enriched in the other component. Does the refractive index of that fraction support your first conclusion? If partial enrichment has been achieved, proceed to the second phase of the distillation.

Redistillation of Fraction 1

Redistill fraction 1 in a clean Hickman still with a thermometer arranged as before (Fig. 6.3), using a 3-mL conical vial and the procedure just outlined. Collect an initial fraction over the boiling range 68–71 °C (~100–200 μL). Remove it from the collar, using the Pasteur pipet, and place it in a 1-dram screw-cap vial.

Characterization of Fraction 1

Determine the ultramicro-boiling point and the refractive index of this lower boiling fraction. Compare the experimental values obtained with those of pure hexane reported in the literature.

Redistillation of Fraction 3

Fraction 3 is placed in a clean Hickman still, using a thermometer and a 3-mL conical vial (Fig. 6.3), and redistilled using the procedure outlined. Collect an initial fraction over the boiling range 95–108 °C (~500 μL), and transfer this fraction by Pasteur pipet to a screw-cap vial. Collect a final fraction at 108–110 °C (~250 μL), and transfer the material to a second vial. *This second fraction is the highest boiling fraction to be collected in the three distillations and should be the richest in the high-boiling component.*

Characterization of Fraction 3

Determine the refractive index and boiling point of the second fraction, and compare your results with those found in the literature for toluene. *Determine the refractive index and boiling point of pure toluene for comparison purposes.*

SEPARATION OF ACID, BASE, AND NEUTRAL COMPOUNDS: SOLVENT EXTRACTION AND IDENTIFICATION OF COMPOUNDS BY MELTING POINT (MP)

This lab is based on Experiment 4C in Mayo, Pike, and Trumper. It is designed to illustrate three basic principles:

(1) Extraction from one solvent into another using a separatory funnel;

(2) Precipitation of a solute from water by changing pH;

(3) Identification of a compound by its melting point.

Please read the section on use of a separatory funnel on pp 82-83 of the lab text.

You will be given a sample of a mixture of 3 compounds and will weigh out a small amount of the mixture (roughly 0.15 g; write the weight in your notebook). Then use chemical methods to separate the basic and acidic components from the neutral component, as described below. Since you will not know the identity of any of the components ahead of time (you are supposed to figure them out) you need to follow the procedure in the textbook carefully. The next 2 pages summarize this procedure.

The basic component will be either ethyl 4-aminobenzoate or 4-chloroaniline:

ethyl 4-aminobenzoate (or ethyl *p*-aminobenzoate)   4-chloroaniline (or *p*-chloroaniline)

The acidic component will be benzoic acid, 2-chlorobenzoic acid, or o-toluic acid:

benzoic acid   2-chlorobenzoic acid (*o*-chlorobenzoic acid)   *o*-toluic acid (2-methylbenzoic acid)

The neutral component will be acetophenone, benzil, benzoin, or biphenyl:

acetophenone   benzil   benzoin   biphenyl

Prelab: Look up the literature values of the melting point (MP [lit]) for all of these compounds. You may consult the Handbook of Chemistry and Physics or the Aldrich Catalogue (or the catalogue of any one of several other chemical suppliers). List these melting points in your lab notebook.

Prepare a flow chart summarizing the sequence of steps you will be performing in this experiment.

PROCEDURE

Weigh approximately 0.15 g of the unknown mixture and add it to a 30 mL separatory funnel. Then add 4 mL of ether [HOOD] and dissolve the solid. More than 4 mL of ether may be required to dissolve all the starting mixture. If so, add extra ether slowly (no more than 1 mL at a time), and make sure that the separatory funnel containing the ether layer stays closed all the time (except when you are adding or removing something). Note the total volume of ether required to dissolve the solid. Using a felt tip marker, mark the volume of solution on the outside of the separatory funnel.

Separation of the Basic Component

Using a plastic pipette, add 2 mL of chilled 3M HCl dropwise to the solution in the separatory funnel. Stopper and thoroughly mix the two-phase system with careful, repeated venting. *Make sure the stopper is greased and snugly inserted.* Once the layers have separated, remove the stopper, open the stopcock, and carefully drain off the bottom (aqueous) layer into a labeled 10 mL flask. (If the volume of ether has diminished in the course of shaking or venting, add more ether dropwise to maintain the original volume of the organic layer). Repeat this step with an additional 2 mL of 3M HCl. Transfer the aqueous layer to the same flask as before. Stopper the separatory funnel and set it onto a ring in the hood.

Isolation of the Basic Component

To the aqueous layer from above add 6M NaOH dropwise with swirling until the solution is distinctly alkaline to litmus paper. Cool the flask in ice for 10 min. Collect the solid precipitate that forms using a Hirsch funnel set-up with a vacuum flask. Wash the precipitate with two 1 mL portions of distilled water. Make sure the solid is dry before weighing and obtaining its melting point (MP).

Extraction of the Acidic Component

Add 2 mL of chilled 3M NaOH to the ether solution in the separatory funnel. Stopper and thoroughly mix the two-phase system with careful repeated venting. Once the layers have separated, drain off the bottom (aqueous) layer into a labeled 10 mL flask. Repeat this step with an additional 2 mL of 3M NaOH. Transfer the aqueous layer to the same flask as before and set aside.

Separation of the Neutral Component

Wash (extract) the remaining ether solution contained in the separatory funnel with two 1-mL portions of water, separating the lower aqueous layer each time. Now add about 300 mg of anhydrous sodium sulfate (Na_2SO_4) to the ether solution in the separatory funnel (to remove water from the ether layer). Add a little more Na_2SO_4 if clumping is observed. Stopper the separatory funnel, swirl the contents briefly, and set the separatory funnel onto a ring in the hood to allow the drying agent to work.

Isolation of the Acidic Component

Add 6M HCl dropwise to the aqueous alkaline solution (which you set aside above) until the solution becomes distinctly acidic to litmus paper. Cool the flask in ice for 10 min. Collect the solid precipitate that forms using a Hirsch funnel set-up with a vacuum flask. Wash the precipitate with two 1 mL portions of cold distilled water. Make sure the solid is dry before weighing and obtaining its MP.

Isolation of the Neutral Component

Transfer the dried ether solution out of the top of the separatory funnel into a tared 10 mL round bottom flask containing a boiling stone using a plastic pipette. Be careful not to transfer any of the Na_2SO_4 into the flask. Rinse the Na_2SO_4 drying agent (all of which should remain in the separatory funnel) with an additional 1 mL of ether, remove it with a plastic pipette, and add this liquid to the tared flask. Concentrate the ether solution on a rotatory evaporator. Obtain the weight of the residue and determine its melting point range.

Taking the Melting Point

Once you have obtained the melting point of each of the separated components of your mixture, set each of them in your lab drawer and let them stand for one week. The next lab period (2nd lab) record the weight again (hopefully it will not all have evaporated away!) and retake the melting point while you are doing the next experiment. Then hand in your lab report with the two sets of melting points and your identification of each of the components by the end of the 2nd lab, as shown for the a hypothetical mixture:

Example of Results

	Recovery		Exptl. Melting Point		Identification	MP[lit]
Component	1st Lab	2nd Lab	1st Lab	2nd Lab		
Acid	45 mg	41 mg	120–122°	121–122°	benzoic acid	122°
Base	29 mg	30 mg	85–89°	85–89°	ethyl-4-aminobenzoate	89°
Neutral	34 mg	34 mg	oil	84–85°	9-fluorenone	84°

NOTES

Melting points are characteristic of many solids. Usually the MP goes down if impurities are present. Your identification will be based on chemical classification (acid, base, or neutral) and the MP you measure. A sample that remains as an oil in the 1st lab may crystallize upon standing for a week.

WRITE-UP

Answer the following prior to coming to the 2nd lab:

(1) Suppose your sample lost weight upon standing for a week. How might you explain that?

(2) Suppose your sample gained weight upon standing for a week. How might you explain that?

(3) If your sample gained weight, what would you expect might happen to its MP?

The isolation of usnic acid experiment makes use of a polarimeter to measure optical activity of the recovered product. The polarimeter used in Chem 112A does not look exactly like the instrument shown in Fig. 5.62 (left-hand column of p. 114). Instead, the view through the eyepiece looks like this

or

To measure optical rotation you rotate the analyzer to find the brightest disk between these two "half moons".

The Isolation of Natural Products

INTRODUCTION

These experiments are designed to acquaint you with the procedures used for the isolation of naturally occurring and often biologically active organic compounds. These substances are known as *natural products* because they are produced by living systems. The particular natural products you are going to study come from the plant kingdom.

At the end of the nineteenth century more than 80% of all medicines in the Western world were natural substances found in roots, barks, and leaves. There was a widespread belief at that time that in plants there existed cures for all diseases. As Kipling wrote, "Anything green that grew out of the mold/ Was an excellent herb to our fathers of old." Even as the power of synthetic organic chemistry has grown during this century, natural materials still constitute a significant fraction of the drugs employed in modern medicine. For example, in the mid-1960s when approximately 300 million new prescriptions were written each year, nearly half were for substances of natural origin. Furthermore, these materials have played a major role in successfully combating the worst of human illnesses, from malaria to high blood pressure; diseases that affect hundreds of millions of people.

Unfortunately, during the latter one-half of this century a number of very powerful natural products that subtly alter the chemistry of the brain have been used in vast quantities by our society. The ultimate impact on civilization is of grave concern. Evidence clearly demonstrates that these natural substances disrupt the exceedingly complex and delicate balance of biochemical reactions that lead to normal human consciousness. How well the brain is able to repair the damage from repetitive exposure is unknown. Unfortunately, we are, whether we like it or not, currently conducting the experiment to answer that question.

The natural products that you may isolate in the following experiments include a bright-yellow crystalline antibiotic (Experiment [11A]), a white crystalline alkaloid that acts as a stimulant in humans (Experiment [11B]), and an oily material with a pleasant odor and taste (Experiment [11C].

Isolation and Characterization of an
Optically Active Natural Product: Usnic Acid

Common name: Usnic acid
CA number: [7562-61-0]
CA name as indexed: 1,3(2*H*,9b*H*)-Dibenzofurandione, 2,6-diacetyl-7,9-dihydroxy-8,9b-dimethyl-

Purpose

To extract the active principle, usnic acid, from one of the lichens that produce it. Usnic acid is a metabolite found in a variety of lichens. For this experiment we will utilize a local (in Maine) species of lichen, *Usnea hirta* (often referred to as *Old Man's Beard*), which is a fruticose lichen (a lichen that possesses erect, hanging, or branched structures). This experiment illustrates an extraction technique often employed to isolate natural products from their native sources (see also Experiment [11B] for another extraction strategy). As usnic acid possesses a single chiral center (stereocenter), and as only one of the enantiomers is produced in *Old Man's Beard*, this experiment also functions as an introduction to the methods used to measure the specific rotation of optically active substances.

LICHENS AND NATURAL PRODUCTS

Lichens, of which there are estimated to be greater than 15,000 species, are an association between an algae and a fungus that live together in an intimate relationship. This association is often termed symbiosis. Symbiosis requires that two different organisms live together in both close structural proximity and interdependent physiological combination. It ordinarily is applied to situations where the relationship is advantageous, or even required, for one or both, but not harmful to either. In the case of lichens, the algae can be grown independently of the fungi that obtain nutrients from the algae cells. The fungi are, therefore, considered to be parasitic and their contribution to the union has been viewed historically only as an aid in the absorption and retention of water and perhaps to provide a protective structure for the algae. It appears, however, that the fungi may play a far more important role in the life of the lichen than earlier appreciated. The fungi appear to generate a metabolite, usnic acid, which is the most common substance found in these primitive systems. This acid can comprise up to 20% of the dry weight of some lichens! Even more intriguing is the original belief that usnic acid appears to have *no biological function* in these plants. Why would a living system channel huge amounts of its precious energy into making an apparently useless substance? Recently, with our increased understanding of the role of chemical communication substances in ecology, it has been recognized that usnic acid very likely makes a major symbiotic contribution as a *chemical defense agent*. Indeed, in 1945 Burkholder demonstrated that several New England lichens possessed antibiotic properties, and usnic acid was subsequently shown to be the active agent against several kinds of bacteria, including staphylococcus. The Finnish company, Lääke Oy Pharmaceutical, has prepared from reindeer lichen a broad-spectrum usnic acid antibiotic for treating tuberculosis and serious skin infections. There is, in fact, evidence that lichens were used in medicine by the ancient Egyptians, and from 1600–1800 AD these plants were considered an outstanding cure for tuberculosis. Usnic acid has been investigated for use as an antibiotic by the U.S. Public Health Service. It proved to be effective in dilutions between 1 part in 100,000 and 1 part in 1,000,000 against several Gram-positive organisms.

This widespread lichen metabolite is the material isolated in this experiment. Usnic acid was first isolated and identified in 1843 by Rochleder, but a molecule of this complexity was beyond the structural knowledge of organic chemistry in those days. The structure was finally determined in 1941 by Schöpf, and not too long after that (1956) it was synthesized in the laboratory by Sir D. H. R. Barton (Nobel Laureate). Barton's route involved a spectacular one-step dimerization of a simple precursor, a synthesis that very closely mimicked the actual biogenetic pathway (see chemistry). The key step was the one-electron (1 e⁻) oxidation of methylphloracetophenone, which leads directly to the dimerization. The mechanism of this reaction, both in the plant and in the laboratory synthesis, is essentially identical to the oxidative coupling of 2-naphthol to give 1,1'-bi-2-naphthol, which is explored in detail in Experiment [5$_{adv}$].

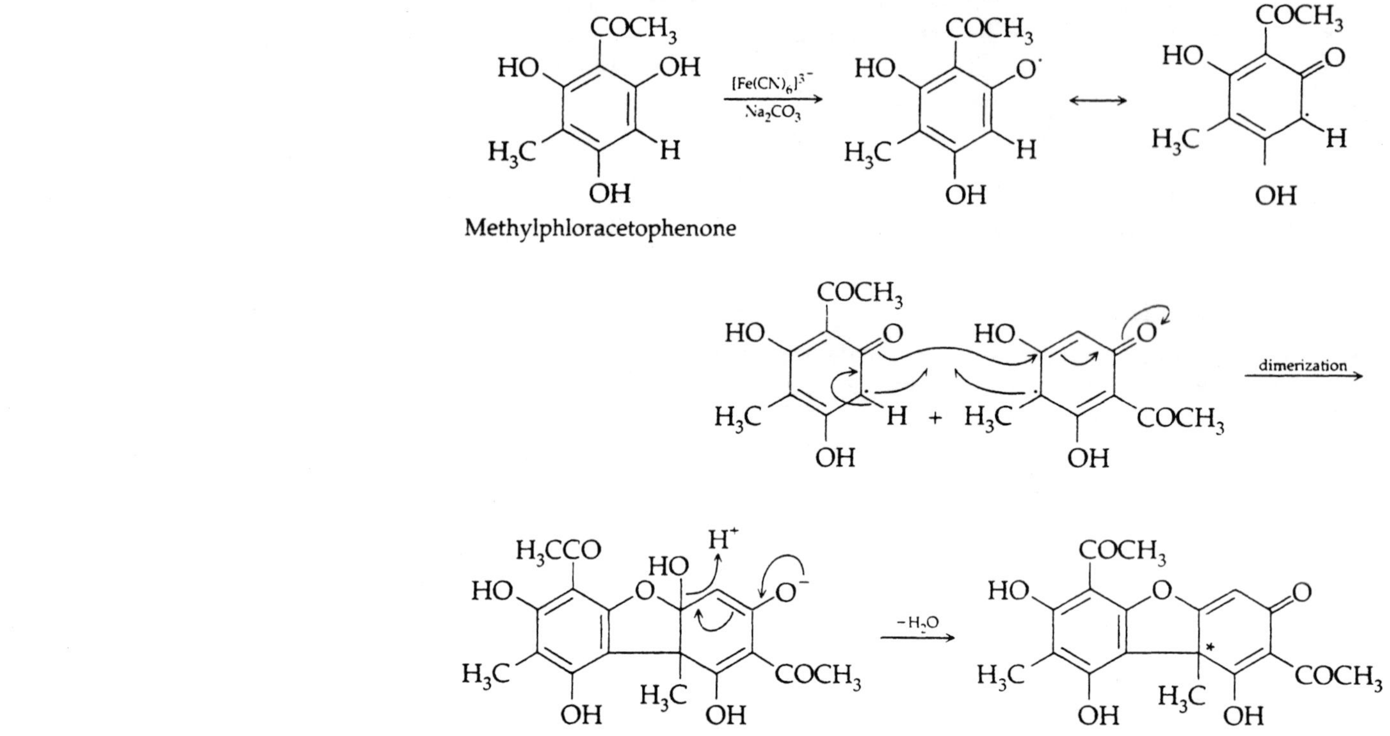

Methylphloracetophenone

Usnic Acid

The chiral center (stereocenter) (*) is bonded to a highly conjugated aromatic ring system (see structure), which gives rise to a very large specific rotation. This enhanced interaction with polarized radiation makes this compound a particularly interesting molecule to examine for optical activity. The production of a single enantiomer in the natural product, which, as discussed above, is formed by an oxidative coupling process, implies that there must be an intimate association between the substrate and an enzyme (a biological catalyst that itself is optically active) during the crucial coupling process.[9]

Prior Reading
Technique 8:   Measurement of Specific Rotation
Optical Rotation Theory (see pp. 111–115).

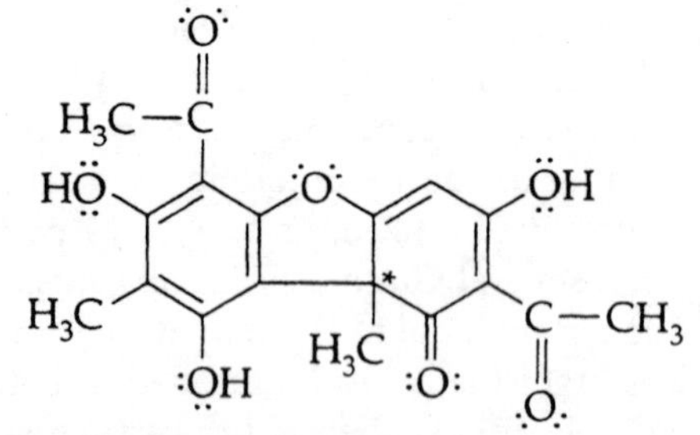

[9] Dean, F. M.; Halewood, P.; Mongkolsuk, S.; Roberston, A.; Whally, W. B. *J. Chem. Soc.* **1953**, 1250. Kreig, M. B. *Green Medicine*; Rand McNally: New York, 1964. Lewis, W.H.; Elvin-Lewis, M. P. F. *Medical Botany*; Wiley: New York, 1977. Hendrickson, J. B. *The Molecules of Nature*, W. A. Benjamin, New York, 1965. Richards, J. H.; Hendrickson, J. B. *The Biosynthesis of Steroids, Terpenes, and Acetogenins*; W. A. Benjamin, New York, 1964. Schöpf, C.; Ross, F. *Annalen* **1941**, 546, 1 (see further references cited in Experiment [5$_{adv}$]).

Nonracemic solutions of chiral substances, when placed in the path of a beam of polarized light, may rotate the plane of the polarized light clockwise or counterclockwise and are thus referred to as *optically active*. This angle of optical rotation is measured using a *polarimeter*. This technique is applicable to a wide range of analytical problems varying from purity control to the analysis of natural and synthetic products in the medicinal and biological fields. The results obtained from the measurement of the observed angle of rotation (α_{obs}) are generally expressed in terms of *specific rotation* $[\alpha]$. The sign and magnitude of $[\alpha]$ are dependent on the specific molecule and are determined by complex features of molecular structure and conformation, and thus cannot be easily explained or predicted. The relationship of $[\alpha]$ to α_{obs} is as follows: $[\alpha]_\lambda^T = \dfrac{\alpha_{obs}}{l \cdot c}$ where T is the temperature of the sample **in degrees Celsius** (°C), l is the length of the polarimeter cell **in decimeters** (1 dm = 0.1 m = 10 cm), c is the concentration of the sample **in grams per milliliter** (g/mL), and λ is the wavelength of the light **in nanometers** (nm) used in the polarimeter. These units are traditional, though most are esoteric by contemporary standards. Thus, the specific rotation for a given compound is normally reported in terms of temperature, wavelength, concentration, and the nature of the solvent. For example: $[\alpha]_D^{25} = +12.3°$ ($c = 0.4$, $CHCl_3$) implies that the measurement was recorded in a $CHCl_3$ solution of 0.4 g/mL at 25 °C using the sodium D line (589 nm) as the light source. Unless indicated the pathlength is assumed to be 1 decimeter in these observations.

Usnic acid contains a single stereocenter (see structure), and therefore it can exist as a pair of enantiomers. In nature, however, only one of the enantiomers (R or S) would be expected to be present. Usnic acid has a very high specific rotation, $[\alpha]_D^{25} = +488°$ ($c = 0.4$, $CHCl_3$), which will give a large α_{obs} even at low concentrations, and for this reason it is an ideal candidate to measure rotation in a microscale experiment.

Racemic (equimolar amounts of each enantiomer) usnic acid has been resolved (separated into the individual enantiomers) through preparation and separation of the diastereomeric (−) brucine salts. This procedure was the route followed in order to obtain an authentic synthetic sample for comparison with the natural material. This separation was required because the dimerization step in the synthesis, which was carried out in the absence of enzymatic, or other chiral, influence, gave a racemic product.

A common method of extracting chemical constituents from natural sources is presented in this experiment. In this case, only one chemical compound, the usnic acid, is significantly soluble in the extraction solvent, acetone. For this reason, the isolation sequence is straightforward.

Isolation of Usnic Acid

Estimated time for completion of the experiment: 2.5 hours.

Physical Properties of Components

Compound	MW	Amount	bp(°C)
Lichen		1.0 g	
Acetone	58.08	15.0 mL	56.2

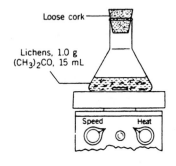

Loose cork

Lichens, 1.0 g
(CH₃)₂CO, 15 mL

Speed   Heat

Reagents and Equipment

Weigh and place about 1.0 g of oven dried (40 °C) crushed, or cut-up, lichens and 15.0 mL of acetone in a 50-mL Erlenmeyer flask containing a magnetic stirrer. Loosely cap the flask with a cork stopper. (■) The lichens used in this experiment are *Usnea hirta*.

Reaction Conditions

Stir or occasionally swirl the mixture for about 30 min at room temperature. If necessary, periodically push the lichens below the surface of the acetone solvent using a glass rod.

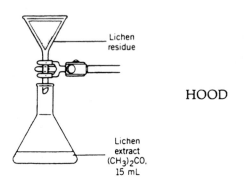

Lichen
residue

Lichen
extract
(CH₃)₂CO,
15 mL

HOOD

Isolation of Product

Filter the resulting mixture by gravity and collect the filtrate in a 25-mL Erlenmeyer flask. (■) A Pasteur filter pipet may be used to make this transfer, if desired. Remove the acetone solvent under a slow stream of air or nitrogen [HOOD] on a warm sand bath nearly to dryness. Allow the remainder of the acetone to evaporate at room temperature to obtain the crude bright yellow or orange usnic acid crystals.

Purification and Characterization

Recrystallize the crude extract from acetone/95% ethanol (10:1). Dissolve the crystals in the minimum amount of hot acetone and add the appropriate volume of 95% ethanol. Allow the mixture to cool to room temperature and then place the flask in an ice bath to complete the recrystallization. Collect the golden-yellow crystals by vacuum filtration (■) and wash them with *cold* acetone. Dry the crystals on a porous clay plate or on a sheet of filter paper. As an alternative and more efficient procedure, the crude material may be recrystallized using a Craig tube, avoiding the filtration step with the Hirsch funnel.

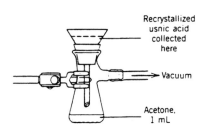

Recrystallized
usnic acid
collected
here

→ Vacuum

Acetone,
1 mL

Weigh the yellow needles of usnic acid and calculate the percent of the acid extracted from the dry lichen. Determine the melting point (use the evacuated melting point technique) and compare your value to that found in the literature. Obtain an IR spectrum and compare it with that of an authentic sample or that given in *The Aldrich Library of IR Spectra*.

Chemical Tests

Chemical tests can assist in establishing the nature of the functional groups in usnic acid. Perform the 2,4-dinitrophenylhydrazine test and the ferric chloride test (see Chapter 10). Are the results significant?

Determination of the Specific Rotation

Though usnic acid is an optically active compound with a very high specific rotation, a low-volume, long-path-length cell must be employed to successfully determine its specific rotation with microscale quantities.

Dissolve usnic acid (80 mg) in 4.0 mL of tetrahydrofuran (THF) solvent and transfer the solution to the polarimeter cell using a Pasteur pipet.

NOTE. *To obtain this quantity (80 mg) of usnic acid will very likely require pooling the recrystallized product of eight or nine students. Spectral grade THF* should be used as the solvent. Many of the early specific rotation values on these substances were recorded with chloroform as the solvent, but, because it possesses some toxicity, it is now avoided if possible.

Place the cell in the polarimeter and measure the angle of rotation. Calculate the specific rotation using the equation given in the discussion section.

6-66. Determine the correct R or S designation for each of the following molecules.

6-67. The structure originally proposed for cordycepic acid, which has $[\alpha] = +40.3°$, was

Why is this not a plausible structure?

6-68. A sample of 150 mg of an organic compound is dissolved in 7.5 mL of water. The solution is placed in a 20-cm polarimeter tube and the rotation measured in a polarimeter. The rotation observed was $-2.676°$. Distilled water, in the same tube, gave a reading of $+0.016°$. Calculate the specific rotation for the compound.

6-69. Compound **A** is optically active and has the molecular formula $C_5H_{10}O$. On catalytic hydrogenation (addition of hydrogen) of **A**, Compound **B** is obtained. Compound **B** has the molecular formula $C_5H_{12}O$ and is optically inactive. Give the structure for Compounds **A** and **B**.

6-70. Which of the following compounds have a meso form?
2,3-Dibromopentane   2,4-Dibromopentane   2,3-Dibromobutane

BIBLIOGRAPHY

This experiment is adapted from that given by:

Todd, D. *Experimental Organic Chemistry*; Prentice-Hall: Englewood Cliffs, NJ, **1979**, p. 57.

Synthesis of usnic acid:

Barton, D. H. R.; DeFlorin, A. M.; Edwards, O. E. *J. Chem. Soc.* **1956**, 530.

Penttila, A., Fales, H. M. *Chem. Commun.* **1966**, 656.

A large scale method of isolation of usnic acid has been reported:

Stark, J.B.; Walter, E. D.; Owens, H. S. *J. Am. Chem. Soc.* **1950**, 72, 1819.

Bromination of E-Stilbene:
meso-Stilbene Dibromide

Common names: *meso*-Stilbene dibromide, *meso*-1,2-dibromo-1,2-di-
    phenylethane
CA number: [13440-24-9]
CA name as indexed: Benzene, 1,1'-(1,2-dibromo-1,2-ethanediyl)-
    bis-, (R*,S*)-

Purpose

To synthesize the *second* intermediate in the **b** series of Sequential Reactions by carrying out the bromination of *(E)*-stilbene to obtain *meso*-stilbene
dibromide. This product is the precursor to diphenylacetylene, the next
synthetic intermediate in the **b** series. A further purpose of this experiment
is to demonstrate the *stereospecific* addition of bromine to alkenes.

NOTE. *If it is planned to continue the synthetic sequence to hexaphenylbenzene,
the semimicroscale procedure described below should be used. If you wish to study
this reaction as an individual microscale experiment, those conditions and other
scaleup options follow the semimicro discussion.*

Prior Reading

    Technique 5:   Crystallization
                  Use of the Hirsch Funnel (see pp. 93–95).

REACTION

(E)-Stilbene   Pyridinium   *meso*-Stilbene
                       ~~bromide~~   dibromide
                       perbromide

DISCUSSION

The bromination of alkenes is an example of an electrophilic addition reaction (also see Experiments [D2] and [F2]).

In the present reaction, bromination of *(E)*-stilbene yields *meso*-
stilbene dibromide. Thus, this reaction is classed as *stereospecific* since the
other possible diastereomers are not formed.

The reaction proceeds in two stages. The first step involves the formation of an intermediate cyclic *bromonium ion*. The concept of a three-membered cyclic intermediate was first proposed as early as 1937. Subsequent
studies have provided solid evidence that cyclic halonium ions do, indeed,
exist. For example, stable solutions of cyclic bromonium ions in liquid SO_2
(-60 °C) have been prepared as SbF_6^- salts. Two examples are given here.

Ethylene bromonium ion salt   Tetramethylethylene bromonium ion salt

Nuclear magnetic resonance spectroscopic measurements have provided powerful evidence that these and other selected alkenes form stable *bridged* bromonium ion salts. A solid bromonium ion tribromide salt of adamantylidene adamantane has been isolated, and its structure determined by X-ray crystallography.

Tribromide salt of adamantylidene adamantane

The bromine molecule (Br_2) is normally symmetrical. However, as it approaches the nucleophilic and electron-rich π bond of the alkene, it becomes polarized by induction and can then function as the electrophile in an addition reaction. The result is the generation of a cyclic bromonium ion.

Induced polarization of Br_2 as it approaches the alkene

Bromonium ion

In the present reaction, both the bromine and the *(E)*-stilbene are achiral. However, the bromonium ion that is produced is chiral. In this ion, the bromine atom bridges both carbon atoms of the original carbon–carbon double bond to form a three-membered ring intermediate. The generation of a cyclic species has a profound effect on the *stereochemistry* of the second step of the bromine addition.

The second stage of the bromination involves nucleophilic attack by bromide ion on the intermediate bromonium ion. As the nucleophile must approach from the face opposite the leaving group, bond formation involves inversion of configuration at the carbon center under attack in the second stage of the bromination reaction.

Note that *either* carbon can be approached by the nucleophile (one attack is shown). This second step is a classic backside S_N2 sequence. The bromination of cyclic alkenes provides further evidence that this type of halogenation is an anti addition, with the bromine atoms introduced trans to one another.

Bromonium ion   Dibromo product

It is important to realize that if two different groups are present on one or both of the sp^2 carbon atoms of the alkene linkage, chiral carbon centers are generated on addition of bromine, though if a chiral product were formed from achiral reagents, one would expect it to be racemic. In the case with *(E)*-stilbene, two chiral centers are generated. However, due to the symmetry of the reactants and the stereoselectivity of the reaction, only the meso diastereomer is formed.

$$\text{(E)-Stilbene} \xrightarrow[\text{acetic acid}]{Br_2} \text{meso-Dibromostilbene}$$

(E)-Stilbene

Identical

meso-Dibromostilbene

Refer to the Discussion section of Experiment [D2] for further information on the stereochemistry of bromination reactions.

Bromination of alkenes using a Br_2–CCl_4 solution (a red-brown color) is frequently used as a qualitative test for the presence of unsaturation in a compound. Rapid loss of color from the reagent solution is a positive test (see Chapter 10).

Pyridinium bromide perbromide, a solid brominating agent, is used as a source of bromine in this experiment. The material is more convenient to handle than liquid bromine (see Experiment [D2]).

(The microscale reaction is increased by a factor of 2.6.)

Estimated time to complete the reaction: 1.0 hour.

SEMIMICROSCALE EXPERIMENTAL PROCEDURE

Physical Properties of Reactants

Compound	MW	Amount	mmol	mp(°C)	bp(°C)
(E)-Stilbene	180.25	600 mg	3.3	122–124	
Glacial acetic acid		12 mL			118
Pyridinium bromide perbromide	319.83	1.2 g	3.7	205	

Reagents and Equipment

In a 50.0-mL round-bottom flask containing a magnetic spin bar and equipped with an air condenser, weigh and place 600 mg (3.3 mmol) of (E)-stilbene. Next add 6 mL of glacial acetic acid (using a graduated cylinder), and warm the resulting mixture in a sand bath at 130–140 °C with stirring until the solid dissolves (~5 min). (■)

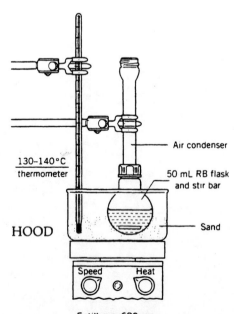

130–140°C thermometer

Air condenser

50 mL RB flask and stir bar

Sand

HOOD

Speed   Heat

E-stilbene, 600 mg + glacial acetic acid, 12 mL + pyridinium bromide perbromide, 1.2 g

HOOD

WARNING: Glacial acetic acid is corrosive and toxic. It is dispensed in the *hood* using an automatic delivery pipet.

Remove the condenser from the flask, and to the warm solution **[HOOD]** add 1.2 g (3.7 mmol) of pyridinium bromide perbromide in one portion. Wash down any perbromide adhering to the sides of the flask with an additional 6 mL of acetic acid using a Pasteur pipet. Reattach the air condenser.

WARNING: The brominating agent is a mild lachrymator. It should be dispensed in the hood. An alternative solid brominating agent is tetra-N-butylammonium tribromide.

Reaction Conditions

With stirring, heat the reaction mixture at a sand bath temperature of 130–140 °C for an additional 5–6 min. (The product often begins to precipitate during this period.)

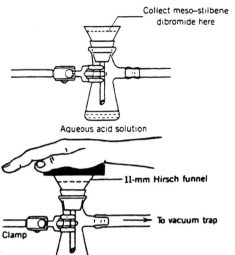

Collect meso–stilbene dibromide here

Aqueous acid solution

11-mm Hirsch funnel

To vacuum trap

Clamp

Isolation of Product

Remove the reaction flask from the heat source and allow it to cool to approximately 40–50 °C (water bath). Add 12 mL of water, with swirling, and then place the flask in an ice bath for 5–8 min. Collect the crystalline solid by vacuum filtration using a Hirsch funnel. (■)

Purification and Characterization

Wash the material with three 2-mL portions of cold water to obtain white crystals, and then with two 2-mL portions of acetone. To dry the solid, place a solid rubber disk over the top of the Hirsch funnel (as illustrated to the left) and press it down with your hand until the vacuum holds it on. Continue suction for 30 minutes to remove the last vestiges of solvent.

Weigh the *meso*-stilbene dibromide and calculate the percent yield. Determine the evacuated melting point and compare your result with the literature value.

Generally, the material is sufficiently pure to be used in the next stage of the **b** series of Sequential Reactions, the preparation of diphenylacetylene. If desired, a small portion (~10–20 mg) may be recrystallized from hot xylene using the Craig tube.

Chemical Tests

You may wish to perform several classification tests on the product (see Chapter 10). Carry out the ignition test to confirm the presence of an aromatic group. The Beilstein test can be used to detect the presence of bromine. The silver nitrate test for alkyl halides should also give a positive result.

OPTIONAL MACROSCALE AND MICROSCALE PREPARATIONS

Macroscale Reaction Procedure

The procedure is similar to that for the 2.6 fold scaleup preparation with the following exceptions.

1. The reagent and solvent amounts are increased approximately 4.3-fold over the microscale preparation.

Physical Properties of Reactants

Compound	MW	Amount	mmol	mp(°C)	bp(°C)
(E)-Stilbene	180.25	1.0 g	5.5	122–124	
Glacial acetic acid		12 mL			118
Pyridinium bromide perbromide	319.83	2.0 g	6.2	205	

2. After cooling the reaction mixture, add 20 mL of water to assist in precipitating the product. Wash the collected crystals with three 3-mL portions of cold water followed by two 3-mL portions of acetone.

Microscale Reaction Procedure

The procedure is similar to that for the 2.6-fold scaleup preparation with the following modifications:

1. Use a 10-mL round-bottom flask
2. The reagent and solvent amounts are *decreased* by a factor of approximately 2.6.

Physical Properties of Reactants

Compound	MW	Amount	mmol	mp(°C)	bp(°C)
(E)-Stilbene	180.25	230 mg	1.28	122–124	
Ethanol		4.2 mL			118
Pyridinium bromide perbromide	319.83	450 mg	1.4	205	

3. Add 2.2 mL of ethanol at the same time as the addition of the (E)-Stilbene
4. An additional 2 mL of ethanol is added with the brominating reagent.
5. The reaction mixture is diluted with 4.5 mL of water, swirled, and placed in an ice bath for 5–8 min.
6. The filter cake is washed with three 2-mL portions of cold water, followed by two 2-mL portions of acetone.

QUESTIONS

8-23. Using suitable structures, draw the sequence for the addition of bromine to (Z)-stilbene.

8-24. Are the results different for the answer in Question 8-23 than for the result in this experiment? If so, how? What is the stereochemical relationship between the products formed in the two reactions?

You are going to use the product of this reaction for the synthesis of diphenylacetylene next week. If you did not recover at least 0.4 grams of product from the bromination of *trans*-stilbene, please run the reaction a second time, so that you can combine the yields of the two preparations to get enough material to run next week's experiment.

If you ran the preparation twice, please be sure to report the yields of both preparations separately in your write-up and, in your Conclusions section, try to account for any differences in yield.

Dehydrohalogenation of *meso*-Stilbene Dibromide: Diphenylacetylene

Common names: Diphenylacetylene, diphenylethyne
CA number: [501-65-5]
CA name as indexed: Benzene, 1,1'-(1,2-ethynediyl)bis-

Purpose

The product formed in this multiple elimination reaction is the *third* intermediate in the b series of Sequence A, and is one of the immediate precursors to our target molecule, hexaphenylbenzene.

To investigate the synthesis and properties of alkynes, and to become familiar with E2 elimination reactions.

NOTE. *If it is planned to continue the synthetic sequence to hexaphenylbenzene, the semimicroscale procedure described below should be used. If you wish to study this reaction as an individual microscale experiment, those conditions, and other scaleup options, follow the semimicro discussion.*

Prior Reading
   Technique 5:   Crystallization
                    Use of the Hirsch Funnel (see pp. 93–95).

REACTION

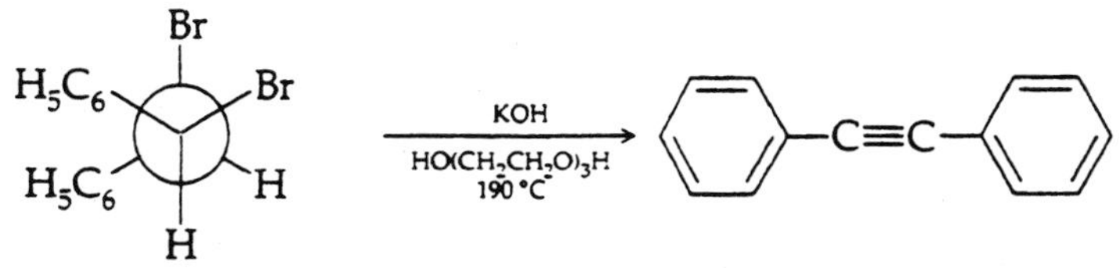

meso-Stilbene dibromide   Diphenylacetylene

DISCUSSION

This reaction illustrates the dehydrohalogenation of a *vicinal* dibromo compound to form an alkyne. It is a useful reaction for the synthesis of alkynes, as the starting dibromides are readily available from alkenes (see, e.g., Experiment [A2$_b$]).

The double dehydrohalogenation reaction is usually run in the presence of a strong base, such as KOH or NaNH$_2$, and proceeds in two stages.

In the first, an intermediate bromoalkene is formed, which can be isolated under more mildly basic conditions. In fact, this reaction is a valuable route to vinyl halides. The mechanism of elimination involves the abstraction of the proton on the carbon atom β to the halogen. The E2 mechanism, which operates under these strongly basic conditions, is fastest when it involves removal of a proton, H^+, antiperiplanar to the leaving group, Br^-. The E2 sequence of bond breakage and formation involves a smooth transition from reactant to product without the formation of an intermediate (concerted mechanism). The general mechanism is shown here.

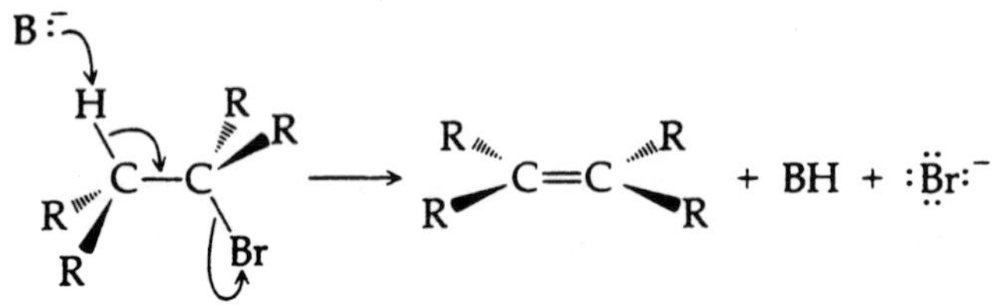

This type of elimination reaction is stereospecific since the geometry of the transition state requires that the H, both Cs, and the Br, all lie in the same plane.

If *meso*-stilbene dibromide is treated with KOH in ethanol solvent, it *is* possible to isolate the monodehydrohalogenation product, the bromoalkene.

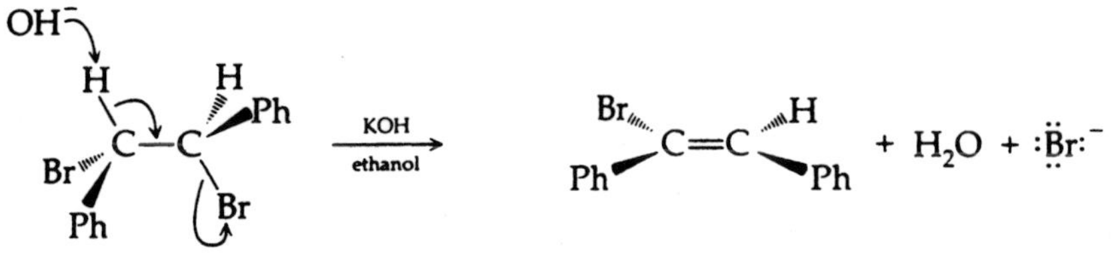

meso-Stilbene dibromide   (E)-1-Bromo-1,2-diphenylethylene

The second stage of the reaction involves a higher activation energy, and therefore it requires higher temperatures to proceed. In the presence of a strong base near 200 °C, the bromoalkene undergoes an E2 elimination to form the triple bond. Part of the reluctance to eliminate, in this particular case, results from the fact that the elimination proceeds by a syn pathway.

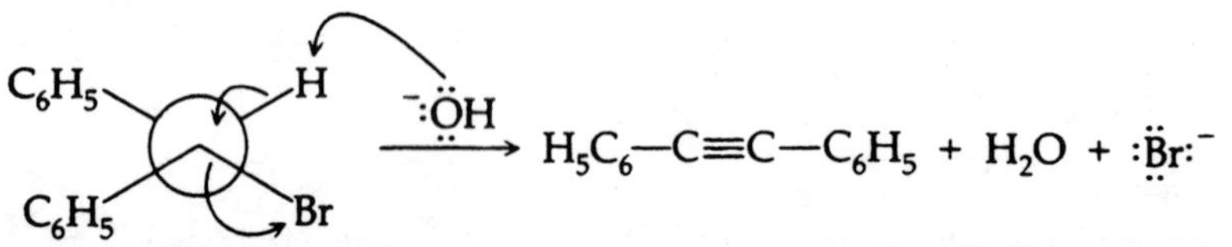

Thus, the stereochemistry of the reactant employed necessitates somewhat higher temperatures for the second elimination reaction.

(The microscale reaction is increased by a factor of 5.)

Estimated time to complete the reaction: 1.0 hour.

SEMIMICROSCALE
EXPERIMENTAL PROCEDURE

Physical Properties of Reactants

Compound	MW	Amount	mmol	mp(°C)	bp(°C)
meso-Stilbene dibromide	340.07	400 mg	1.2	241 dec	
Potassium hydroxide	56.11	387 mg	6.9	360	
Triethylene glycol	150.18	2 mL			278

Reagents and Equipment

Weigh and place 400 mg (1.2 mmol) of *meso*-stilbene dibromide and 387 mg (6.9 mmol) of KOH flakes in a 10-mL Erlenmeyer flask containing a magnetic stir bar. Using a graduated cylinder, measure and add 2 mL of triethylene glycol to the flask.

Reaction Conditions

Place the reaction flask in a *preheated* sand bath set at a temperature of 190–195 °C, and stir the reaction for 7–8 min.

Isolation of Product

Allow the resulting dark-colored reaction mixture to cool to approximately 40–50 °C (water bath), and then add 5.0 mL of water. Now place the flask in an ice bath for 15 min. Collect the solid product by filtration under reduced pressure using a Hirsch funnel. (■)

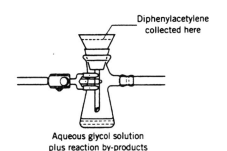

Diphenylacetylene collected here

Aqueous glycol solution plus reaction by-products

Purification and Characterization

Rinse the product crystals with two 1-mL portions of cold 70% ethanol, and air-dry them on a porous clay plate or on filter paper. These crystals can be recrystallized from 95% ethanol (~2.0 mL). If desired, a small portion may be recrystallized from 95% ethanol using the Craig tube.

Weigh the recrystallized product and calculate the percent yield. Determine the melting point and compare your result with the literature value. Obtain IR and NMR spectra of the material and compare them with those recorded in *The Aldrich Library of IR Spectra* or *The Aldrich Library of NMR Spectra*.

NOTE. *If you have synthesized the diphenylacetylene from benzaldehyde, calculate the overall yield to this point in the synthesis of hexaphenylbenzene. Base these calculations on the starting amount of benzaldehyde.*

Chemical Test
The ignition test for aromatic groups indicates the presence of the phenyl groups. Decolorization of a Br_2–CH_2Cl_2 solution should give a positive test for unsaturation (see Chapter 10).

OPTIONAL MACROSCALE AND MICROSCALE PREPARATIONS

Macroscale Reaction Procedure

(This reaction is scaled up by a factor of 10 over the microscale procedure.)

The procedure is similar to that outlined above with the following exceptions:

1. Carry out the reaction in a 25-mL Erlenmeyer flask containing a boiling stone. Run the reaction in the **hood**.   HOOD

2. Increase the reagent and solvent amounts approximately twofold over the semimicroscale procedure, as indicated here.

Physical Properties of Reactants

Compound	MW	Amount	mmol	mp(°C)	bp(°C)
meso-Stilbene dibromide	340.07	800 mg	2.4	241 dec	
Potassium hydroxide	56.11	756 mg	13	360	
Triethylene glycol	150.18	4 mL			278

3. After cooling the reaction mixture, add 10 mL of water.

4. Rinse the product crystals with two 1-mL portions of cold 70% ethanol. They can be recrystallized from 95% ethanol (~5.0 mL).

Microscale Reaction Procedure

The procedure is similar to that outlined above with the following exceptions:

1. Carry out the reaction in a 3-mL conical vial containing a boiling stone.

2. The reaction is heated in a sand bath at 190 °C for 5 min.

3. Decrease the amounts of reagents and solvents as given here.

Physical Properties of Reactants

Compound	MW	Amount	mmol	mp(°C)	bp(°C)
meso-Stilbene dibromide	340.07	80 mg	0.24	241 dec	
Potassium hydroxide	56.11	75 mg	1.3	360	
Triethylene glycol	150.18	0.4 mL			278

4. After cooling of the reaction mixture to 40–50 °C (water bath), add 1.0 mL of water, and place the reaction vessel in an ice bath for 15 min.

5. Rinse the product crystals with one 0.25-mL portion of cold 70% ethanol. The alkyne can be recrystallized from 95% ethanol (~0.5 mL).

8-28. Both (E)- and (Z)-2-chlorobutenedioic acids dehydrochlorinate to give acetylene dicarboxylic acid.   **QUESTIONS**

$$HO_2C-C(Cl)=CH-CO_2H \rightarrow HO_2C-C\equiv C-CO_2H$$

The Z acid reacts about 50 times faster than the E acid. Explain.

8-29. Compounds containing a carbon–carbon triple bond undergo the Diels–Alder reaction. Formulate the product formed by the reaction of (E,E)-1,4-diphenyl-1,3-butadiene with diethyl acetylenedicarboxylate.

Purpose

To explore the conditions under which ethers are prepared by the well-known Williamson' ether synthesis. To prepare alkyl aryl ethers by S_N2 reactions of alkyl halides with substituted phenoxide anions. To demonstrate the use of phase-transfer catalysis.

Prior Reading

Technique 4: Solvent Extraction
Liquid-Liquid Extraction (see pp. 80–82).

Technique 6: Chromatography
Column Chromatography (see pp. 98–101).

For Optional Scaleup: Separatory Funnel Extraction (see pp. 82–83).

REACTION

CH$_3$—⟨benzene⟩—ÖH + CH$_3$CH$_2$CH$_2$—I $\xrightarrow[\text{(C}_4\text{H}_9\text{)}_4\text{N}^+\text{, Br}^-]{\text{NaOH}}$ CH$_3$—⟨benzene⟩—Ö—CH$_2$CH$_2$CH$_3$ + Na$^+$, I$^-$

p-Cresol   Propyl iodide   Propyl p-tolyl ether

DISCUSSION

The two compounds whose preparations are described in Experiments [22A] and [22B] are alkyl aryl ethers. The general method of preparation is the Williamson synthesis, an S_N2 reaction specifically between a phenoxide ion (ArO$^-$) nucleophile and an alkyl halide. This reaction is often used for the synthesis of symmetrical and unsymmetrical ethers where at least one of the ether carbon atoms is primary or methyl, and thus amenable to an S_N2 reaction. Elimination (E2) is generally observed if secondary or tertiary halides are used, as phenoxide ions are also bases.

The conditions under which these reactions are conducted lend themselves to the use of phase-transfer catalysis. The reaction system involves two phases, the aqueous phase and the organic phase. In the present case, the alkyl halide reactant acts as the organic solvent, as does the product formed. The phase-transfer catalyst plays a very important role. In effect, it carries the phenoxide ion, as an ion-pair, from the aqueous phase, across the phase boundary into the organic phase, where the S_N2 reaction then occurs. The ether product and the corresponding halide salt of the catalyst are produced in this reaction. The halide salt then migrates back into the aqueous phase, where the halide ion is exchanged for another phenoxide ion, and the process repeats itself. The catalyst can play this role since the large organic groups (the four butyl groups) allow the solubility of the ion-pair in the organic phase, while the charged ionic center of the salt renders it soluble in the aqueous phase. For further discussions of phase-transfer catalysis, see Experiments [19B] and [19D].

In the reactions described below, the mechanism is a classic S_N2 process, and involves a backside nucleophilic attack of the phenoxide anion on the alkyl halide.

CH$_3$—⟨benzene⟩—ÖH + NaOH $\rightleftharpoons$ CH$_3$—⟨benzene⟩—Ö$^-$, Na$^+$ + H$_2$O

CH$_3$—⟨benzene⟩—Ö$^-$, Na$^+$ + CH$_3$CH$_2$—C(H)(H)—I $\longrightarrow$ CH$_3$—⟨benzene⟩—Ö—CH$_2$CH$_2$CH$_3$ + Na$^+$, I$^-$

It is of interest to contrast the acidity of phenols with that of simple alcohols. A phenol is more acidic than an alcohol. In a typical aliphatic alcohol (e.g., ethanol) loss of the proton forms a strong anionic base, alkoxide ion (ethoxide ion).

$$R—CH_2—OH \rightleftharpoons H^+ + R—CH_2—O^-$$
Alkoxide ion

The strongly basic characteristics of the alkoxide species is due to the fact that the negative charge is localized on the oxygen atom. Ethanol has a $pK_a = 16$. In contrast, the conjugate base of a phenol can delocalize its negative charge.

Phenoxide ion

Thus, the phenoxide ion is stabilized by this resonance delocalization; therefore it is a weaker base than the alkoxide ion. Conversely, the phenol is a stronger acid than a typical aliphatic alcohol. Phenol has a $pK_a = 10$ and is thus 1 million times more acidic than ethanol.

Propyl *p*-Tolyl Ether

The reaction for Experiment [22A] is shown above.

Estimated time of the experiment: 2.5 hours.

EXPERIMENTAL PROCEDURE

Physical Properties of Reactants

Compound	MW	Amount	mmol	mp(°C)	bp(°C)	d	n_D
p-Cresol	108.15	160 µL	1.56	32–34	202	1.02	1.5312
25% NaOH solution		260 µL					
Tetrabutyl-ammonium bromide	322.38	18 mg	0.056	103–104			
Propyl iodide	169.99	150 µL	1.54		102	1.75	1.5058

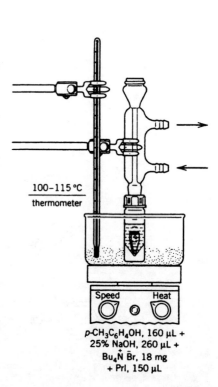

100–115 °C thermometer

p-CH₃C₆H₄OH, 160 µL + 25% NaOH, 260 µL + Bu₄N B̄r, 18 mg + PrI, 150 µL

Reagents and Equipment

Weigh and place 160 µL (168 mg, 1.56 mmol) of *p*-cresol in a 5.0-mL conical vial containing a magnetic spin vane. Now add 260 µL of 25% aqueous sodium hydroxide, and thoroughly mix the resulting solution. (■) To this solution weigh and add the tetrabutylammonium bromide (Bu₄N⁺,Br⁻) catalyst (18 mg), followed by 150 µL (262 mg, 1.54 mmol) of propyl iodide. Immediately attach the vial to a reflux condenser.

HOOD **NOTE.** *Warm the cresol in a hot water bath to melt it. Dispense this reagent and the propyl iodide in the hood using an automatic delivery pipet.*

CAUTION: Propyl iodide is a cancer suspect agent.

Reaction Conditions

Place the reaction vessel in a sand bath, and stir vigorously at 110–115 °C for 45–60 min.

Isolation of Product

Cool the resulting two-phase mixture to room temperature, and remove the spin vane with forceps. Rinse the spin vane with 1.0-mL of diethyl ether, adding the rinse to the two-phase mixture. Cap the vial, agitate, vent, and transfer the bottom aqueous layer, using a Pasteur filter pipet, to a 3.0-mL conical vial. A Vortex mixer, if available, can be used to good advantage in this extraction step. Wash this aqueous fraction with 1.0 mL of diethyl ether. Save this, and all subsequent aqueous fractions together in a small Erlenmeyer flask until your final product has been isolated and characterized. Now transfer this diethyl ether wash to the 5-mL conical vial containing the ether solution of the product. Extract the resulting ether solution with a 400-μL portion of 5% aqueous sodium hydroxide solution. Cap the vial, agitate, vent, and remove and save the bottom aqueous layer, using a Pasteur filter pipet. Wash the product–ether solution with 200 μL of water. Remove, and save, the aqueous phase to obtain the crude, wet ether solution of the product. Place the 5 mL vial on the rotary evaporator and concentrate the solution to afford the crude product.

Purification and Characterization

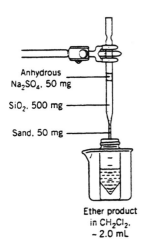

Anhydrous
Na₂SO₄, 50 mg

SiO₂, 500 mg

Sand, 50 mg

Ether product
in CH₂Cl₂,
~ 2.0 mL

The crude product is purified by chromatography on silica gel. Prepare a microchromatographic column by placing 500 mg of activated silica gel in a Pasteur filter pipet, followed by 50 mg of anhydrous sodium sulfate. (■) Dissolve the crude product in 250 μL of methylene chloride, and transfer the resulting solution to the dry column by use of a Pasteur pipet. Elute the material with 2.0 mL of methylene chloride, and collect the eluate in a tared 5 mL conical vial. Place the vial on the rotary evaporator and concentrate the solution to afford the product.

Weigh the pure propyl *p*-tolyl ether and calculate the percent yield.

In the course of this experiment run a Ferric Ion Test (see next page) on the starting material, *p*-cresol, using a 6-well spot plate (please check one out from the stockroom and return it at the end of lab). Then run the Ferric Ion Test on a small drop of the crude product that you get after removal of the ether. Finally, run the Ferric Ion Test on a small drop of the purified product after you have removed the methylene chloride. In the Conclusions section of your final write-up, discuss (among other things) the results of these spot tests, especially whether the product gives the same type of spot test as the starting material.

Please use a white porcelain 6-well spot plate to run the Ferric Ion Tests. Ferric chloride solution is available in the hoods. Compare the color of ferric chloride solution with the colors you observe in the spot test. Please clean the 6 well plate thoroughly and return it to the stockroom before you leave the laboratory.

Ferric Ion Test   **Phenols and Enols**

Most phenols and enols form colored complexes in the presence of ferric ion, Fe^{3+}.

Phenols give red, blue, purple, or green colors. Sterically hindered phenols may give a negative test. Enols generally give a tan, red, or red-violet color.

On a white spot plate place 2 drops of water, or 1 drop of water plus 1 drop of ethanol, or 2 drops of ethanol, depending on the solubility characteristics of the unknown. To this solvent system add 1 drop (10 mg if a solid) of the substance to be tested. Stir the mixture with a thin glass rod to complete dissolution. Add 1 drop of 2.5% aqueous ferric chloride ($FeCl_3$) solution (light yellow in color). Stir and observe any color formation. If necessary, a second drop of the $FeCl_3$ solution may be added. Additional points to consider:

1. The color developed may be fleeting or it may last for many hours. A slight excess of the ferric chloride solution may or may not destroy the color.
2. An alternate procedure using $FeCl_3$–CCl_4 solution in the presence of pyridine is available.[11]

Bromine Water

Phenols, substituted phenols, aromatic ethers, and aromatic amines, since the aromatic rings are electron rich, undergo aromatic electrophilic substitution with bromine to yield substituted aryl halides. For example,

---

CAUTION: The test should be run in the *hood*.   HOOD

---

[11] Soloway, S.; Wilen, S. H. *Anal. Chem.* **1952**, *4*, 979.

Glossary

Absorb To take up matter (to dissolve), or to take up radiant energy.

Active methylene A methylene group with hydrogen atoms rendered acidic due to the presence of an adjacent (α) electron withdrawing group, such as a carbonyl.

Activity (of alumina) A measure of the degree to which alumina adsorbs polar molecules. The activity (adsorbtivity) of alumina may be reduced by the addition of small amounts of water. Thus the amount of water present in a sample of alumina determines the activity grade. Alumina of a specific activity can be prepared by dehydrating alumina at 360 °C for about 5–6 hours and then allowing the dehydrated alumina to absorb a suitable amount of water. The Brockmann scale of alumina activity is based on the amount of water (weight percent) that the alumina contains: Grade I = 0%, Grade II = 3%, Grade III = 6%, Grade IV = 10%, and Grade V = 15% . For further information, see Brockmann, H.; Schodder, H. *Chem. Ber.* **1941**, *74*, 73.

Adsorb The process by which molecules or atoms (either gas or liquid) adhere to the surface of a solid.

Aliquot A portion.

Anilide A compound that contains a C_6H_5NHCO group. An amide formed by acylation of aniline (aminobenzene).

Capillary action The action by which the surface of a liquid, where it contacts a solid, is elevated or depressed because of the relative attractions of the molecules of the liquid for each other and for the solid. It is particularly observable in capillary tubes, where it determines the ascent (descent) of the liquid above (below) the level of the liquid in which the capillary tube is immersed.

Characterize To conclusively identify a compound by the measurement of its physical, spectroscopic, and other properties.

Condensation reaction A condensation reaction is an addition reaction that produces water (or another small neutral molecule such as CH_3OH or NH_3) as a byproduct.

Deliquescent Liquefying by the absorption of water from the surrounding atmosphere.

Dihedral angle The angle between two intersecting planes. In organic chemistry the term *dihedral angle* (or *torsional angle*) is used to describe the angle between two atoms (or groups) bonded to two adjacent atoms, such as H—C—C—H, and can be determined from a molecular model by looking down the axis of the bond between the two central atoms.

Eluant A mobile phase in chromatography.

Eluate The solution that is eluted from a chromatographic system.

Elute To cause elution.

Elution The flow, in chromatography, of the mobile phase through the stationary phase.

Emulsion A suspension composed of immiscible drops of one liquid in another liquid (e.g., oil and vinegar in salad dressing).

Enol A functional group composed of a hydroxyl group bonded to an alkene.

Enolate The conjugate base of a enol, that is, a negatively charged oxygen atom bonded to an alkene. An enolate results from deprotonation of a carbon α to a carbonyl group.

Filter cake The material that is separated from a liquid, and remains on the filter paper, after a filtration.

Glacial acetic acid Pure acetic acid containing less than 1% water.

Heterolysis Cleavage of a covalent bond in a manner such that both the bond's electrons end up on one of the formerly bonded atoms.

Homogeneous Consisting of a single phase.

Homolysis Cleavage of a covalent bond in a manner such that the bond's electrons are evenly distributed to the formerly bonded atoms.

Hygroscopic Absorbs moisture.

In situ In chemistry, the term usually refers to a reagent or other material generated directly in a reaction vessel and not isolated.

Lachrymator A material that causes the flow of tears.

Ligroin A solvent composed of a mixture of alkanes.

Metabolites The compounds consumed and produced by metabolism.

Metabolism The chemical processes performed by a living cellular organism.

Methine A CH group (with no other hydrogen atoms attached to the carbon atom).

Methylene A CH_2 group (with no other hydrogen atoms attached to the carbon atom).

Mother liquor The residual, and often impure, solution remaining from a crystallization.

Olefin An older term for an alkene.

Oxonium ion A trivalent oxygen cation with a full octet of electrons (e.g., H_3O^+).

Polymer A large molecule constructed of repeating smaller (monomer) units.

Racemic Consisting of an equimolar mixture of two enantiomers.

Reagent A chemical or solution used in the laboratory to detect, measure, react with, or otherwise examine other chemicals, solutions, or substances.

Reflux The process by which all vapor evaporated or boiled from a vessel is condensed and returned to that vessel.

Rotamers Conformational isomers that can be interconverted by rotation about one or more single bonds (e.g., gauche and anti butane).

Tare A tared container is one whose weight has been measured. The term may also refer to the process of zeroing a balance after a container has been placed on the weighing platform.

Triturate To grind to a fine powder.

Zwitterion A neutral molecule containing separated opposite formal charges.